SPECTRAL LINE FORMATION

A Blaisdell Book in the Pure and Applied Sciences

Spectral
Line Formation

JOHN T. JEFFERIES

UNIVERSITY OF HAWAII

BLAISDELL PUBLISHING COMPANY

A DIVISION OF GINN AND COMPANY

Waltham, Massachusetts / Toronto / London

FOR *CHARMIAN*

AND TO

THE MEMORY OF MY PARENTS

Preface

The purpose of this book is to discuss certain aspects of the theory of the formation and analysis of the line spectrum of a hot gas. The underlying motivation for most of the studies discussed here lies in a desire to develop a physically sound procedure for interpreting the line spectrum of a stellar atmosphere; correspondingly, the major emphasis is given to problems encountered in astrophysics. The theory is, nevertheless, equally applicable to a discussion of the spectrum of a steady laboratory source.

While studies of this kind have been carried out for many years—in keeping with their fundamental role in astrophysics—they have not been uniformly successful in giving consistent results and so have evoked no universal confidence. Within the past decade or so, strong criticism has been leveled at the assumption of local thermodynamic equilibrium (LTE) which underlies by far the greatest number of the standard analyses of stellar spectra. In an effort to escape this assumption, a more general formulation—rather misleadingly designated non-LTE—has been developed on the basis of earlier work of the 1930's; this theory has gained substantial support along with its own measure of criticism. Much of the relevant literature on the generalized theory of line formation is widely diffused, known only to the few workers in the field, and, perhaps, can well be criticized as being overly esoteric. Correspondingly, perhaps, widespread misunderstanding exists as to its nature and limitations, why and how it differs from the LTE assumption and, especially, how it is to be applied in practice.

In this book I have attempted to present a logical development of the generalized—or non-LTE—theory of line formation and analysis; indeed, this has been my single concern and no attempt has been made to abstract the conventional LTE theories of line formation for which an adequate literature exists already.

The subject matter of the following chapters finds a natural division, depending on its relevance either to the synthetic problem of computing the radiation emerging from a gas in a specific state or to the inverse, analytical, aspect of determining the state of the gas from a study of the emergent spectrum. The synthetic problem is studied first; this is more natural and, as will be seen, provides the insight needed to make progress with the analysis. The epoch of the book is late 1965; the subject is developing rapidly and much will certainly be added to the literature before this book is published. Still, it is hoped that the basis is sound enough and the applications sufficiently clear to allow the student not only to apply the principles for himself but to see how and where new developments modify or extend the theory.

My first wandering and hesitant steps in this subject were guided by my friend and teacher R. G. Giovanelli—now Chief, CSIRO Division of Physics, Sydney—when I first began work at that laboratory. For the example of his physical insight, no less than his patient supervision, I shall remain always in his debt. In R. N. Thomas, now of the Joint Institute for Laboratory Astrophysics, Boulder, Colorado, I have again found the best of teacher, friend, and colleague. Impatient of equivocation, generous of his time, experience, and insight, his example continues as a guide in all my work.

A first outline for this book arose in a set of lectures delivered in the 1961 spring semester in the Department of Astro-Geophysics, University of Colorado. In a modified and extended form these were repeated two years later. I am grateful to the students attending these classes for their criticisms, explicit and implicit. Especially am I indebted to G. W. Curtis and O. R. White for their polite, but nevertheless insistent, demands that I complete the manuscript. To F. Q. Orrall and J. B. Zirker, long-time colleagues and friends, I owe my sincere thanks for encouragement and help generously and unfailingly given in all aspects of my work.

To R. D. Dietz and G. D. Finn I offer my grateful thanks for the many hours which they have spent in a detailed study of this manuscript. Their attention and criticism have resulted in the removal of many obscurities, ambiguities, and errors. For those which remain I am alone responsible; for the fact that these are far fewer than they might have been I can only give credit to the care of these colleagues.

The final draft of the manuscript was completed at the Department of Astrophysical Sciences, Princeton University, during October and November, 1965. I am the more grateful to Dr. Lyman Spitzer for the opportunity to spend those two months in his Department since, without this, the manuscript would certainly have remained unfinished.

The complete manuscript was typed with skill and dedication by Miss Jo Ann Baker; for her cheerful acceptance of this difficult and often tedious task I owe and offer my sincerest thanks.

Finally, to my wife for the years of love, sympathy, encouragement, and understanding which leave an unpayable debt, this book is given in inadequate tribute.

J.T.J.

Contents

List of Symbols

This list is not intended to be exhaustive but is confined to the more commonly used symbols. Of necessity some symbols are occasionally used to represent different physical or mathematical quantities. In such cases the reader should be able to resolve the ambiguity from the context of the discussion.

GREEK SYMBOLS

α	η_0/kT
α_ν	Atomic absorption coefficient
γ_r, γ_c	Radiative or collisional damping constants
δ	Damping constant ($\equiv \gamma/4\pi$); see also Equation (7.34)
$\Delta\nu, \Delta\lambda$	Frequency (wavelength) interval
$\Delta\nu_D, \Delta\lambda_D$	Doppler frequency (wavelength) width
$\varepsilon_\nu, \varepsilon$	Volume emission coefficient (ε_ν); see also Equation (3.30)
η_ν	r_ν^{-1}
η, η_0	Energy, threshold energy
θ	Angle between outward normal $\mathbf{n}$ and the direction of a ray; also $5040/T$
$\kappa_\nu, \kappa_0, \kappa_c$	Absorption coefficient, per unit path length, respectively at frequencies ν and ν_0, and in the continuum
λ	Wavelength
λ_μ	$1 - \varpi_0$

μ	$\cos\theta$
ν, ν_0	Frequency, line center frequency
ξ	Frequency in frame of an atom; microturbulent velocity
ϖ_0	Albedo for the single scattering of line radiation
ϖ_ν	Corresponds to ϖ_0, see Equation (7.9)
ρ	Mass density
ρ_W	Weisskopf radius, see Equation (4.55)
σ	Cross section
τ	Optical depth or optical thickness, characteristic time
τ_1 or τ^1	Total optical thickness of a finite layer
τ_c	Continuum optical depth
τ_ν	Usually, composite (line plus continuum) optical thickness
ϕ_λ	Saturation function, see Equation (10.26)
ϕ_ν	Normalized absorption coefficient profile $\int_0^\infty \phi_\nu\, d\nu = 1$
ϕ_ν'	Ratio of atomic absorption coefficient at frequency ν to that at the line center
ϕ	Phase angle
χ_ν	Normalized profile of atomic emission coefficient $\int_0^\infty \chi_\nu\, d\nu = 1$
χ_i	Excitation potential of state i
χ_{ion}	Ionization potential from ground state of ion
χ_u, χ_ℓ	Excitation potential of upper, lower, state of a transition
ψ	Phase angle, wave function
ψ_ν	χ_ν/ϕ_ν
ω, Ω	Solid angle—usually as an element $d\omega$, $d\Omega$; also angular frequency

ROMAN SYMBOLS

a	Dimensionless damping constant $\delta/\Delta\nu_D$
A_{ij}	Einstein coefficient for spontaneous $i \to j$ photoelectric transition, see Equations (4.35) through (4.42)
$b_n(t)$	Probability amplitude for occupation of state n at time t
b_n	Factor measuring departure of state n from its LTE value with respect to the continuum state at the ambient electron temperature and density, see Equation (6.3)
B_ν^*	See Equation (7.34)
$B_\nu(T)$	Planck function at temperature T, see Equation (3.2)

B_{ij}, B_{ji} Einstein coefficients for upward or downward transitions under the influence of radiation, see Equations (4.35) through (4.40)

c Velocity of light

C_{ij} Rate of collision transition $i \to j$ per atom in state i

C Interaction parameter, see Equation (4.44)

f, f_{abs} Absorption f-value

f_{em} Emission f-value

F_ν See H_ν

F_0 Normal field strength, see Equation (4.72)

$g(v, v')$ Redistribution function, see Equation (5.18)

g_i Statistical weight of level i

G_λ Weighting function, see Equation (10.19)

h Planck constant, $\hbar \equiv h/2\pi$

$H(a, v)$ Profile of line absorption coefficient, see Equation (4.98)

H_ν Radiant flux $1/4\pi \int I_\nu \, \mu \, d\omega$

$h(\mathbf{n}, \mathbf{n}')$ Scattering phase function, see Equation (5.2)

I_i Incident intensity

I_ν Specific intensity

j_ν Mass emission coefficient, ε_ν/ρ

J_ν Mean intensity $1/4\pi \int I_\nu \, d\omega$

k_ν Mass absorption coefficient κ_ν/ρ

LTE   Local thermodynamic equilibrium

n_i Number of atoms per unit volume in state i

n_e Number of electrons per unit volume

$\mathbf{n}$ Outward normal at the top of plane parallel atmosphere

p Probability factor

p_{ij} The probability P_{ij}/T_i

P_{ij} Rate, per atom in state i, of the transition $i \to j$, $P_{ij} = C_{ij} + R_{ij}$

$q_{ij,k}$ Probability factor—see Section 6.1.3

$Q_{ij}(\eta)$ Collision cross section, for a relative energy η, for the transition $i \to j$

r_ν, r_0 The ratio κ_c/κ_ν, κ_c/κ_0

R_{ij} Rate, per atom in state i, of the radiative transition $i \to j$

$R(v, v')$ Redistribution function, see Chapter 5

$\mathbf{s}$ Direction of a ray

S_l Line source function in the frequency-independent case

S_ν Composite source function, see Equation (2.55)

$S_H(\alpha)$ Holtsmark intensity distribution, see Equation (4.77)

T	Temperature, electron temperature, characteristic time, total optical thickness
T_e	Electron temperature
T_k, T_{kin}	Kinetic temperature
T_{ex}	Excitation temperature
T_i	Total rate, per atom in state i, of all transitions from state i
TE	Thermodynamic equilibrium
t_ν, t_0, t_c	Optical depths, respectively, at frequency ν, at frequency ν_0, in the continuum
t^0	Characteristic time
t_0^T	Thermalization (optical) length; see Equation (7.44)
$t^\dagger$	Characteristic optical length, see Equation (8.29)
v, V	Velocity
v	Dimensionless frequency interval, usually $(\Delta\nu/\Delta\nu_{\mathrm{D}})$
W	Equivalent width, dilution factor
$x(t_c)$	Function defined by Equation (10.27)
Y_ℓ	Net radiative bracket for the (u, ℓ) line, see Equation (6.79)
Z_ℓ	Net radiative bracket for the (u, ℓ) line, see Equation (6.77)
z, Z	Depth variables

Lycinus: ... you are dragged on by consistency; it never occurs to you that a thing may be self-consistent and yet false. ... *Hermotimus, or the Rival Philosophies*—Lucian. TR. H. W. AND F. G. FOWLER.

1

Introduction

1.1 The Basic Problem

The slit spectrum of a glowing gas shows in general a series of lines each of which, under sufficiently high dispersion, exhibits definite structure. These lines are normally superposed on a continuous background of radiation and are sometimes conveniently designated as "emission" or "absorption" lines according to whether their intensities lie above or below that of the continuum. The center of such an emission or absorption line may usually be readily distinguished and, after correction for any velocity shifts, a measurement of its wavelength almost always allows an identification to be made of the atom responsible for the emission. We owe this possibility to the patience and dedication of a long succession of workers, and it clearly forms a basic aspect to any study of line spectra. The techniques and limitations of such qualitative spectrochemical analysis lie outside our present interests, however, and their results will be presumed.

Our purpose here is different: We wish to deduce the physical properties of the atmosphere emitting the radiation from observations of the strengths and shapes of spectral lines originating from known transitions in known atoms. Conceptually, we may envisage two general ways in which to proceed to this goal.

First, if we could develop a theory which would enable us to compute the radiation emerging from a gas of given physical structure, then an

1

investigation of an observed spectrum might proceed through the postulation of a model, the computation of the emergent radiation, and the comparison of the computed and observed spectra. To the extent that the comparison did not yield agreement we could hope to change the model until it did. If, however, this agreement were not attained, or were attained for some lines but not for others, we would have either to question the properties of the model, the quality of the theory, or the validity of the basic atomic data involved in the computation. Unfortunately, this often gives so much flexibility to the interpretation that an appearance of consistency may be obtained by a judicious assignment of model parameters or the recognition that the atomic data may be inaccurate, while actually using an incorrect theory.

The second general approach, which is the inverse to the above, would proceed directly from the observed radiation to infer the properties of the gas. This *analytic* procedure cannot be formulated, however, without our first having solved the *synthetic* problem posed in the preceding paragraph. Accordingly, our attention in the first part of this book—through Chapter 8—is devoted to the problem of the computation of the radiation emerging from a gas of given structure. On this basis we are able, in the final two chapters, to turn to the question of the analysis of an observed spectrum.

To compute the radiation emerging from a radiating gas, and so to solve our problem, it is evident that we have only to specify, at each point in the gas and for each frequency in the line, the rates at which the relevant radiant energy is absorbed and emitted by a unit volume of the gas, to enter these rates in the equation governing the flow, or transfer, of radiation through the gas, and finally to solve this equation.

A knowledge of the bulk coefficients of emission and absorption, which we shall denote by ε_ν and κ_ν, respectively, is therefore central to our problem. It often turns out to be more convenient, however, to work not in terms of ε_ν and κ_ν but in the related quantities κ_ν and $\varepsilon_\nu/\kappa_\nu$; this ratio is known as the *source function* and is denoted by S_ν.

From what we have said already it is clear that the spectroscopic state of the gas, i.e., the set of variables which directly determines the radiation field in the gas, is specified by the values of κ_ν and S_ν as functions of position and frequency. In other words, if we can specify these two quantities we can immediately compute the emergent radiation; inversely, if we know the emergent radiation we may be able to infer both S_ν and κ_ν but we can certainly find no more information directly.

This point has been considered in detail in an important and far-reaching investigation by Thomas (1965).

Our fundamental problem, therefore, lies in the specification of S_ν and κ_ν—or of ε_ν and κ_ν—and this will occupy much of our attention in the subsequent chapters. The emission and absorption coefficients are *macroscopic* parameters whose values depend on the details of the microscopic interactions between radiation and atoms, and also on the populations, or numbers of atoms per unit volume, which are in states capable of emitting or absorbing the line radiation. The central problem with which we shall be concerned lies in the computation of these atomic populations. The whole "non-LTE" theory differs from the LTE theory simply in this: that the LTE hypothesis makes an assumption on the relative populations of the states of an atom, while our generalized, or non-LTE, theory seeks to compute these populations self-consistently, recognizing that the intensity of the radiation in the gas not only is controlled by the atomic populations but in turn controls these populations by influencing the transition rates between the states.

It is instructive, before discussing further the basis of our general formulation, to look in some detail at the two simpler situations of the thermodynamic equilibrium and local thermodynamic equilibrium specifications of the spectroscopic state parameters S_ν and κ_ν.

1.2 Approximate State Representations—TE and LTE

The simplest conceptual state of excitation of a gas is that of thermodynamic equilibrium (TE) which applies to the material inside an isolated isothermal enclosure when the material has reached equilibrium with the (opaque) container walls. In this condition the energy is equally partitioned among the various degrees of freedom and the energy distribution functions take well-known forms involving—apart from atomic parameters—only the thermodynamic temperature T. In particular, the distribution functions are independent of the details of the mechanisms of interaction, while the same value of T applies to all points inside the enclosure. The source function S_ν is simply given by the Planck function $B_\nu(T)$; the absorption coefficient is of little consequence in this case.* For a gas in thermodynamic equilibrium, it is

---

* The only requirement is that the optical depth be infinite—corresponding to the definition of a blackbody as one in which the radiation is completely absorbed. Mathematically this implies that κ_ν is infinite at the walls of a *finite* enclosure.

a straightforward matter to compute the internal radiation intensity, while the inversion of the observed intensity is equally immediate. Thus, in thermodynamic equilibrium the temperature T constitutes the complete set of parameters describing the spectroscopic state of the gas. We need know nothing else to compute the emergent radiation; we can determine nothing else from its value. Note, in particular, that the auxiliary physical parameters, volume, pressure, and chemical composition are not observationally accessible from the radiation intensity which, being given by the Planck function, depends on temperature alone.

While strict thermodynamic equilibrium must be rejected both on theoretical and observational grounds for an open system like a stellar atmosphere, it has been argued that the flux of radiation from the gas, whose existence prevents the application of strict TE, is often small compared to the corresponding total radiative energy content. In this case it may not be unreasonable to adopt the slightly modified assumption of local thermodynamic equilibrium (LTE) in which situation it is presumed that the distribution of energy among the kinetic and internal (e.g., excitation, ionization) degrees of freedom is the same as in thermodynamic equilibrium, except that these distributions are now controlled by the *local* value of the "temperature." Note, however, that this can no longer be the *thermodynamic* temperature since the intensity of the local radiation field can in general no longer be described by its TE distribution—the Planck function $B_\nu(T)$—since the radiation at a point does not have a local origin but rather reflects conditions within a photon mean free path; and these are not constant except in the degenerate case of strict thermodynamic equilibrium.

When we adopt LTE for an open gas of given thermal structure we implicitly assume that the equilibrium among the kinetic and internal degrees of freedom is reached independently of the details of the interaction mechanisms, i.e., we assume that the state populations are governed by the Boltzmann relations, and this, as we shall see in Chapter 3, is equivalent to the specification $S_\nu = B_\nu(T)$. Nevertheless, a radiative flux is transmitted in these circumstances, and its magnitude certainly depends on the absorptive and emissive properties of the specific gas, i.e., on the specific mechanisms of interaction between the radiation and the given material. Hence, to compute the emergent radiation for a gas in LTE we shall require more information than in the case of strict TE; specifically, we must know the local value of the kinetic temperature T_k to obtain $S_\nu = [B_\nu(T_k)]$ and the composition of the gas at each point to obtain κ_ν. In terms of our general discussion above, this information would constitute a description of the spectroscopic state of the gas *provided* that we knew, from laboratory experiments or theoretical computations, the relevant cross sections for photoelectric absorption so that we could compute the absorption coefficient. Similarly, if LTE were assumed one would presume it possible, as indeed it turns out to be, to determine from the observed spectral characteristics the depth distribution of kinetic temperature together with some additional information on the other spectroscopic parameter, κ_ν. However, the validity of the analysis would clearly depend on whether or not the basic assumption of LTE were valid.

As emphasized above, in LTE the radiative intensity at a point in the gas depends on the mechanisms of interaction between radiation and the gas, while the atomic populations, *by assumption*, do not. Hence, granted that the kinetic energy distribution follows the Boltzmann law, we shall strictly be justified in assuming LTE *only* if we can show either that the rate of each radiative transition is small compared to that of the corresponding collisional transition, or that the photoelectric transition rates, up and down, balance in detail.*

1.3 The Basic Assumptions of a Generalized Theory

Our viewpoint is to be more fundamental than LTE. We do not reject this assumption as such, rather we choose as a starting point the more basic assumption of *statistical equilibrium* in which the usual ensemble averages are independent of time.† This condition obviously includes LTE, and strict thermodynamic equilibrium, as limiting cases, so that this theory is not properly designated "non-LTE"; however, since this name will no doubt remain with us we should understand that there is implied no automatic dismissal of LTE or of its replacement by an alternative assumption. Consistent with the requirement of statistical equilibrium, the equilibrium of the gas at each point is determined by the condition that the rates of entry to and exit from any given state

---

* In either of these two cases the assumption of a Maxwell-Boltzmann form for the kinetic energy distribution leads to a TE distribution among the internal energy states; see Chapter 6.

† The assumption of time independence is removable, of course, but it applies to the majority of cases of interest here; for a discussion of some time-dependent cases see Curtis (1963).

are equal; the theory is therefore in its very nature a "rate-process theory." In general, the transitions between the atomic levels take place under the influence both of collisions and radiation; the collisional rates are determined by the relevant cross sections, by the electron density, and by the electron velocity distribution—if, as is nearly always the case, electrons are responsible for the great majority of the collisional transitions—while the radiative transition rates depend on the intensity and on the radiative cross sections. Throughout we shall *assume* that the electron energy distribution needed to compute the collisional rates has the Boltzmann form characterized by a parameter T_e which is referred to as the "electron temperature." This assumption can be shown to be physically reasonable in most cases, it is essentially a reflection of the fact that elastic collisions between electrons and other gas constituents occur at a much greater rate than the corresponding inelastic or radiative processes.

The specification of the radiation intensity needed to compute the rates of photoelectric absorption and stimulated emission is less straightforward. We cannot assume its value, indeed our whole problem is to compute it.

As mentioned above, to determine the radiation intensity at any location we must first specify the values of ε_ν and κ_ν, enter these in an equation of radiative transfer, and solve the equation. However, the radiation intensity enters directly in the statistical equilibrium equations—it determines the rate of photoelectric absorption—while at the same time the solutions of these equations are needed to determine the populations entering the factors ε_ν and κ_ν in the radiative transfer equation, which in turn determines the intensity. Therefore, we must clearly solve the radiative transfer and statistical equilibrium equations simultaneously if we wish to get a consistent result.

In a full theory of line formation this coupling between radiation and state populations is inevitable. In the special case of LTE, one *assumed* that the solution of the statistical equilibrium equations was that giving the usual Boltzmann relations between the populations of the atomic states at the local value of T_e, and so one removed by assumption the dependence on the radiation intensity of the emission and absorption terms in the equation of transfer. In other words, one introduced an assumption which had the effect of *uncoupling* the radiative transfer and the statistical equilibrium equations. In the still more special case of strict thermodynamic equilibrium, one also presumed a solution to the radiative transfer equation—by letting the opacity tend to infinity.

1.4 Outline of the Following Chapters

The first part of this study is to be devoted to the synthetic aspect of computing the radiation emerging from an atmosphere of given physical conditions. Correspondingly, in Chapter 2 we shall consider the formulation of the equation of radiative transfer, whose solution determines the radiation intensity as a function of position and direction. We shall see, in keeping with the above, that the solution of the transfer equation can be effected immediately if we specify, as a function of depth and frequency, the two quantities ε_ν and κ_ν, or the source function S_ν and the absorption coefficient κ_ν. In Chapter 3 we consider some aspects of the specification of S_ν, giving particular attention to the evolution of the theories developed over the years, how they differ one from another, to what situations they may be applicable, where they fail, and how our theoretical treatment relates to these earlier studies.

In Chapter 4 we turn attention to the line absorption coefficient. This has an extensive literature and it is impossible in the more widespread context of this book to do justice to such a vast subject. Some aspects of astrophysical interest have been included, but these largely reflect the author's personal bias. It is hoped that, if nothing else, the reader will at least gain a glimpse of the basic problems involved and perhaps be able to approach the literature with a little more confidence. The succeeding Chapter 5 deals with the frequency dependence of the emission coefficient ε_ν. Here an attempt is made to summarize our knowledge on the degree of frequency coherence to be expected in the absorption–re-emission (or scattering) process. Especially we shall be interested in the degree to which we may confidently assume that the emission and absorption coefficients share a common frequency dependence.

Chapter 6 turns to the study of the equations of statistical equilibrium, the determination of the rate processes for collisional excitation and de-excitation and of the corresponding radiative processes. As has been indicated above, an *a priori* specification of the radiation intensity is not in general possible. Nevertheless, certain approximate results apply in the special cases where an atmosphere is either optically thick, or optically thin, in some or all of the transitions and the corresponding solutions of the statistical equilibrium equations are discussed at that point.

Chapter 7 contains a first discussion of the more complete problem of the solution of the coupled equations of transfer and statistical equilibrium. For simplicity, attention is here confined to a two-level atom. In spite of its obvious shortcomings, this study is able to throw a great deal of light on the physical factors governing line formation in a stellar atmosphere and, at the same time, to predict the broad features of such diverse line shapes as those of the solar Balmer lines on the one hand and of Ca II H and K lines on the other. Chapter 8 describes the generalization to a multilevel system and sets out some preliminary results which are nevertheless of profound significance.

In Chapter 9 we turn to the second general aspect of this book, the analytical problem of determining the atmospheric structure from observed spectral line profiles. We outline a scheme for the analysis of close multiplet lines in the solar atmosphere and illustrate the procedure using observations of the sodium D lines. More restrictive analyses of the solar Balmer series are also discussed.

In Chapter 10 we present a review of the important analytical work of Pecker and his associates on the solar photospheric spectra of the neutral atoms. Their analyses are examined in detail along with the criticisms directed against them.

REFERENCES

CURTIS, G. W., 1963, "Aspects of the Radiation Cooling of a Hot Gas," *Ph.D. Thesis*. Boulder: University of Colorado (*unpublished*).

THOMAS, R. N., 1965, *Some Aspects of Non-Equilibrium Thermodynamics in the Presence of a Radiation Field*. Boulder: University of Colorado Press.

2

The Equation of Transfer

The equation of radiative transfer which we shall discuss in this chapter is readily derived in terms of simply defined photometric quantities introduced to describe the radiation field and its sources and sinks. Our needs are simple, however, and we shall limit our discussion accordingly. In particular, we consider the refractive index of the medium to be unity; we suppose the radiation to be unpolarized when emitted, and to remain unpolarized in its interactions with atoms. We consider only time-independent problems; and we shall regard the atmosphere as being stratified in plane parallel layers so that the only linear dimension entering the description of the atmosphere is the depth, z, which we shall agree to measure increasing toward the bottom of the atmosphere. There are, of course, very many problems in radiative transfer where these approximations would be totally inadequate—for example, the scattering of sunlight in a planetary atmosphere. Reference should be made to the extensive literature for the specific modifications needed to treat cases lying outside the range of our restrictions.

A word may be added on the homogeneous and plane parallel assumptions, especially having in mind the nonuniformity observed in monochromatic, and white-light, photographs of the solar atmosphere, and the evident curvature of a stellar atmosphere. The fact that nonuniform structure is seen does not necessarily imply that an analysis in terms of a homogeneous model is totally worthless; its applicability clearly depends on the relative values of the mean free path of the photon and the scale length of the atmospheric inhomogeneities. Furthermore, to the extent that the fluctuations in values of the physical parameters are a relatively small fraction of the values themselves, one may expect that the space-averaged emission would reflect the space-averaged properties of the gas. Nevertheless, a good deal of work is needed before we can approach the analysis of an inhomogeneous source with confidence.

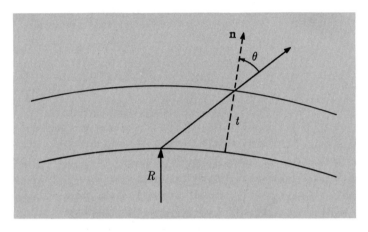

Figure 2.1. Geometry of a curved emitting atmosphere of thickness t on a star of radius R. Radiation emerges at the angle θ to the normal **n**.

In regard to the neglect of curvature one may be more definite. Let us suppose, as in Figure 2.1, that the thickness of the emitting region is t while the radius of the star is R. The validity of the plane-parallel approximation may be measured in terms of the departure from unity of the ratio, $l/(t \sec \theta)$, of the actual slant length of the emitting region to that adopted in the approximation. Suppose we limit this ratio to a value not exceeding $(1 + \delta)$*; then it follows simply that the plane-parallel approximation would be acceptable for all angles θ such that

$$\cos \theta \geq \sqrt{t/2R\delta}. \qquad (2.1)$$

As a typical example, say $t = 10^2$ km, $R = 10^6$ km, $\delta = 0.05$, then the approximation would be as accurate as permitted by the observations up to $\cos \theta \simeq 0.03$. On a 10-in.-diameter solar image this limiting

---

* In practice the value of δ will depend on the accuracy of an observation and on the observed rate of variation of intensity with $\cos \theta$, i.e., on the "limb darkening."

value would occur at about 2.5×10^{-3} in.—or about 0.5 seconds of arc —from the limb.

2.1 The Specific Intensity and Its Moments

Consider, as in Figure 2.2, an element of area $d\sigma$ through which radiation is streaming in a direction $\mathbf{s}$ making an angle θ with the outward normal $\mathbf{n}$ to $d\sigma$. Through a point P of $d\sigma$ describe a cone of solid angle $d\omega$ about the direction $\mathbf{s}$. The envelope of those cones described as the

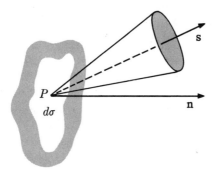

Figure 2.2. Geometric basis for the definition of a unit of solid angle in photometry.

point P takes all possible positions on $d\sigma$ will determine a truncated cone of base area $d\sigma$ whose opening defines our element of solid angle $d\omega$. It is a matter of experience that the radiant energy dE_ν in a frequency band $d\nu$ which flows in time dt through $d\sigma$ and is confined within the solid angle $d\omega$ about $\mathbf{s}$, can be written

$$dE_\nu \propto d\nu \, dt \, d\omega \, d\sigma \cos\theta. \tag{2.2}$$

The constant of proportionality is defined as the *specific intensity*, or more briefly as the intensity, and is denoted by I_ν. Thus I_ν is, in general, a function of time, position, frequency, and direction. Since $d\sigma \cos\theta$ is the projected area of $d\sigma$ normal to the beam direction, I_ν is equivalently the energy per unit solid angle and per unit frequency interval which in unit time flows through a unit area *normal to its direction of flow*. Evidently I_ν gives a complete specification of an unpolarized radiation field at frequency ν, and it is thus the fundamental quantity whose value we seek.

Rather than I_ν, it is frequently more convenient to use I_λ—the corresponding energy per unit wavelength interval. From Equation (2.2) it follows that

$$\frac{dE}{dt\, d\omega\, d\sigma\, \cos\theta} = I_\nu\, d\nu = I_\lambda\, d\lambda \tag{2.3}$$

or, since $|d\nu| = c\, d\lambda/\lambda^2$, the conversion between I_ν and I_λ is simply

$$I_\lambda = \frac{I_\nu c}{\lambda^2}, \qquad I_\nu = \frac{I_\lambda c}{\nu^2}, \tag{2.4}$$

when we choose to regard I_λ and I_ν as positive quantities, i.e., we measure both $d\nu$ and $d\lambda$ increasing.

Since we shall only be concerned with cases where the intensity is symmetrical in the azimuth angle ϕ, and is independent of time, its functional dependence at any given location in the gas will be expressed in its representation as $I_\nu(\mu)$ with $\mu = \cos\theta$. In our subsequent discussion we shall make frequent reference to three angular moments of $I_\nu(\mu)$ defined by the relations

$$J_\nu = \frac{1}{2}\int_{-1}^{+1} I_\nu(\mu)\, d\mu, \tag{2.5}$$

$$H_\nu = \frac{1}{2}\int_{-1}^{+1} I_\nu(\mu)\mu\, d\mu, \tag{2.6}$$

$$K_\nu = \frac{1}{2}\int_{-1}^{+1} I_\nu(\mu)\mu^2\, d\mu. \tag{2.7}$$

The important quantity J_ν is known as the mean intensity. In this notation we follow Chandrasekhar (1950); Kourganoff (1952), following Schwarzschild's original notation, has represented it by $\bar{I}_\nu$ and this notation is often found in the literature. A direct physical interpretation for the mean intensity is provided by the relationship

$$u_\nu = \frac{4\pi J_\nu}{c}, \tag{2.8}$$

in which u_ν is the energy density of radiation in unit frequency interval about ν. For a derivation of this result see, e.g., Unsöld's (1955) treatise.

The quantity H_ν, as given by the definition (2.6), is simply $1/4\pi$ times the net flux, i.e., the outward flow of energy—per unit time and frequency interval—across unit area in the plane of stratification. Unlike the related quantities I_ν, J_ν, and K_ν, H_ν may be either positive or negative; for an isotropic radiation field it is evidently zero. Chandrasekhar and Kourganoff define a quantity F_ν by the equation

$$F_\nu = 2 \int_{-1}^{+1} I_\nu(\mu)\mu \, d\mu = 4H_\nu, \qquad (2.9)$$

but this definition is less convenient for our purposes.

The K_ν integral defined by Equation (2.7) is related to the radiation pressure $p_r(\nu)$ by the equation

$$p_r(\nu) = \frac{4\pi}{c} K_\nu, \qquad (2.10)$$

but we shall have no occasion to use this fact; for isotropic radiation this equation reduces to the well-known result $p_r(\nu) = u_\nu/3$.

2.2 The Absorption and Emission Coefficients

In its passage through a medium, a beam of radiation is observed to be weakened by interaction with the material. To express this absorption quantitatively we appeal to experiment to determine how the weakening depends on the macroscopic parameters of the medium.

Let us imagine an experiment in which a collimated beam of flux $4\pi H_\nu$ is incident normally on a slab of matter of thickness ds, which lies between the planes P_1 and P_2 in Figure 2.3, and suppose that we were to measure the change dH_ν in H_ν arising from the insertion of

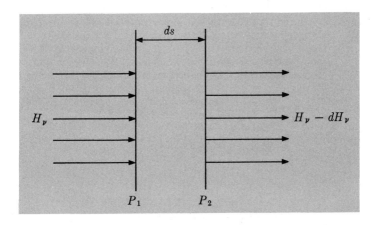

Figure 2.3. Arrangement of an ideal experiment for the determination of the macroscopic absorption coefficient of the material lying between the planes P_1, P_2.

successively thinner slabs of the same material in the same physical condition into the beam. It is consistent with physical experience that, in the limit $ds \to 0$, we find the fractional change $(-dH_\nu)/H_\nu$ to be directly proportional to the thickness ds. We may express this experimental result in the form

$$dH_\nu = -\kappa_\nu H_\nu \, ds, \tag{2.11}$$

and we shall refer to the quantity κ_ν as the *linear absorption coefficient*. In general κ_ν will depend on the particular material, on its physical condition and, as indicated by the subscript, on the frequency of the radiation being absorbed. It is often convenient to define a *mass absorption coefficient*, denoted by k_ν, such that Equation (2.11) is written

$$dH_\nu = -k_\nu \rho H_\nu \, ds, \tag{2.12}$$

where ρ is the density of material at the point s.

For an uncollimated beam of specific intensity I_ν it follows readily that the attenuation is given by

$$dI_\nu = -\kappa_\nu I_\nu \, ds, \tag{2.13}$$

where ds is measured along the direction of the beam.

The absorption coefficient κ_ν specifies only the fractional energy removed from the radiation which is traveling in the same direction both before and after its interaction with the absorbing material. The energy removed may not be wholly, or even partly, lost to the *total* radiation field; some of it may be re-emitted (or scattered) as radiation in other directions, or in other frequencies, or both.

The macroscopic emission coefficient may be defined in an analogous way. If we were to study experimentally the radiant energy emitted by a thin block of gas, we would find it possible to define a monochromatic volume emission coefficient ε_ν such that the energy dE_ν emitted from a volume element dV, into an element $d\omega$ of solid angle, in the frequency range $(\nu, \nu + d\nu)$ in time dt could be written, to the first order in the differentials,

$$dE_\nu = \varepsilon_\nu \, d\nu \, d\omega \, dV \, dt. \tag{2.14}$$

Correspondingly, we could define a mass emission coefficient j_ν by the relation

$$dE_\nu = j_\nu \rho \, d\nu \, d\omega \, dV \, dt, \tag{2.15}$$

where again ρ is the local value of the density.

It is to be noted that neither κ_ν nor ε_ν has been given an explicit angular dependence. These are *macroscopic* quantities; unless we are dealing with an ordered macroscopic system—like a crystal, or a gas flow—we shall not expect either the monochromatic emission or absorption coefficients to show any preferential angular dependence. In any case, we shall neglect it here though it is simple enough to generalize the definitions for special cases even if this leads to substantial mathematical problems in the subsequent solution of the transfer equation.

2.3 The Equation of Transfer

The basic transfer equation governing the variation of the specific intensity I_ν through an atmosphere which absorbs and emits radiation of frequency ν, is obtained by counting the gains and losses to a pencil of radiation traversing, in solid angle $d\omega$, the cylindrical volume element—shown in Figure 2.4—of cross section $d\sigma$ and length ds *in the direction of the beam.*

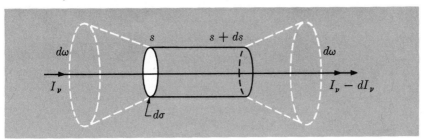

Figure 2.4. The geometric volume element considered in the derivation of the equation of radiative transfer.

The change in the radiant energy lying in the frequency interval $d\nu$ which, while confined to a solid angle $d\omega$ about the s-direction, passes in time dt through $d\sigma$ may be written as

$$[I_\nu(s + ds) - I_\nu(s)]\, d\sigma\, d\omega\, dt\, d\nu$$

or in the limit $ds \to 0$,

$$\frac{dI_\nu}{ds}\, ds\, d\sigma\, d\omega\, dt\, d\nu. \tag{2.16}$$

This energy change arises entirely from emission of radiation into the direction s, the frequency interval $d\nu$, and the solid angle $d\omega$, and by the corresponding absorption processes. From the definition (2.14) of the emission coefficient, the corresponding energy emitted is

$$\varepsilon_\nu \, d\sigma \, ds \, d\omega \, dt \, d\nu, \qquad (2.17)$$

while that absorbed is, from Equation (2.13),

$$\kappa_\nu \, ds \, I_\nu \, d\sigma \, d\omega \, dt \, d\nu. \qquad (2.18)$$

Thus equating the gain in radiant energy given by Equation (2.16) to the difference between the emission (2.17) and absorption (2.18) in the same frequency interval and solid angle, we find the general equation of transfer for this time-independent case, namely

$$\frac{dI_\nu}{ds} = -\kappa_\nu I_\nu + \varepsilon_\nu. \qquad (2.19)$$

This equation refers to the specific intensity in the direction **s**. In the particular case of a stratified atmosphere (Figure 2.5) $ds = -dz \sec \theta$

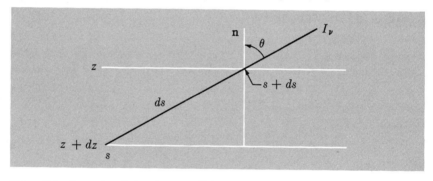

Figure 2.5. Geometry of the plane parallel atmosphere; the depth variable z increases downward, the top of the atmosphere is up.

so that, writing $\cos \theta = \mu$, we obtain the equation of transfer for a plane parallel atmosphere homogeneous over the xy-plane in the form,

$$\mu \frac{dI_\nu}{dz} = \kappa_\nu I_\nu - \varepsilon_\nu. \qquad (2.20)$$

The consideration of linear differential equations of this type is frequently simplified by a change of the independent variable; here it is convenient to introduce the *monochromatic optical depth* τ_ν defined by the equation

$$\tau_\nu(z) = \int_Z^z \kappa_\nu \, dz, \qquad (2.21)$$

where Z is the depth coordinate of the top of the atmosphere—by convention usually set equal to zero. Since z increases inward, so, at a given frequency, does τ_ν; note that τ_ν is dimensionless. The final form of the transfer equation now follows at once as

$$\mu \frac{dI_\nu}{d\tau_\nu} = I_\nu - S_\nu, \qquad (2.22)$$

where $S_\nu \equiv \varepsilon_\nu/\kappa_\nu$ is a fundamental quantity known as the *source function*.

Equation (2.20) illustrates the point made in Chapter 1 that the specification of the quantities ε_ν and κ_ν as functions of frequency and position allows us completely to solve the problem of the computation of the radiation intensity I_ν. The transformation (2.21) and the equation (2.22) illustrate the assertion in Chapter 1 that the related quantities S_ν and κ_ν are frequently a more convenient pair.

2.4 The Concept of Optical Depth

The monochromatic optical depth—or the corresponding quantities optical thickness, and optical path length—determines the amount by which a collimated beam is attenuated at a given frequency. The concept is most simply illustrated by a colored glass filter, a red filter having a higher optical thickness (or opacity) in the blue than in the red. A more subtle interpretation is required, and a quite important difference is illustrated, in the case of a diffuser such as the foggy atmosphere discussed by K. Schwarzschild (1906) in his classic memoir. It is a commonplace that the presence of a light in a fog may be detected long before one can see such details as the shape of the lamp. In terms of our definition of κ_ν, the optical path length between the lamp and the observer is greater than unity when we can no longer make out the *outline* of the lamp since this means that light emitted from the lamp is "absorbed" before it reaches our eyes. However, this radiation obviously cannot all be lost to the radiation field *as a whole*, otherwise the glow would not be seen farther away than the outline. It is, to a large extent, merely redirected. Nevertheless, in terms of our definition of the absorption coefficient it is to be regarded as absorbed. It may be objected that the word "absorption" is a poor one to apply to a situation in which light is only redirected, and that for clarity some sort of scattering coefficient should be introduced, as well as a "true" absorption coefficient. However, as we will see, this proves to be rather difficult in line-transfer problems, and is, in any case, unnecessary. We shall continue to regard as an absorption any interaction which results in the removal of energy from a beam of definite frequency and direction no matter what subsequently happens to the radiation. It is perhaps as well to mention that the scattered light is not simply ignored but is, of course, included in the *emission* coefficient. In other words, just as "absorption" in our sense of the word does not necessarily mean that radiant energy is lost to the *total* radiation field (in all directions and frequencies), neither does "emission" mean that fresh photons are necessarily added to the *total* radiation field. All this, of course, is implicit in our definitions of ε_v and κ_v; at the risk of laboring the point these examples have been given to make it explicit.

A quantitative meaning for τ_v follows immediately from the transfer equation in the case where ε_v (and so S_v) may effectively be neglected. For example, in the case of a high-quality optical glass filter it follows at once, from Equation (2.22), that the emergent intensity $I_v(0, \mu)$ is given by

$$I_v(0, \mu) = I_v(\tau_v^1, \mu) \exp\left[-\frac{\tau_v^1}{\mu}\right], \tag{2.23}$$

where τ_v^1 is the total optical thickness and $I_v(\tau_v^1, \mu)$ is the intensity incident at τ_v^1 in the direction specified by μ. Thus, τ_v^1/μ measures the logarithmic depletion at frequency v of the beam incident in the direction μ.

2.5 A Formal Solution of the Equation of Transfer

Consider, as in Figure 2.6, a plane parallel slab of material of optical thickness* τ_1 and suppose it to be illuminated from above uniformly over the top surface ($\tau = 0$) with radiation of intensity $I_i(0, \mu)$—with μ necessarily negative—while the intensity incident on the bottom surface ($\tau = \tau_1$) is $I_i(\tau_1, \mu)$ with μ necessarily positive.

The linear differential equation of transfer (2.22) gives, in the usual fashion, a solution for the specific intensity at optical depth τ of the form,

$$I(\tau, \mu) = -\int_k^\tau S(t)e^{-(t-\tau)/\mu} \frac{dt}{\mu}, \tag{2.24}$$

* For clarity frequency subscripts are suppressed throughout this section.

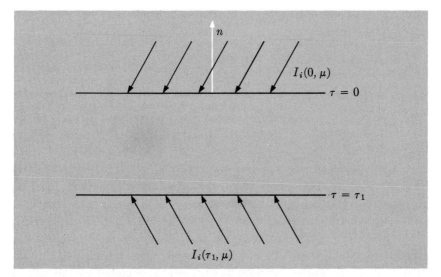

Figure 2.6. A plane parallel layer of optical thickness τ_1 diffusely illuminated uniformly over the top and bottom surfaces; only one incident beam direction is shown.

where k is an integration constant determined by the boundary condition. Since the inward- and outward-directed beams have different boundary values, it is convenient to consider them separately and we may distinguish between them with subscripts $+$ or $-$ depending respectively on whether they refer to the beams directed outward ($\mu > 0$) or inward ($\mu < 0$) with respect to the outward normal at the surface $\tau = 0$. The boundary condition at $\tau = \tau_1$ then requires that, for the outward-directed beam,

$$I_+(\tau_1, \mu) \equiv I_i(\tau_1, \mu) = -e^{\tau_1/\mu} \int_{k_+}^{\tau_1} S(t)e^{-t/\mu}\, \frac{dt}{\mu} \qquad (\mu > 0), \quad (2.25)$$

which is an equation determining k_+ in terms of the known values of $I_i(\tau_1, \mu)$ and τ_1. Indeed, it then follows at once that the specific intensity of the outward-flowing beam at depth τ is given by

$$I_+(\tau, \mu) = I_i(\tau_1, \mu)e^{-(\tau_1 - \tau)/\mu} + \int_{\tau}^{\tau_1} S(t)e^{-(t-\tau)/\mu}\, \frac{dt}{\mu} \qquad (\mu > 0). \quad (2.26)$$

Similarly, the boundary condition at $\tau = 0$ requires that

$$I_-(0, \mu) \equiv I_i(0, \mu) = -\int_{k_-}^{0} S(t)e^{-t/\mu}\, \frac{dt}{\mu} \qquad (\mu < 0), \quad (2.27)$$

which correspondingly gives immediately the intensity of the inward beam in the form:

$$I_-(\tau, \mu) = I_i(0, \mu)e^{\tau/\mu} - \int_0^\tau S(t)e^{(\tau-t)/\mu}\frac{dt}{\mu} \qquad (\mu < 0). \qquad (2.28)$$

In particular, from Equation (2.26) the emergent intensity is expressible as

$$I_+(0, \mu) = I_i(\tau_1, \mu)e^{-\tau_1/\mu} + \int_0^{\tau_1} S(t)e^{-t/\mu}\frac{dt}{\mu}. \qquad (2.29)$$

For a semi-infinite atmosphere—for which τ_1 is infinite—the limit in the expressions (2.26) and (2.29) may be taken provided that, as $\tau_1 \to \infty$, the product $S(t)e^{-t}$ tends to zero.

A physical interpretation of these formal solutions is straightforward. At depth τ the specific intensity in the μ-direction is the sum of the depleted incident intensity and the integral, along the direction specified by μ, of the source function at each depth, depleted by the optical path length $(t - \tau)/\mu$. Thus, the quantity S is, in a real sense, the source for the specific intensity I, a fact which accounts for the nomenclature. In general, $I(\tau, \mu)$ is determined by local values of the source function S (that is, values within optical path length unity or so) because of the exponential damping factor under the integration signs in Equations (2.26) and (2.28). However, this is not at all the same thing as saying that the intensity is determined by local values of the *temperature* and *density*. This would be so only if the *source function* were so controlled, and as we shall see this is not necessary, or even usual, in a tenuous gas such as that in a stellar atmosphere.

The formal solutions (2.26) and (2.28) represent the complete solution to our basic problem once S is known. Thus, the *fundamental problem of line formation* (and of transfer theory as a whole) *lies in the specification* of S as a function of position and frequency and, in more general cases, of direction and polarization state also. In general, as we have already indicated, the source function S will depend on the specific intensity I; if the form of this dependence is known, the formal solutions given above can be used immediately to find an integral equation for the source function. This procedure sometimes gives a more convenient representation than the differential equation (2.22). We shall find examples of both approaches in later chapters.

Formal solutions for the mean intensity J_ν and the flux H_ν may be obtained immediately from the definitions (2.5) and (2.6) with the formal solutions (2.26) and (2.28). In the particular case of a semi-infinite atmosphere with no incident radiation on the surface $\tau = 0$, we find

$$J(\tau) = \frac{1}{2} \int_0^\infty S(t) E_1(|t - \tau|) \, dt \qquad (2.30)$$

and

$$H(\tau) = \frac{1}{2} \int_\tau^\infty S(t) E_2(t - \tau) \, dt - \frac{1}{2} \int_0^\tau S(t) E_2(\tau - t) \, dt. \qquad (2.31)$$

2.6 Eddington's Approximation and Krook's Extension

Before discussing some of the special approximations to S_ν which have been introduced in the past, it is instructive to consider the forms of J_ν, H_ν, and K_ν which result when I_ν is expanded—as it may essentially always be—in a series of Legendre polynomials in the angular variable μ, that is, when we write

$$I_\nu(\tau, \mu) = \sum_0^\infty a_n(\tau) P_n(\mu). \qquad (2.32)$$

Because of the orthogonality relation for Legendre polynomials,

$$\int_{-1}^{+1} P_n(\mu) P_m(\mu) \, d\mu = \frac{2}{2n + 1} \delta_{nm}, \qquad (2.33)$$

where δ_{nm} is the Kronecker delta, and because $\mu = P_1(\mu)$ and $\mu^2 = \frac{2}{3} P_2(\mu) + \frac{1}{3} P_0(\mu)$, we find from the definitions (2.5), (2.6), (2.7), and the expansion (2.32), that

$$J_\nu = a_0, \qquad H_\nu = \frac{a_1}{3}, \qquad K_\nu = \frac{a_0 + \frac{2}{5} a_2}{3}. \qquad (2.34)$$

Eddington's (1926) approximation follows by supposing that in the expansion (2.32) the single coefficient a_2 is zero—cf. Giovanelli (1963), Krook (1955)—so that

$$K_\nu(\tau) = \frac{1}{3} a_0(\tau), \qquad (2.35)$$

or, in view of Equation (2.34),

$$K_\nu(\tau) = \frac{1}{3} J_\nu(\tau), \qquad (2.36)$$

which is the usual expression of this approximation.

Consider the application of the approximation (2.36) to the transfer equation in a case where S_ν is independent of direction. Applying successively the operators

$$\frac{1}{2} \int_{-1}^{+1} \ldots d\mu, \qquad \frac{1}{2} \int_{-1}^{+1} \ldots \mu\, d\mu$$

to Equation (2.22), and using the definitions (2.5), (2.6), and (2.7), we find

$$\frac{dH_\nu}{d\tau_\nu} = J_\nu - S_\nu \qquad (2.37)$$

and

$$\frac{dK_\nu}{d\tau_\nu} = H_\nu. \qquad (2.38)$$

If we adopt the Eddington approximation (2.35) the above expression takes the form

$$\frac{1}{3}\frac{dJ_\nu}{d\tau_\nu} = H_\nu, \qquad (2.39)$$

so that finally,

$$\frac{1}{3}\frac{d^2 J_\nu}{d\tau_\nu^2} = J_\nu - S_\nu. \qquad (2.40)$$

This is Eddington's form of the transfer equation which provides the starting point for many of the investigations in this book. Its great advantage for approximate computations will become clear in Chapter 7 when we turn to the simultaneous solution of the transfer and statistical equilibrium equations.

It is frequently desirable to express this equation in terms of the optical depth at some definite frequency ν_0, for example that at the center of an absorption line. In this case it is readily seen that the equation assumes the form

$$\frac{d^2 J_\nu}{d\tau_0^2} - \frac{d}{d\tau_0}(\ln \phi_\nu')\frac{dJ_\nu}{d\tau_0} = x_\nu^2(J_\nu - S_\nu), \qquad (2.41)$$

in which τ_0 is the optical depth at the frequency ν_0, ϕ_ν' is the ratio of the absorption coefficient at frequency ν to that at ν_0, and $x_\nu = \sqrt{3}\,\phi_\nu'$.

A generalization of Eddington's approximation was given by Krook (1955). If we define the moments M_k of $I(\mu)$ by the relation

$$M_k = \frac{1}{2}\int_{-1}^{+1} I(\mu)\mu^k\, d\mu \qquad (2.42)$$

and then apply the operator

$$\frac{1}{2} \int_{-1}^{+1} \ldots \mu^k \, d\mu$$

to the transfer equation (2.22), we obtain the set of coupled equations

$$\frac{dM_{k+1}(t)}{dt} = M_k(t) - \left(\frac{1 + (-1)^k}{2(k+1)}\right) S(t), \qquad (2.43)$$

where k successively takes the values $0, 1, \ldots, 2n - 1$. We may solve this set of differential equations if we can express M_{2n} in terms of some or all of the lower-order moments. Krook suggests as the proper choice the relationship

$$a_0 M_{2n} + a_1 M_{2n-2} + \cdots + a_n M_0 = 0, \qquad (2.44)$$

where the coefficients a_j are those of μ^{2n-2j} in the Legendre polynomial $P_{2n}(\mu)$. As he points out, Equation (2.44) is equivalent to the requirement

$$\int_{-1}^{+1} P_{2n}(\mu) I(\mu) \, d\mu = 0. \qquad (2.45)$$

The relation (2.44) reduces, of course, to the Eddington relation (2.36) in the case $n = 1$.

For the exact transfer equation there is no difficulty in specifying the boundary conditions; indeed we have already done this in deriving the formal solutions (2.26) and (2.28). For the Eddington approximation, however, the position is less straightforward. If we write

$$J = \frac{1}{2} \int_0^1 I(\mu) \, d\mu + \frac{1}{2} \int_{-1}^0 I(\mu) \, d\mu, \qquad (2.46)$$

it is clear that to specify J at the boundary we need to know both the incident and emergent intensities. The former is specified and so presents no problem, but we do not know the latter—in fact, we are seeking to compute it. One commonly used procedure is to suppose for the purpose of forming the boundary condition, that the emergent intensity is independent of μ, in which case we would find that, at $\tau = 0$,

$$J(0) = \frac{1}{2} \bar{I} + \frac{1}{2} \int_{-1}^0 I_i^-(\mu) \, d\mu \qquad (2.47)$$

with $\bar{I}$ the (assumed constant) emergent intensity and I_i^- the incident intensity on the surface at $\tau = 0$. In a similar manner, and to the same approximation, we find that

$$H(0) = \frac{1}{4}\bar{I} + \frac{1}{2}\int_{-1}^{0} I_i^-(\mu)\mu \, d\mu. \qquad (2.48)$$

Eliminating the unknown $\bar{I}$, and using the Eddington approximation (2.39) we determine the following approximate boundary condition, at $\tau = 0$,

$$J(0) = \frac{2}{3}\left(\frac{dJ}{d\tau}\right)_0 + \frac{1}{2}\int_{-1}^{0}(1 - 2\mu)I_i^-(\mu)\,d\mu \qquad (2.49)$$

and, at $\tau = \tau_1$,

$$J(\tau_1) = -\frac{2}{3}\left(\frac{dJ}{d\tau}\right)_{\tau_1} + \frac{1}{2}\int_{0}^{1}(1 + 2\mu)I_i^+(\mu)\,d\mu, \qquad (2.50)$$

with $I_i^+(\mu)$ the incident intensity on the lower boundary.

In the work referenced above, Krook also studied the best representation for the boundary conditions in his approximation to the transfer equation. For the case $n = 1$, this amounts to replacing by $1/\sqrt{3}$ the factor $\frac{2}{3}$ in the above equations; in this work we shall adopt Krook's boundary conditions in the form:

$$J(0) = \frac{1}{\sqrt{3}}\left(\frac{dJ}{d\tau}\right)_0 + \frac{1}{2}\int_{-1}^{0}(1 - 2\mu)I_i^-(\mu)\,d\mu, \qquad (2.51)$$

$$J(\tau_1) = -\frac{1}{\sqrt{3}}\left(\frac{dJ}{d\tau}\right)_{\tau_1} + \frac{1}{2}\int_{0}^{1}(1 + 2\mu)I_i^+(\mu)\,d\mu. \qquad (2.52)$$

In the particular case of a semi-infinite atmosphere the second boundary condition is determined from the requirement that $J(\tau)$ is not to increase exponentially—which usually means that it remains finite in the limit $\tau_1 \rightarrow \infty$.

2.7 The Transfer Equation for Both Line and Continuum Absorption

Since most stellar spectral lines are seen against a continuous background, we must usually consider not only line absorption—as has been done for simplicity above—but continuous opacity as well. The extension is straightforward and can be derived in essentially the same way as we obtained Equation (2.22) from Equation (2.20). Thus, the balance of gains and losses to a pencil of radiation which may be absorbed by continuous or line processes, and which may receive contributions from these two sources, can be written in analogy with Equation (2.20) as

$$\mu \frac{dI_\nu}{dz} = (\kappa_\nu + \kappa_c)I_\nu - (\varepsilon_\nu + \varepsilon_c), \tag{2.53}$$

in which κ_ν and ε_ν refer to the line while κ_c and ε_c refer to the corresponding continuum processes. In subsequent work we shall find it desirable to refer to the two separate modifications of this equation obtained by defining a line (τ_ν) or a continuum (τ_c) optical depth. If, first, we divide throughout Equation (2.53) by κ_ν we will obtain the transfer equation

$$\mu \frac{dI_\nu}{d\tau_\nu} = (1 + r_\nu)\{I_\nu - S_\nu\} \tag{2.54}$$

with the composite source function S_ν defined by the equation

$$S_\nu = \frac{S_l + r_\nu S_c}{1 + r_\nu}, \tag{2.55}$$

while

$$S_l \equiv \frac{\varepsilon_\nu}{\kappa_\nu}, \qquad S_c \equiv \frac{\varepsilon_c}{\kappa_c}, \qquad \text{and} \qquad r_\nu \equiv \frac{\kappa_c}{\kappa_\nu}.$$

On the other hand, dividing by the continuous absorption coefficient, we obtain the equation

$$\mu \frac{dI_\nu}{d\tau_c} = (1 + \eta_\nu)\left\{I_\nu - \frac{S_c + \eta_\nu S_l}{1 + \eta_\nu}\right\}, \tag{2.56}$$

where $\eta_\nu \equiv \kappa_\nu/\kappa_c$.

The corresponding formal solutions for I_ν, J_ν, and H_ν are, of course, immediate. For example, from Equation (2.56) we obtain the following expression for the intensity emerging from a semi-infinite plane parallel atmosphere

$$I_\nu(0, \mu) = \int_0^\infty \left(\frac{S_c + \eta_\nu S_l}{1 + \eta_\nu}\right) \exp\left[-\int_0^{\tau_c} (1 + \eta_\nu)\frac{d\tau_c}{\mu}\right](1 + \eta_\nu)\frac{d\tau_c}{\mu}. \tag{2.57}$$

A substantial algebraic development has been built up about such expressions as Equation (2.57), particularly for the case of LTE and for the computation of the "equivalent width" of an absorption line through the equation:

$$W = \int_0^\infty \frac{I_c - I_\lambda}{I_c}\, d\lambda, \qquad (2.58)$$

in which I_λ is the intensity given by Equation (2.57), while I_c is the corresponding value of the integral in the limit of zero line opacity, i.e., when η_ν is zero. We shall not here discuss the forms which have been derived to represent the integral on the right of Equation (2.58); a comprehensive summary is given by Aller (1960).

REFERENCES

ALLER, L. H., 1960, "Quantitative Analysis of Normal Stellar Spectra," *Stellar Atmospheres*, edited by J. L. Greenstein. Chicago: University of Chicago Press, Ch. 4.

CHANDRASEKHAR, S., 1950, *Radiative Transfer*. Oxford: Clarendon Press.

EDDINGTON, A. S., 1926, *The Internal Constitution of the Stars*. Cambridge: Cambridge University Press.

GIOVANELLI, R. G., 1963, "Diffusion Through Non-uniform Media," *Progress in Optics*, II. Amsterdam: North Holland Publ. Co., p. 111.

KOURGANOFF, V., 1952, *Basic Methods in Transfer Problems*. Oxford: Clarendon Press.

KROOK, MAX, 1955, "On the Solution of Equations of Transfer I," *Astrophys. J.* *122*, 488.

SCHWARZSCHILD, K., 1906, "Über das Gleichgewicht der Sonnenatmosphäre," *Göttinger Nachr. 41.*

UNSÖLD, A., 1955, *Physik der Sternatmosphären*, Second ed. Berlin, Springer-Verlag.

3

The Source Function

In the previous chapter we saw that our basic experience of radiant energy in nature suggested a definition of the specific intensity, the absorption coefficient, and the emission coefficient. Nothing was said about the physical mechanisms responsible for production or destruction of the radiation, nor how ε_ν and κ_ν depended on the specific characteristics, and the environment, of the emitting and absorbing matter; as introduced they are purely phenomenological parameters.

In general, the value of the source function S_ν—or the ratio $\varepsilon_\nu/\kappa_\nu$—must be sought from a microscopic analysis of the excitation processes occurring in the medium. In one special case this is unnecessary, namely when the emitting and absorbing material is enclosed in a cavity whose walls are opaque and maintained under constant conditions. For such a case Kirchhoff showed that

$$\varepsilon_\nu = \kappa_\nu B_\nu(T), \tag{3.1}$$

where $B_\nu(T)$ is a universal function of the thermodynamic temperature of the walls. The form of B_ν was derived by Planck (the function is now known as the Planck function) and is given by the well-known relation

$$B_\nu(T) = \frac{2h\nu^3}{c^2} \left[\exp\left(\frac{h\nu}{kT}\right) - 1 \right]^{-1}. \tag{3.2}$$

27

In a stellar atmosphere, or under usual conditions in a laboratory discharge, material is neither in temperature equilibrium nor in a cavity, and Kirchhoff's law (3.1) is not obviously applicable. Nevertheless, it may be in a state approximating this closely enough for practical purposes, and under these circumstances a state of local thermodynamic equilibrium is said to exist. Whether this is so for any particular situation can only be decided, however, from a microscopic analysis.

The fundamental problem in the theory of formation of spectral lines lies in the specification of S_ν, or equivalently of ε_ν and κ_ν, as a function of position, of frequency, and possibly of direction. As such it has received considerable attention and it is appropriate to give here a brief review of previous attempts to solve this central problem in spectral line formation. These attempts may conveniently be considered under three separate categories, (1) theories for purely scattering atmospheres, (2) theories studying the detailed atomic processes of emission and absorption, and (3) theories based on the assumption of LTE or of small departures from this state.

3.1 The Meaning of Line Scattering

A situation which is in some respects the antithesis of local thermodynamic equilibrium is that of pure scattering. The state of LTE is reached if the radiant and thermal (i.e., kinetic) energies couple so strongly that the energy of an absorbed photon is immediately converted to kinetic energy by a de-exciting collision—or, in other words, if collisions dominate all transition processes. In assuming pure scattering, however, we suppose that no such interaction ever takes place; the energy of the radiation field is supposed to be conserved as radiation, although its directional and frequency distributions may be modified in its passage through the gas.

In practice, some such re-emission will in general occur and some authors have introduced a scattering coefficient (often denoted by σ) which is intended to measure the fraction of the absorbed energy which is re-emitted.* In this case κ_ν is taken as the sum of a "true" absorption coefficient and a "scattering" coefficient. This may lead to considerable confusion when examined on a microscopic scale. To illustrate the difficulty let us consider the scattering of Lyman β of hydrogen.

---

* This energy is, of course, included in our macroscopic emission coefficient ε_ν.

On absorption the atom is raised from the ground to the $n = 3$ state, from which it may leave—ultimately to return to the ground state—by various processes. The de-excitation may take place by Lβ emission, by Hα and Lα emission, by collisional de-excitation, either directly $(3 \to 1)$ or via the 2 state $(3 \to 2 \to 1)$, or by part collision and part spontaneous de-excitation. Since the collisional de-excitation rate depends linearly on the local particle density, and to a lesser extent on the local electron temperature, it is obvious that the probability that Lβ will be re-emitted (this process would surely be a scattering) is fundamentally a function of the atmospheric parameters. Thus, neither the wavelength-integrated atomic scattering coefficient nor the "true" atomic absorption coefficient would then be representable as a purely atomic constant—although their sum (the absorption coefficient per atom) certainly would be. In a stellar atmosphere, it may well be objected, the density is so low that spontaneous de-excitation from the 3 state—either directly or through the 2 state—would be several orders of magnitude more important than collisional processes, which, it could be argued, would then be negligible. Even granting this,* what should we take as the scattering coefficient? It is frequently suggested that it should be given by the relation,

$$\frac{\sigma_\nu}{\kappa_\nu} = \frac{A_{31}}{A_{31} + A_{32}}$$

where the A's are the Einstein transition probabilities; for hydrogen this ratio is about 0.6. This may be suitable for describing the scattering of Lβ from a thin low-density slab of material; however, in an optically thick slab, such as a stellar atmosphere, this procedure leaves open the fundamental question as to what happens to the Lα and Hα photons which are emitted in nearly all the cases when Lβ is not re-emitted. These photons may be absorbed again and give rise to a new Lβ photon. This photon, however, would not have been present but for the absorption of a previous one and so, in a very real sense, the process

$$\text{L}\beta \to \text{L}\alpha + \text{H}\alpha \to \text{L}\beta \tag{3.3}$$

constitutes what we intuitively would regard as a "scattering" of the original photon. The probability of the process (3.3) depends on the

---

* Which we would not, since it contains the fundamental flaw that the radiation then has no source in the atmosphere.

radiation strengths; if we regard it as a "scattering" to be included in the scattering coefficient, it poses the unpleasant problem that then σ_ν would depend in an obscure manner on the solution of the transfer equation in which it enters.

These difficulties are unnecessary; we shall not introduce a "scattering" coefficient, not only because its definition would be ambiguous but simply because its introduction is unnecessary and irrelevant; the "scattering" terms appear quite naturally in the transfer equation.*

Consider a photon arising as a result of a collisional excitation at some location in the gas. Its energy will be transmitted through the atmosphere in the form of radiation until it ultimately escapes, or is converted back to thermal energy. If radiative de-excitation is more probable than collisional, the energy travels in the form of radiation a mean distance which is greater than the mean distance $1/\kappa$ traveled between an individual emission and absorption. Thus we may anticipate (as indeed we find) that the local radiation field at a point in the atmosphere will then not in general reflect average thermodynamic conditions within an absorption scale length $1/\kappa$, but within a—larger— *diffusion* scale length. If on the other hand, the particle density is high enough that the probability of radiative de-excitation becomes small, i.e., scattering becomes negligible, then the radiation field within a distance $1/\kappa$ will reflect the local thermal conditions. When this latter situation occurs we have a state of local thermodynamic equilibrium since then the radiation is closely coupled, via collisions, with the thermal kinetic energy of the gas.

3.2 Theories of S_ν for Purely Scattering Atmospheres

Early attempts to understand the formation of the Fraunhofer spectrum were made by Schuster (1905) and by Schwarzschild (1906). They adopted an atmospheric model—known now as the Schuster-Schwarzschild model—consisting of a "photospheric" layer having only continuous opacity (and so emitting a continuous spectrum) overlying which was a "reversing layer" having only line opacity. Most consideration was given to the case in which the line opacity arose from pure scattering.

---

* The situation is different for electron scattering of radiation where we may introduce unambiguously a scattering coefficient.

The specification of S_ν in such a scattering atmosphere is straightforward. Consider the absorption and emission of radiation in an element of volume of thickness dz and cross section $d\sigma$ in the xy-plane. The radiant energy in the frequency interval $d\nu'$ absorbed by this element in unit time is

$$\int_{4\pi} I'_\nu(\mu)\kappa'_\nu \, d\nu'(dz/\mu)(\mu \, d\sigma) \, d\omega, \qquad (3.4)$$

and this is all re-emitted, by the hypothesis of pure scattering. Suppose, for simplicity, that the re-emission is isotropic and that the probability that energy absorbed at ν' is re-emitted into the frequency interval $d\nu$ about ν is $R(\nu', \nu) \, d\nu$, then

$$\varepsilon_\nu = \int J'_\nu R(\nu', \nu)\kappa'_\nu \, d\nu', \qquad (3.5)$$

so that

$$S_\nu = \frac{\int J'_\nu R(\nu', \nu)\kappa'_\nu \, d\nu'}{\kappa_\nu}. \qquad (3.6)$$

The form of $R(\nu', \nu)$ will be considered in Chapter 5 in reference to a more general theory than that considered here; however, we should mention two cases which have been extensively studied in the literature. The first is that of *coherent scattering*, in which

$$R(\nu', \nu) = \delta(\nu' - \nu), \qquad (3.7)$$

δ being the Dirac delta function; in this approximation an absorbed photon is, therefore, assumed to be re-emitted with no change in frequency. The other extreme case is that of *complete redistribution*, for which

$$R(\nu', \nu) = \phi(\nu), \qquad (3.8)$$

where $\phi(\nu)$—defined as the ratio $\kappa_\nu/\int \kappa_\nu \, d\nu$—is the normalized profile of the absorption coefficient; in this case, therefore, the frequencies of the absorbed and re-emitted photons are completely uncorrelated.

Corresponding to these extreme cases we find, from Equation (3.6), that for coherent scattering,

$$S_\nu = J_\nu, \qquad (3.9)$$

while for complete redistribution,

$$S_\nu = \int J_\nu \phi_\nu \, d\nu. \qquad (3.10)$$

Early studies were set almost entirely in terms of coherent scattering in which case Eddington's approximation to the transfer equation gives, in the "reversing layer,"

$$\frac{d^2 J_\nu}{d\tau_\nu^2} = 0, \tag{3.11}$$

which has the solution

$$J_\nu = \alpha_\nu + \beta_\nu \tau_\nu, \tag{3.12}$$

and it is to be noted that τ_ν is a monochromatic—"scattering"—optical depth in the line. If no external radiation is incident on the top of the atmosphere, $I_i^- = 0$ in the boundary condition (2.51) appropriate to the top of the line-forming region; we therefore obtain the following relationship between the integration constants:

$$\alpha_\nu = \frac{1}{\sqrt{3}} \beta_\nu. \tag{3.13}$$

At the lower boundary of the reversing layer $\tau_\nu = \tau_1$, and the boundary condition (2.52) then requires that

$$\alpha_\nu + \beta_\nu \tau_1 = -\frac{1}{\sqrt{3}} \beta_\nu + C_\nu, \tag{3.14}$$

with

$$C_\nu = \frac{1}{2} \int_0^1 I_i^+(\mu)(1 + 2\mu) \, d\mu, \tag{3.15}$$

where $I_i^+(\mu)$ represents the photospheric intensity incident from below on the base of the reversing layer, that is, $I_i^+(\mu)$ is the continuum intensity $I_c(0, \mu)$ near ν.

Equations (3.13), (3.14), and (3.15) lead immediately to the solution

$$J_\nu(\tau_\nu) = \frac{C_\nu(1 + \sqrt{3} \, \tau_\nu)}{(2 + \sqrt{3} \, \tau_1)}, \tag{3.16}$$

and, by Equation (3.9), this also represents the source function. Within the limits of the Eddington approximation and the assumption of coherent scattering, the emergent intensity $I_\nu(0, \mu)$ then follows immediately from the formal solution (2.29) with $S_\nu(\tau)$ given by Equation (3.16). Thus,

$$I_\nu(0, \mu) = I_i^+(\mu)e^{-\tau_1/\mu} + \int_0^{\tau_1} \left(\frac{C_\nu}{2 + \sqrt{3} \, \tau_1}\right)(1 + \sqrt{3} \, t)e^{-t/\mu} \, dt/\mu \tag{3.17}$$

or

$$I_v(0, \mu) = I_i^+(\mu)e^{-\tau_1/\mu} + \frac{[1 + \sqrt{3}\,\mu - (1 + \sqrt{3}\,\mu + \sqrt{3}\,\tau_1)e^{-\tau_1/\mu}]C_v}{(2 + \sqrt{3}\,\tau_1)}.$$

(3.18)

In particular, for large τ_1 (greater than 10, say),

$$I_v(0, \mu) \simeq \frac{C_v(1 + \sqrt{3}\,\mu)}{\sqrt{3}\,\tau_1},$$

(3.19)

so that the "depth" of the line is, roughly, given as

$$\frac{I_v(0, \mu)}{I_c(0, \mu)} \sim \frac{1}{\tau_1}.$$

(3.20)

For lines for which τ_1 is large, therefore, the emergent central intensity is predicted to be correspondingly small—this arises simply because the reversing layer reflects nearly all the incident photospheric flux.

It is important to note that the emergent intensity (3.19) is not directly controlled by the intensive parameters (temperature, density) of the line-forming region; two pure scattering atmospheres of entirely different structure but with a common value of τ_1 at the line center would produce a line of the same central depth. In particular, the temperature of the line-forming region may be higher, lower, or equal to that of the photosphere but an absorption line will still be produced.

We can look at this result in another and fundamentally important way. The source function given by Equation (3.16) for this case of pure coherent scattering does not explicitly depend on the temperature in the line-forming region. The observation of a deep absorption line—as predicted by Equation (3.20)—does not necessarily mean that the *temperature* of the line-forming region is lower than in the "photosphere"—it simply means that the *source function* is lower. In our everyday experience we become used to the idea that cold bodies absorb radiation, and so we have a natural tendency to associate an absorption line with the presence of a cold gas overlying a hotter one. In situations far removed from LTE—as, for example, in this case of pure scattering—we shall have to revise this preconception. The presence of an absorption line in a stellar spectrum is no guarantee at all that the line-forming region is colder than the region producing the continuum.

Of course, this is not to say that the Schuster-Schwarzschild model of a pure coherent scattering reversing layer is at all valid for a stellar atmosphere, though it finds application elsewhere. Indeed, the very low value predicted for the intensity in the line core led to its rejection long before more powerful theoretical arguments forced its abandonment. At the same time, the model serves as a forceful illustration of the important point made in the preceding paragraph.

3.3 Theories of S_v Based on the Study of Detailed Atomic Processes

Under this heading may be classed those approaches which seek to specify the individual values of ε_v and κ_v by a study of the detailed atomic processes which maintain the relative populations of the upper and lower states of the transition. Knowing these populations and the frequency dependence of the emission and absorption coefficients, we may uniquely specify S_v. Logically this would seem the most satisfactory procedure if it is at all feasible, and it is, in any case, the one adopted throughout this book.

Transitions maintaining the populations of the atomic levels are, in general, both radiative and collisional. A good deal of attention has been given to situations where collisional effects are presumed to be negligible. We shall discuss that degenerate case first, noting that, in a very definite sense, the pure scattering atmosphere of Schuster and Schwarzschild is the prototype.

3.3.1 Theories neglecting Collisions

In this category the earliest study appears to be that of Rosseland (1926). In his "theory of cycles," Rosseland studied the equilibrium populations of the states of a three-level atom bathed in a "dilute" field of blackbody radiation, i.e., one for which the radiation intensity is given by

$$J_v = W \frac{2h\nu^3}{c^2} (e^{h\nu/kT} - 1)^{-1}, \qquad (3.21)$$

where the "dilution factor" W is less than unity. Rosseland was able to show that, under these conditions, an atmosphere would tend to degrade the shortest wavelength 1–3 photons into the longer wavelength 1–2 and 2–3 radiation. Equivalently, the cycle of transitions 1–2–3–1

is less favored than that proceeding in the reverse direction, 1–3–2–1;*
the ratio of the rates of the cycles being roughly equal to W.

The cycles would proceed at the same rate when $W = 1$ since this implies that the material is in a cavity where detailed balance applies. The origin of the different rates for the two cycles lies in the fact that, while the rate of an absorption transition is reduced by the factor W below its value in a full field of blackbody radiation, the spontaneous transition rates are unaffected. A cycle which can be completed with two absorptions and one emission therefore occurs roughly at a rate proportional to W^2, while the rate for a cycle needing one absorption and two emissions for its completion depends only on the first power of W. The fact that the radiation is dilute ($W < 1$) therefore causes the atmosphere to "fluoresce" in the 1–2 and 2–3 radiation, i.e., to emit radiation at longer wavelengths at the expense of absorption in the shorter. This mechanism is frequently held to be responsible for the presence of emission lines in stellar spectra, it being argued that their strength arises from the degradation of shorter wavelength photons.

A strict application of Rosseland's ideas requires the following conditions to be met. First, the radiation field at all relevant frequencies must be specifiable in terms of Equation (3.21) with a single temperature T; second, the atmosphere which is excited by the incident radiation must be optically thin; and third, it must be possible to demonstrate that collisional excitation plays a negligible part in the formation of the line radiation. This is not to say that Rosseland's theorem is not applicable under more general conditions; for example, if W is very small only a correspondingly gross departure from the distribution (3.21) can prevent its applicability, provided that the second and third points above are satisfied. Nevertheless, it is not entirely clear how one may be certain *a priori* of its correctness, and until this is clarified it seems safer to start any analysis from more general considerations.

Since the determination of the source function for cases of pure radiative excitation is a special case of the following section, we shall not proceed further with it here, but shall instead turn to the more general case.

---

* In fact, we encounter a difficulty that such cycles are not physically possible for optically permitted transitions since they would violate the selection rules on the angular quantum number l. We may disregard this problem in our descriptive approach. The difficulty does not arise when level 3 is the continuum.

3.3.2 Theories Including Collisions

The most fundamental early analyses of line formation in stellar atmospheres were given by Eddington and by Milne. Although limited to simple atomic models, their results have such an essential bearing on our development that they merit a detailed study here. Milne (1928) considered the case only of coherent scattering: Although this is now known to be a generally poor representation, we adopt it for an illustration of the Milne-Eddington formulation.

Consider the excitation of a two-level atom in which the upper and lower levels are respectively labeled 2 and 1. The relative populations of these states are governed by the requirement that the rate of exit from one is equal to the rate of entrance to the other. Algebraically this condition may be stated as

$$\left(4\pi B_{12}\int J_\nu\phi_\nu\,d\nu + C_{12}\right)n_1 = \left(A_{21} + 4\pi B_{21}\int J_\nu\phi_\nu\,d\nu + C_{21}\right)n_2,$$

(3.22)

in which C_{12} and C_{21} are rates of collisional excitation and de-excitation, the A- and B-factors are the usual Einstein radiation coefficients defined in Chapter 4, while ϕ_ν is the normalized profile of the absorption coefficient, which we assume to equal that of the stimulated emission. Well-known relationships hold between A_{21}, B_{21}, and B_{12}; as shown in Chapter 4, we may write

$$B_{12} = \frac{c^2}{8\pi h\nu^3}\frac{g_2}{g_1}A_{21}$$

(3.23)

and

$$B_{21} = \frac{c^2}{8\pi h\nu^3}A_{21},$$

(3.24)

where g_1 and g_2 are statistical weights. It follows from the principle of detailed balance (Chapter 6) that the collision rates are related through the equation

$$C_{12} = C_{21}\frac{g_2}{g_1}\exp\left(-\alpha_{12}\right),$$

(3.25)

with $\alpha_{12} = \eta_{12}/kT_e$, η_{12} being the energy separation of the two states and T_e the distributional temperature of the particles (usually electrons) causing the collision transitions.

For isotropic emission and absorption we may write

$$\varepsilon_\nu = \frac{A_{21}h\nu n_2}{4\pi}\chi(\nu) \tag{3.26}$$

and

$$\kappa_\nu = \left(B_{12} - B_{21}\frac{n_2}{n_1}\right)h\nu n_1\phi(\nu), \tag{3.27}$$

where $\chi(\nu)$ is the normalized profile of the emission coefficient. Equation (3.26) is simply a formal expression and is to be used with care. The profile $\chi(\nu)$ will be considered in some detail in Chapter 5; here we merely note the necessity to pay due regard to the way in which the emission arises. First, there will be a certain amount of emission due directly to collisional excitation, the excited atoms subsequently giving up energy by spontaneous emission. Provided that the energy spectrum of the colliding particles is constant over the range of energies corresponding to the line width, the profile of the emission coefficient for *collisionally* excited emission must be identical to that of the absorption coefficient. The point is considered in detail in Chapter 5. The remainder of the emission, however, arises from "scattering," i.e., from photoelectric absorption followed by re-emission. If this scattering is coherent—as Milne assumed it to be—then the total emissivity from collisional excitation and scattering must be expressible as the sum

$$\varepsilon_\nu = p\left[\kappa_\nu J_\nu + \frac{C_{12}h\nu\phi(\nu)n_1}{4\pi}\right], \tag{3.28}$$

in which the first term in the bracket on the right-hand side represents the coherently scattered contribution, while the second arises from collisional excitation. The multiplier p represents the probability that an atom in the upper state will decay by spontaneous emission, that is,

$$p = \frac{A_{21}}{A_{21} + C_{21} + 4\pi B_{21}\int J_\nu\phi_\nu\,d\nu}.$$

On the basis of Equations (3.22) to (3.28) we readily deduce, after some algebra, the Milne expression for S_ν appropriate to this case, namely

$$S_\nu = \frac{J_\nu + \varepsilon B_\nu(T_e)}{1 + \varepsilon} \tag{3.29}$$

with

$$\varepsilon = \frac{C_{21}[1 - \exp(-\alpha_{12})]}{A_{21}}. \tag{3.30}$$

In order to apply these expressions we must be able to demonstrate that the scattering is indeed coherent and, which is more important still, that the assumption of a two-level atom gives an adequate description of the physical problem.   The simple dichotomy into a scattering and a collisional term was early realized to be inadequate for the theoretical interpretation of stellar spectra.   Pannekoek (1930) investigated the size of ε under stellar atmospheric conditions and showed that, even for weak lines it was so extremely small that "scattering" would dominate in line formation for Milne's two-level atom.   This, however, would imply an almost zero central intensity for the line—for exactly the same reason that it did in the Schuster-Schwarzschild case of Section 3.2—unless the electron temperature in the line-forming region were considerably higher than that in the photosphere. This apparent difficulty was overcome by Strömgren (1935), who took account of ionization to, and recombinations from, the continuum and hence was able to show that under certain circumstances a nonzero central intensity was not incompatible with "scattering" being the dominant source of line formation.   Like Milne, Strömgren assumed the scattering to be coherent.

As long ago as 1929 Eddington, in a frequently quoted passage, urged the cruciality of the question as to "whether light absorbed in one part of the line is re-emitted in precisely the same part of the line."   He pointed out that if this were so, i.e., if coherent scattering applied, the intensity at any frequency in the line could be computed independently of that at all others.   If, however, the frequency of a photon is not preserved on scattering, the intensity at one frequency depends, in general, on that at all others so that the computational problem is much more difficult and the physical basis of line formation is greatly modified.

On general quantum mechanical grounds Spitzer (1944) studied the question as to whether the scattering is coherent, and pointed out its close relationship to the problem of line broadening.   He advanced strong arguments in favor of noncoherent scattering as the mechanism most likely to be operative in stellar atmospheres.   Spitzer's study was stimulated by the work of Houtgast (1942), who considered the observational implications of noncoherent scattering and concluded it to be necessary in order to account for the observed wing shapes of solar Fraunhofer lines.   This, however, is probably not a question to be decided on the basis of spectral line observations of stars, since the result may well be sensitive to the model adopted for their interpretation. Rather it should be answered as far as possible on purely quantum mechanical grounds, preferably supported by laboratory experiments. With the theoretical techniques recently evolved for handling problems of line broadening this question may now be amenable to a fairly precise treatment.

3.4 Theories of S_ν Based on the Assumption of LTE or Near-LTE

An entirely different approach to the specification of S_ν has been urged by Unsöld and others in recent years and has been extensively applied to the analysis of solar and stellar spectra. Doubting, quite reasonably, that a simple two- or three-level approximation is adequate for computing the emergent radiation, with a reliability sufficient for observational analysis, in a line of an atom with a complex level structure, Unsöld (1955, 1963) has given the following arguments for adopting the enormous simplification of LTE.

If the radiation field in an atmosphere is "bounded" in the sense that it cannot escape, then it is effectively in an enclosure and so couples completely with the kinetic energy of the particles making up the atmosphere. Consequently a unique thermodynamic temperature can be assigned to describe the way in which the energy of the atoms is partitioned among the various degrees of freedom. Suppose the possibility of line scattering is granted. If this is of such a character that the photon frequency is changed on scattering—and this is the most physically meaningful case in a stellar atmosphere—then it will be preferentially re-emitted toward the line center where the value of the absorption coefficient profile ϕ_ν is greatest. Hence, the essential condition we require is that the photons in the line center be bounded. However, the crucial question is to decide what is meant by "bounded," or equivalently, how great is the optical depth over which a photon's energy is propagated before being converted into heat by a de-exciting collision. It is implied in Unsöld's analysis of the problem that this depth is unity in the line center so that, since the observed radiation at all but the line center arises at lower depths, almost the whole line may be taken to be formed in LTE.

This conclusion is premature, however. The condition of "boundedness" is one which has meaning only when applied to the radiation of the atom in *all* its emitted frequencies. It is incorrect to consider a photon as bounded if, on absorption, it has a significant probability of being re-emitted, in another line altogether, as a photon which can then escape from the atmosphere.

The essential requirement for the applicability of LTE is that the radiation field *as a whole* couples fully with the local thermal field (through exciting and de-exciting collisions). It is not sufficient that a photon merely be absorbed, the essential question is what happens after it is absorbed, and this question is not answered by Unsöld. Hence, the radiation field needs to be bounded, in the above sense, in *all* lines emitted by the atom before one can expect it to couple so completely with the thermal energy that LTE is applicable. Even then LTE will only be applicable to the extent that the thermal structure does not change appreciably in the distance between the creation of a photon and the destruction of its energy by a de-exciting collision. This condition is relaxed somewhat if the continuum radiation field is Planckian since then it is only necessary that those atomic radiations be bounded which contribute significantly more to the local intensity than does the continuum. This would seem to require boundedness in all lines for which the line center absorption coefficient exceeds that of the continuum; this, however, is a necessary condition for the line to be distinguishable at all from the continuous background.

For a simple atomic structure Unsöld's argument cannot hold since in a tenuous gas the radiation will be scattered many times before its energy is converted to thermal energy, and the diffusion length of the photon is then much greater than unit optical path length. While his emphasis was to the application of LTE to the energy-level populations of atoms of complex structure, the same general remarks nevertheless hold in that case; the mere possibility of the transfer of photon energies back and forth between different lines does not help to establish an LTE distribution.

An essentially similar approach to that of Unsöld has been adopted by various authors (e.g., Böhm (1960), Swihart (1956)) mainly in connection with attempts to establish the validity of the Saha relation. In this procedure one attempts to estimate the ratio

$$C = \frac{\int J_\nu \kappa_\nu \, d\nu / h\nu}{\int B_\nu \kappa_\nu \, d\nu / h\nu} \tag{3.31}$$

(or some similar function) and compares the computed value of C with its LTE value of unity which is demanded to satisfy detailed balance. Were J *known* at all frequencies and at each atmospheric location we could, of course, test the applicability of LTE in this or some other way. The adopted procedure, however, lies in assuming LTE and thus computing the ratio C. When, as almost automatically happens for $\tau \gtrsim 0.1$, this gives values of C close to unity, the assumption of LTE below this depth is *consistent*; it most certainly does not prove it is valid. Granted that the tests are sometimes claimed as consistency tests, the implication that they are also validity tests is usually very strongly made. Certainly when C differs greatly from unity, LTE is invalid (since it is then inconsistent with its own assumption).

The point, of course, is that one cannot establish the validity of an assumption without appealing outside the assumption—indeed, in this case one must make a microscopic analysis of the excitation state of the gas as has been done, for example, by Pagel (1957) in his attempts to establish the applicability of LTE to the H^- continuum in the sun.

An attempt by Lecar (1962) to estimate the departures from LTE in a pure hydrogen atmosphere—modeled after an AO star atmosphere— is pertinent here. Lecar's procedure was to assume LTE and then to solve in a standard manner for the temperature and density distributions through the conditions of radiative and hydrostatic equilibrium. For each depth he was then able to compute a radiation intensity for each pertinent wavelength and on this basis to determine the steady-state hydrogen populations from the statistical equilibrium equations; these populations he compared with the initially assumed LTE values. He concluded that the populations of the bound and free hydrogen levels were not, in fact, in LTE, although this was found to have little effect on the computed atmospheric structure.

Recognizing this procedure to be only the first step in an iterative process which should presumably converge if continued far enough, Lecar (1965) extended it to a hundred iterations. Convergence was not achieved, however, nor was an accelerated iteration procedure any more successful. Hence, finally Lecar decided that his earlier conclusion was premature and, in fact, that the influence of departures from LTE on the computed structure of an atmosphere is still an open question.

In a series of papers similar in spirit to the above, Henyey (1946), Henyey and Grasberger (1955), and Grasberger (1957) have attempted to derive a method for handling departures from LTE under the assumption that these departures are small. The linearity following from this assumption allows an elegant solution of the problem; however, as Thomas has clearly shown in his analysis of this question, a small perturbation approach is predestined to failure in a situation where the absorption coefficient fluctuates widely from line to line and from line to the neighboring continuum. The essential difference between this radiative case and the corresponding small departures approach adopted in the usual discussions of transport phenomena which neglect radiation lies in two factors, the existence of a boundary from which photons may escape, and the wide range of variation of the absorption coefficient—coupled with the possibility that a photon in one line may be converted into a photon in an entirely different spectral region with a different absorption coefficient and diffusion scale length. In the elastic collision interactions entering the usual discussions of transport phenomena these difficulties do not occur—in Thomas' (1965) words "the elastic collisional ensemble is 'gray,'—all the particles have effectively the same free-path."

3.5 A General Formal Expression for S_ν

The formal expressions (3.26) and (3.27) for the emission and absorption coefficients may be combined to form an expression for the source function

$$S_\nu = \frac{A_{21}n_2\chi(\nu)}{4\pi(B_{12}n_1 - B_{21}n_2)\phi(\nu)} \tag{3.32}$$

provided that we assume that the profiles of the stimulated emission and the absorption coefficients are identical.* If we introduce the well-known relations between the Einstein A- and B-coefficients, the formal expression (3.32) reduces at once to the form

$$S_\nu = \frac{2h\nu^3}{c^2} \left(\frac{n_1}{n_2}\frac{g_2}{g_1} - 1\right)^{-1} \psi(\nu), \tag{3.33}$$

with $\psi(\nu)$ the ratio $\chi(\nu)/\phi(\nu)$. If we define an excitation temperature T_{ex} by the relation

$$\frac{n_2}{n_1} = \frac{g_2}{g_1} \exp\left[-\frac{E_{12}}{kT_{\text{ex}}}\right], \tag{3.34}$$

* It has been suggested—Oxenius (1964)—that this is not so although it is difficult to see how it could be otherwise since stimulated emission is physically identical to negative absorption.

Equation (3.33) may be written

$$S_\nu = B_\nu(T_{ex})\psi(\nu) \tag{3.35}$$

an expression introduced by Thomas (1957) in a slightly different notation. In the important case of complete redistribution $\psi(\nu)$ is unity and

$$S_\nu = B_\nu(T_{ex}), \tag{3.36}$$

which clearly reduces to the LTE result if $T_{ex} = T_e$, that is, if the population ratio (3.34) is given by the Boltzmann relation at the local "temperature."

While these formal expressions are frequently useful and are completely general, it must be remembered that they are only formal, and in no sense constitute a solution to the problem. Indeed, as we have remarked above, the population ratio n_2/n_1 depends in general on the radiation intensity and so on the distribution of S_ν through the gas. Thus, the excitation temperature is implicitly a function of the excitation state of the gas as a whole.

REFERENCES

Böhm, K-H., 1960, *Stellar Atmospheres*, edited by J. L. Greenstein. Chicago: Chicago University Press, Ch. 3.

Eddington, A. S., 1929, "The Formation of Absorption Lines," *Mon. Not. R. Astr. Soc. 89*, 620.

Grasberger, W., 1957, "Hydrogen Lines in an Atmosphere with Near Thermodynamic Radiative Equilibrium," *Astrophys. J. 125*, 750.

Henyey, L. G., 1946, "Near Thermodynamic Radiative Equilibrium," *Astrophys. J. 103*, 332.

Henyey, L. G., and W. Grasberger, 1955, "Near Thermodynamic Equilibrium II," *Astrophys. J. 122*, 498.

Houtgast, J., 1942, "The Variations in the Profiles of Strong Fraunhofer Lines Along a Radius of the Solar Disc." Dissertation, University of Utrecht.

Lecar, M., 1962, "Departures from Local Thermodynamic Equilibrium in an AO Star Atmosphere," *NASA Tech. Note D-2110*.

Lecar, M., 1965, *Discussion, Proceedings, Second Harvard-Smithsonian Conference on Stellar Atmospheres*, p. 217.

Milne, E. A., 1928, "The Effect of Collisions on Monochromatic Radiative Equilibrium," *Mon. Not. R. Astr. Soc. 88*, 493.

Oxenius, J., 1964, "Transfer Equation for a Two-Level Atom in a Scattering Atmosphere (I)," *JILA Report No. 8*.

Pagel, B. J., 1957, "The Emission of Continuous Radiation in Stellar Atmospheres," *Astrophys. J. 125*, 298.

PANNEKOEK, A., 1930, "The Theoretical Contours of Absorption Lines," *Mon. Not. R. Astr. Soc. 91,* 139.

ROSSELAND, S., 1926, "On the Origin of Bright Lines in Stellar Spectra," *Astrophys. J. 63,* 218.

SCHUSTER, A., 1905, "Radiation through a Foggy Atmosphere," *Astrophys. J. 21,* 1.

SCHWARZSCHILD, K., 1906, "Über das Gleichgewicht der Sonnenatmosphäre," *Göttinger Nachr. No. 41.*

SPITZER, L., 1944, "Notes on the Theory of Non-coherent Scattering," *Astrophys. J. 99,* 1.

STRÖMGREN, B., 1935, "The Influence of Electron Captures on the Contours of Franhofer Lines," *Z. Astrophys. 10,* 237.

SWIHART, T., 1956, "Model Atmospheres and the Solar Continuum," *Astrophys. J. 123,* 143.

THOMAS, R. N., 1957, "The Source Function in a Non-Equilibrium Atmosphere; I, The Resonance Lines," *Astrophys. J. 125,* 260.

THOMAS, R. N., 1965, *Some Aspects of Non-Equilibrium Thermodynamics in the Presence of a Radiation Field.* Boulder: University of Colorado Press.

UNSÖLD, A., 1955, *Physik der Sternatmosphären,* Second ed. Berlin: Springer-Verlag.

UNSÖLD, A., 1963, "Über Abweichungen vom lokalen thermodynamischen Gleichgewicht in der Sonnenatmosphäre," *Z. Phys. 171,* 44.

4

The Line Absorption Coefficient

It has been quite clear from the beginning of this book that a detailed knowledge of the absorption and emission coefficients in a gas must be sought in order to study the formation of spectral lines. We have seen in the preceding chapters how these quantities may be defined in terms of ideal experiments; as introduced they are macroscopic quantities defined in terms of everyday experience. An adequate understanding of their physical characteristics, however, must be sought from a detailed microscopic examination of the interaction of electromagnetic radiation with the atoms comprising the gas. In this chapter we shall look at this problem in much less than its full generality but in sufficient detail for most of our needs.

In the special case of thermodynamic equilibrium, ε_ν and κ_ν are related by Kirchhoff's law, namely

$$\varepsilon_\nu = \kappa_\nu B_\nu(T), \tag{4.1}$$

with $B_\nu(T)$ the Planck function. For the limited frequency range covering a given spectral line, $B_\nu(T)$ is effectively constant so that the frequency dependences of the emission and absorption are identical. We may look at this in another way and say that a sufficient (but not necessary) condition that ε_ν and κ_ν have the same frequency dependence is that, over the small energy range covered by the line, the excitation of the atoms from the lower to the upper state is caused by a constant energy spectrum of radiation (if excitation is primarily by radiation) or by a uniform spectrum of particle energies (if excitation is by inelastic collisions). This is the condition for so-called "natural" excitation.

The above carries some implications for the case of excitation by line radiation in a stellar atmosphere. The very presence of an emission or an absorption line means that the radiation spectrum is *not*, in fact, at all depths constant with frequency within a line. If excitation of the atom is due to absorption of radiation, we need not, therefore, expect the ratio ε_v/κ_v to be independent of frequency. This goes to the source of the question of coherency in line scattering which is to be discussed in more detail in the following chapter.

Provided that the excitation *is* "natural" in the above sense, we can as well discuss the frequency dependence of ε_v as that of κ_v. In practice this is usually found to be more convenient—nearly all modern treatments of line broadening consider the Fourier spectrum of the spontaneous emission.

Although largely superseded by the quantum mechanical theory, the classical theory of absorption and emission by a simple harmonic oscillator retains a good deal of interest both for correspondence reasons and for the quite detailed analogies presented between the two general approaches. We shall therefore review the classical theory before considering the modifications arising from quantum mechanical principles.

It is convenient to consider separately a first-order approximation giving the total energy emitted or absorbed in the *whole* line and then to add a perturbation term which accounts for the detailed shape of the emission coefficient; we shall follow that plan here.

4.1 Classical Theory of Emission and Absorption

4.1.1 Total Emission from a Classical Dipole

The classical theory of radiation, as summarized, for example, by Heitler (1954) proceeds from Maxwell's equations to determine the electric and magnetic fields due to a moving charge or system of charges. Apart from a radial coulomb contribution to **E** (whose magnitude decreases as the square of the distance from the charge), the fields are found to be transverse to each other and to the radius vector **R** from the charge to a given point P. By evaluating the Poynting vector one may show that the expression for the total energy flux through unit area at P is directed parallel to $\mathbf{R}$ and is given by

$$|\mathbf{S}| = \frac{|\ddot{\mathbf{Z}}|^2 \sin^2 \theta}{4\pi c^3 R^2}, \tag{4.2}$$

where θ is the angle between $\mathbf{R}$ and the Hertzian vector $\mathbf{Z}$, while, as usual, dots represent differentiation with respect to time. The dominant term in $\mathbf{Z}$ represents electric dipole radiation; higher-order contributions—magnetic dipole, electric quadrupole, etc.,—can be obtained from the same expression with successive terms in the expansion of the Hertzian vector (cf. Heitler for details).

Most studies have supposed the radiator to be representable by a classical dipole in which the dipole moment oscillates at the natural frequency, so producing emission, or is driven by the action of the varying electric field of a passing electromagnetic wave which would consequently be absorbed. For a free oscillator the appropriate Hertzian vector is simply

$$|\mathbf{Z}| = ex_0 \cos \omega_0 t, \tag{4.3}$$

where ex_0 is the maximum value of the dipole moment and ω_0 the natural frequency of the oscillator. The total energy emitted into all directions then follows from Equations (4.2) and (4.3) by integration over the surface of a sphere of radius R as

$$S = \frac{2}{3} \frac{e^2}{c^3} \omega_0^4 x_0^2 \cos^2 \omega_0 t \tag{4.4}$$

or, in the time average,

$$S = \frac{1}{3} \frac{e^2}{c^3} \omega_0^4 x_0^2. \tag{4.5}$$

4.1.2 Emission Line Width

Evidently this power flux cannot continue indefinitely. The emitted energy can only come at the expense of the kinetic energy of the oscillator, but in the deriving of the result (4.5) radiative reaction has been implicitly ignored. The procedure is adequate, however, provided that the radiative reaction force on the oscillator is small compared with the restoring force, of magnitude $m\omega_0^2 x$. Expressed in an equivalent way, this means that the motion of the oscillator should be only lightly damped by the radiation.

The fact that there *is* such damping, while not significantly influencing the *quantity* of radiation emitted in a given time, has a profound influence on its *quality*. The emitted wave is no longer purely sinusoidal and as a result has no longer a unique frequency but must be represented in terms of a spectrum of frequencies. The radiation will, therefore, appear to have a finite frequency width when observed with a Fourier analyzer such as a perfect spectrograph.

Following Heitler, we may analyze the situation as follows: The work done by the reactive force F_R during one cycle of the oscillation must be equal to the energy radiated; thus, from Equation (4.4),

$$\int F_R \, dx = \int F_R v \, dt = -\frac{2}{3} \frac{e^2}{c^3} \int \dot{v}^2 \, dt. \tag{4.6}$$

By a partial integration of the right-hand term, this equation is seen to be satisfied if

$$F_R = \frac{2}{3} \frac{e^2}{c^3} \ddot{v}. \tag{4.7}$$

This relation may be simplified, providing that F_R is small compared with the restoring force, for then the motion will be almost harmonic and we can therefore write,

$$F_R \simeq -\frac{2}{3} \frac{e^2}{c^3} \omega_0^2 \dot{x} \equiv -m\gamma\dot{x}, \tag{4.8}$$

where γ is known as the *classical damping constant*. The condition that the damping be small is $|F_R| \ll m\omega_0^2 x_0$, which is readily seen to be equivalent to the requirement $\lambda_0 \gg r_0$, where λ_0 is the wavelength of the emitted radiation and r_0 ($= e^2/mc^2$) is the classical electron radius (2.82×10^{-13} cm). Clearly this represents no restriction for any case amenable to classical treatment.

With a damping force given by Equation (4.8), the equation of motion of the free oscillator has the form

$$\ddot{x} + \gamma\dot{x} + \omega_0^2 x = 0, \tag{4.9}$$

whose solution (for $\gamma \ll \omega_0$),* is

$$x = x_0 e^{-\gamma t/2} \cos \omega_0 t. \tag{4.10}$$

This corresponds to an exponentially damped oscillation whose energy

---

* So that the small shift of the central frequency is negligible.

decreases with a characteristic time $1/\gamma$, which is accordingly spoken of as the "lifetime" of the oscillator.

We may, therefore, write the amplitude of the emitted light wave as

$$a = \text{Re}\left\{a_0 \exp\left[-i\left(\omega_0 - \frac{i\gamma}{2}\right)t\right]\right\},$$

where Re indicates that the real part is to be taken. In the focal plane of an ideal spectrograph the amplitude distribution will therefore be given by the Fourier integral;

$$a(\omega) \propto \int_0^\infty e^{i\omega t}e^{-i(\omega_0 - i\gamma/2)t}\, dt \propto \frac{1}{i(\omega_0 - \omega) + \gamma/2}, \qquad (4.11)$$

and the observed distribution $I(\nu)$ of intensity with frequency (i.e., the line shape) is therefore equal to $|a(\omega)|^2$, or

$$I(\nu) = \frac{I_0}{\pi}\frac{\delta}{(\nu_0 - \nu)^2 + \delta^2}, \qquad (4.12)$$

where $\delta = \gamma/4\pi$ and I_0 is a normalizing factor equal to the total emission in the line as given by Equation (4.5).

It follows from Equation (4.8) that the (half)halfwidth of the emitted line is given by

$$\delta = \frac{2\pi e^2 \nu_0^2}{3mc^3};$$

in wavelength units this classical total halfwidth is

$$\Delta\lambda_{\text{cl}} = \frac{2\lambda_0^2}{c}\delta = 1.18 \times 10^{-4} \text{ Å} \qquad (4.13)$$

and is independent of wavelength.

4.1.3 Absorption by a Classical Dipole

The corresponding problem of *absorption* of an electromagnetic wave by an oscillating dipole introduces some different features.

A Fourier component of the electric field of the driving wave may be represented by $E(\omega) \cos(\omega t + \psi)$. We shall ultimately suppose the incident wave to be completely incoherent, so that corresponding to any angular frequency ω all phases ψ are present and are randomly distributed.   For this particular component, the equation of motion of the oscillator is then

$$\ddot{x} + \gamma\dot{x} + \omega_0^2 x = \frac{eE_0(\omega)}{m} \cos(\omega t + \psi). \tag{4.14}$$

Again γ denotes a damping constant; however, its interpretation is now less clear; it should strictly be interpreted as the sum of an "emission" γ and an "absorption" γ which would be negative since it represents a growth of the amplitude.   In the limiting cases of small t, that is, before the dipole oscillation has been significantly influenced by the incident wave, or large t—when the oscillation has attained its equilibrium amplitude—the value of the damping constant is just equal to that given in Equation (4.8).   Corresponding to these limiting cases we may distinguish respectively the two cases of absorption, or of scattering.   The general solution of the equation of motion (4.14) may be written

$$x = \frac{eE_0(\omega)}{m} \left[\frac{(\omega_0^2 - \omega^2)[\cos(\omega t + \psi) - e^{-\gamma t/2}\cos(\omega_0 t + \psi)]}{(\omega_0^2 - \omega^2)^2 + (\omega\gamma)^2} \right.$$
$$\left. + \frac{\omega\gamma[\sin(\omega t + \psi) - e^{-\gamma t/2}\sin(\omega_0 t + \psi)]}{(\omega_0^2 - \omega^2)^2 + (\omega\gamma)^2} \right] + be^{-\gamma t/2}\cos(\omega_0 t + \theta),$$
$$\tag{4.15}$$

where b and θ represent the initial amplitude and phase of the oscillator.
    The work done by the wave in a time t_1 is given by;

$$W(t_1) = \int_0^{t_1} e\dot{x}E_0(\omega)\cos(\omega t + \psi)\, dt. \tag{4.16}$$

This integration leads to a rather cumbersome expression which we shall not reproduce; to the first order we find by averaging over the random phase relation between ψ and θ that,* for $\nu \simeq \nu_0$,

$$W(t_1) = \frac{e^2 E_0^2(\omega)}{8m} \frac{\gamma t_1}{(\omega - \omega_0)^2 + (\gamma/2)^2}. \tag{4.17}$$

This result may be expressed in terms of the radiation flux H via the relation

$$H(\omega) = \frac{c}{8\pi} E_0^2(\omega), \tag{4.18}$$

---

* If the phase ψ were unique, $W(t_1)$ could assume negative values for certain relations between ψ and θ.   This corresponds to a "stimulated" emission by which process the oscillator transfers energy to the light wave.

so that Equation (4.17) becomes

$$W(t_1) = \frac{2\pi^2 e^2 H(\omega) t_1}{mc\pi} \frac{\gamma/2}{(\omega - \omega_0)^2 + (\gamma/2)^2}. \tag{4.19}$$

The energy absorbed is thus found to be proportional to the incident flux of radiation, and to increase linearly with time. In normal frequency units (cycles per second), the absorption coefficient per oscillator is therefore to be expressed as

$$\alpha_\nu = \frac{\pi e^2}{mc} \frac{\delta/\pi}{(\nu - \nu_0)^2 + \delta^2}, \tag{4.20}$$

with $\delta = \gamma/4\pi$; note that the emission and absorption profiles are equal. The total energy absorbed by one oscillator in unit time from a unit intensity beam follows by integration as

$$\int \alpha_\nu \, d\nu = \frac{\pi e^2}{mc}. \tag{4.21}$$

4.1.4 Scattering by an Oscillator

Scattering of radiation by a dipole is a different mechanism from absorption, since in this process no net energy is transferred to the oscillator, which merely acts to redirect the passing wave. The process may be investigated in the usual way by considering the free vibration solution of the equation of motion

$$\ddot{x} + \gamma \dot{x} + \omega_0^2 x = \frac{e}{m} E_0 \cos \omega t, \tag{4.22}$$

namely [see Equation (4.15)]

$$x = \frac{eE_0}{m} \frac{\cos(\omega t - \psi)}{\sqrt{(\omega^2 - \omega_0^2)^2 + (\gamma\omega)^2}},$$

where

$$\tan \psi = \frac{\omega\gamma}{\omega_0^2 - \omega^2}.$$

The total re-emitted energy $I(\omega)$ which passes in unit time through unit area at a distance R from the dipole and which is confined to unit (angular) frequency about ω is then given, from Equation (4.2), by the expression

$$4\pi R^2 I(\omega) = \frac{e^4 E_0^2}{m^2 c^3} \frac{\omega^4 \sin^2 \theta \cos^2(\omega t - \psi)}{(\omega_0^2 - \omega^2)^2 + (\omega\gamma)^2}. \tag{4.23}$$

The phase change ψ is small except near the resonant frequency. In the average over time the energy scattered into unit solid angle per second may therefore be written

$$\varepsilon_s = H\sigma(\theta),$$

with the *cross section* $\sigma(\theta)$ given by

$$\sigma(\theta) = \frac{e^4}{m^2 c^4} \frac{\omega^4 \sin^2 \theta}{(\omega_0^2 - \omega^2)^2 + (\omega\gamma)^2}. \qquad (4.24)$$

The total energy scattered into all directions is obtained by an angular integration and yields a *mean* scattering cross section

$$\sigma = \frac{8\pi}{3} \frac{e^4}{m^2 c^4} \frac{\omega^4}{(\omega_0^2 - \omega^2)^2 + (\omega\gamma)^2}. \qquad (4.25)$$

As a particularly important special case, consider the scattering by free electrons for which the restoring force is zero—and so $\omega_0 = 0$. Since $\gamma \ll \omega$ for all cases in which we shall be interested, we find

$$\sigma_e = \frac{8\pi}{3} \frac{e^4}{m^2 c^4} = \frac{8\pi}{3} r_0^2 = 6.65 \times 10^{-25} \quad \text{cm}^2. \qquad (4.26)$$

In contrast to the case of oscillator scattering (4.25), which is strongly (λ^{-4}) wavelength-dependent away from the resonant frequency, the electron scattering cross section is a universal constant independent of the frequency of the incident light.

4.2 Quantum Theory of Emission and Absorption

In order to overcome divergence difficulties in predicting the spectrum of blackbody radiation, Planck was forced to the conclusion that the energy, E, of a monochromatic electromagnetic wave of frequency ν could only take values satisfying the equation

$$E = nh\nu,$$

with n integral and h a universal constant. Thus, on this hypothesis any emission or absorption process must be accompanied by the creation or destruction of just one, or two, or some integral number of the elementary quanta (photons) of energy $h\nu$. Correspondingly, in a one-photon transition from a state with energy E_a to one of energy E_b, a photon is emitted whose frequency, in order to conserve energy, must be given by

$$\nu_{ab} = \frac{E_a - E_b}{h}. \tag{4.27}$$

This relationship embodies Bohr's frequency condition.

Planck's concept was entirely incompatible with the classical theory and, as such, necessitated a fundamental revision of the earlier conclusions. The resulting quantum theory of radiation has been brought to a level of sophistication beyond the scope of this book; we shall for the most part have to be content with a very brief sketch of the theory. For further details Heitler's monograph should be consulted: The following section largely parallels his treatment.

4.2.1 Integrated Quantities; the Einstein Relations

Following the lines of our discussion of the classical theory of radiation, we shall consider first the total radiation emitted or absorbed in the interaction of an atom and the (now quantized) electromagnetic field. As in the classical theory, we may separate the discussion of total emission and line-width effects since again the reaction of the emitted energy on the atom is, in general, small; in other words, the line breadth is small compared with the line frequency.

The starting point for the discussion is the wave equation

$$i\hbar \frac{\partial \psi}{\partial t} = H'\psi,$$

in which H' is a modified Hamiltonian of the interaction between the radiation field and the electrons. To solve this equation we expand ψ in the series

$$\psi(t) = \sum_n b_n(t)\psi_n, \tag{4.28}$$

where the eigenfunctions ψ_n are characteristic of the unperturbed system of radiation and atoms for which the interaction is zero. In this case $|b_n(t)|^2$ is to be understood as the probability that, at time t, the system is in the state n. The basic differential equations describing the evolution of the system may then be shown to be

$$i\hbar \dot{b}_n(t) = \sum_m H_{nm} e^{i(E_n - E_m)t/\hbar} b_m(t), \tag{4.29}$$

where H_{nm} is the matrix element of the interaction Hamiltonian taken between the states n and m. This set of simultaneous equations is hopelessly complicated, and progress is only possible by regarding the interaction H as small. The simplest application of the resulting perturbation theory is to the so-called first-order processes involving the emission or the absorption of only one photon. Suppose the system of atoms and photons to be in a given state 1 at time $t = 0$ (so that $b_1(0) = 1$) and let us seek, through the equation (4.29), the time development of the system under the influence of the interaction. The perturbation equations may then be represented approximately as

$$i\hbar\dot{b}_n = H_{n1}b_1 e^{i(E_n - E_1)t/\hbar} \qquad (n \neq 1), \qquad (4.30)$$

since for small enough times the only significant transition to n will come directly from the initial state 1. So long as these times are short compared with the lifetime of the state, we may also put $b_1(t) = 1$.* The solution of these equations, consistent with the initial conditions $b_n(0) = 0$, is found at once to be

$$b_n(t) = H_{n1}\left[\frac{\exp(i\overline{E_n - E_1}t/\hbar) - 1}{E_1 - E_n}\right], \qquad (4.31)$$

so that

$$|b_n(t)|^2 = \frac{2|H_{n1}|^2[1 - \cos(E_n - E_1)t/\hbar]}{(E_1 - E_n)^2}. \qquad (4.32)$$

As shown by Heitler we can select a time t small compared to the lifetime of state 1 (so that b_1 remains unity in this time, as required) and yet large compared to $\hbar/E_n$ or $\hbar/E_1$. We are therefore justified, in Equation (4.32), in taking the limit as $t \to \infty$, in which case the factor on the right-hand side of Equation (4.32) reduces to the product of t and a delta function of argument $(E_n - E_1)$. We therefore find that

$$\frac{1}{t}|b_n(t)|^2 = \frac{2\pi}{\hbar}|H_{n1}|^2\delta(E_n - E_1). \qquad (4.33)$$

Note that the energy of the system is conserved in the transition since E represents the sum of the energies of the atom and the photon.

We are concerned only with systems in which the precise phase relations and energies of the photons are not specified; the photon may therefore be assigned to any one of the modes of the radiation field which have energy within an infinitesimal range dE. The probability

---

* This is the counterpart of the classical assumption, of Section 4.1.1, that the emission does not react on the oscillator. Its removal leads to a theory of the line shape.

that the system of atom and photons makes a transition to state n is then found from Equation (4.33) by weighting with the number of such modes $E_n^2/(hc)^3$ in unit energy range and integrating over dE_n. In this way we find—for the appropriate range of t given above—that $|b_n(t)|^2$ is proportional to t and is given by

$$\frac{1}{t}\,|b_n(t)|^2 = \frac{\nu^2}{\hbar^2 c^3}\,|H_{n1}|^2 \tag{4.34}$$

for photons emitted into or absorbed from a unit solid angle.

The expression on the right-hand side of Equation (4.34) gives the transition probability per unit time and per unit solid angle for radiation of a particular polarization. To relate this result to the empirical emission and absorption coefficients introduced in Chapter 2, we need to evaluate the matrix elements $|H_{n1}|$. Heitler derives their explicit dependence on the wave functions of the states n and 1 and on the photon intensity. He shows that three separate physical processes can be distinguished in the first-order interaction of an electromagnetic wave and an atom, namely spontaneous emission, stimulated emission, and absorption. His conclusions may be expressed as follows in the familiar notation introduced by Einstein. In a time t short compared with the natural lifetime of the state, the probability that an emission transition takes place so that an atom is carried from an upper (u) to a lower (ℓ) state is expressible as

$$\left[\frac{A_{u\ell}}{4\pi} + B_{u\ell}I_\nu\right]t. \tag{4.35}$$

The corresponding probability of an absorption transition taking place in time t may be expressed by

$$B_{\ell u}I_\nu t,$$

where I_ν is the specific intensity of the incident radiation (supposed constant over the line). The coefficients $A_{u\ell}$, $B_{u\ell}$, $B_{\ell u}$ are not independent; their relationship may be found as follows: The principle of detailed balance requires that, *in thermodynamic equilibrium*, the total number of emission transitions giving photons with momentum directed in a given element of solid angle must exactly balance those absorbed from the radiation in the same solid angle, i.e., we must have in this case,

$$B_{\ell u}I_\nu n_\ell = \left(\frac{A_{u\ell}}{4\pi} + B_{u\ell}I_\nu\right)n_u, \tag{4.36}$$

with n_u and n_ℓ respectively the number density of atoms in the upper and lower states. Since we are considering a thermodynamic equilibrium situation, however, the relative populations are given by the Boltzmann relation, so that by solving Equation (4.36) for I_ν we find

$$I_\nu = \frac{A_{u\ell}/4\pi}{(g_\ell/g_u)B_{\ell u}e^{E/kT} - B_{u\ell}}. \tag{4.37}$$

where E is the energy separation of the states and the g-factors are the relevant statistical weights. For arbitrary frequency this is equivalent to the Planck distribution (which must describe I_ν in this case) if

$$A_{u\ell} = \frac{8\pi h\nu^3}{c^2} B_{u\ell}, \tag{4.38a}$$

and

$$B_{\ell u} = \frac{g_u}{g_\ell} B_{u\ell}, \tag{4.38b}$$

from which it follows also that

$$A_{u\ell} = \frac{8\pi h\nu^3}{c^2} \frac{g_\ell}{g_u} B_{\ell u}. \tag{4.39}$$

We have derived these relations for the special case of thermodynamic equilibrium; the relations must remain valid, however, for an arbitrary state of the gas, since the coefficients A and B are properties of the atom itself.

To the first order, the total energy absorbed by an atom from a unit intensity beam, i.e., the integrated absorption coefficient, may be shown to be given by the equation

$$\int \alpha_\nu \, d\nu \equiv h\nu B_{\ell u} = \frac{8\pi^3 e^2 \nu}{3hc} |X_{u\ell}|^2, \tag{4.40}$$

where $|X_{u\ell}|$ is the matrix element of the space coordinate of the atomic electron.*

It is found convenient in quantitative spectroscopy to define a number f such that a given atom is equivalent in its total absorption in a particular line to a classical oscillator of strength f. We may then use the classical result (4.21) to define its quantal analogue

$$\int \alpha_\nu \, d\nu = \frac{\pi e^2}{mc} f \tag{4.41}$$

* If the angular parts of the two wave functions are orthogonal the matrix element $X_{u\ell}$ will vanish. In this case, of an optically "forbidden" transition, higher-order transitions may still be possible.

and for compatibility with Equations (4.38) to (4.40) we must then require that

$$f = \frac{8\pi^2}{3}\frac{mv}{h}|X_{u\ell}|^2$$

$$= \frac{mc^3}{8\pi^2e^2v^2}\frac{g_u}{g_\ell}A_{u\ell}$$

$$= 1.499 \times 10^{-16}\lambda_A^2 A_{u\ell}\frac{g_u}{g_\ell}, \tag{4.42}$$

with λ_A in angstrom units and A in reciprocal seconds.

The oscillator strength defined by these equations is referred to as the *absorption f*-value. We can define an analogous *emission f*-value such that the two are related by the equation $-g_u f_{em} = g_\ell f_{abs} \equiv gf$; because of its unambiguous meaning the quantity gf is frequently tabulated. Throughout we shall regard an unsubscripted f as referring to the *absorption f*-value.

Because of their obvious significance to spectral-line analysis, a great deal of attention has been given to both the theoretical and the experimental determination of f-values. It would not be feasible, here, to attempt a review of this vast subject; fortunately this is not necessary, in any case, since a comprehensive abstraction has been given by Glennon and Wiese (1962). It is understood that this abstraction is to be kept up to date so that periodic additions to the original bibliography are to be anticipated.

Perhaps the most comprehensive single tabulation of f-values is that given by Corliss and Bozman (1962) for 25000 lines between λ2000 and λ9000 for 112 spectra of 70 elements. This extensive table was based on absolute intensity measurements of the lines excited in an arc burning between copper electrodes to which had been added a small quantity of the element under study.

4.2.2 Natural Line Width in the Quantum Theory

The solutions to the perturbation equations derived in the previous section are incapable of accounting for the line width, since they were based on the assumption $b_1(t) = 1$ while the line breadth arises because the occupation probability b_1, in fact, decreases with time. Thus the emission process reacts back on the atom. A solution to Equation (4.29) which took account of variation of b_1 with time was given by

Weisskopf and Wigner (1930), who found that, for a resonance line, the spontaneous emission at frequency ν was given by the dispersion formula

$$I(\nu) \propto \frac{\delta/\pi}{(\nu - \nu_0)^2 + \delta^2},\tag{4.43}$$

with the damping constant $\delta = \gamma/4\pi$, where, for an upper level j,

$$\gamma = \sum_\ell A_{j\ell},$$

and the sum is to be extended to all levels $\ell < j$. In the time $2/\gamma$ the occupation probability b_1 decreases by a factor e. The form (4.43) also represents the emission profile for a subordinate line provided that we interpret the damping factor δ as the sum of the individual damping constants of the two levels involved in the transition. The line shape is thus the same as in the classical theory, but the damping constant has the significantly different characteristic that it depends on the particular transition in question.

The relationship between the halfwidth δ and the transition rate A may be simply interpreted from the uncertainty relation, $\Delta E\, \Delta t \sim \hbar$, between the energy uncertainty and the time available for measuring the energy. Since we cannot conceive of this time interval being shorter than the decay time $1/\gamma$, we may associate an effective width ΔE_j with level j in accordance with the relation

$$\Delta E_j \sim \hbar \sum_\ell A_{j\ell}.$$

The Bohr relation would then predict a line width $\Delta \nu = (\Delta E_j + \Delta E_k)/h$, where k and j reference the two states of the transition. This, of course, is simply a statement of the fact that radiation which is emitted only during a finite time cannot have a single frequency. If we wish to preserve the Bohr relation we must do so by associating an energy width to the states.

4.3 Pressure Broadening of Spectral Lines

We have seen earlier that an isolated atom will emit a spectral line of finite width. However, other atoms, ions, or electrons, will in general be in the neighborhood of the emitter and may contribute significantly to the broadening by modifying the state of the atom while it is radiating. In practice such *pressure broadening* is often much more impor-

tant than the natural broadening considered in Section 4.2.2; to study
it, it is convenient to take the state lifetime to be infinite and to study
simply the influence of collisional perturbations on an otherwise monochromatic wave.   If these perturbations in fact produce a broadening
small compared to the radiative width then they may, obviously, be
neglected in comparison with the natural broadening governed by
Equation (4.43).   Again, we suppose the radiating atom to be stationary; broadening arising from the Doppler effect consequent on a
motion of the emitting atoms will be discussed separately in Section 4.6.

The literature on pressure broadening is extensive and expanding,
due largely to the application of spectroscopy as a plasma diagnostic
tool.   For pressures of astrophysical interest some of the more sophisticated aspects can be neglected; we shall, in any case, confine attention
to the more elementary features.   The interested reader will find
detailed treatments in the review articles referenced at the end of this
chapter, and in Griem's (1964) text *Plasma Spectroscopy*.

Pictorially, the influence of perturbers on the energy levels of a
radiating atom—and so on the emitted frequencies—may be visualized
in terms of interaction curves of the type shown in Figure 4.1, in which
the ordinate represents the potential energy of an atomic state in the
presence of a perturber at a distance r.   The vertical distance between
the curves measures the frequency which would be emitted if a perturber were situated, and remained at, a distance r from the emitting
atom.   Evidently the interaction curves must have different shapes for
any frequency *change* to result from the interaction.   For many purposes it is sufficient to represent the frequency shift $\Delta \nu$ by a power-law
formula of the kind [see Margenau and Watson (1936)]

$$\Delta \nu = C/r^n, \tag{4.44}$$

where different values of the integer n apply for different types of
interactions, while the constant C is a function both of the transition
and of the interaction.

The representation (4.44) is strictly applicable only to a static perturbation.   In fact, the perturbers and atoms are in motion, and more
than one perturber will be interacting with a given atom at any time.
We will therefore find it necessary, in general, to average over all
possible paths in space and time of all the perturbers in order to compute the shape of the spectral line emitted from a gas.   In fact, this
averaging turns out to be essentially impossible except in two limiting

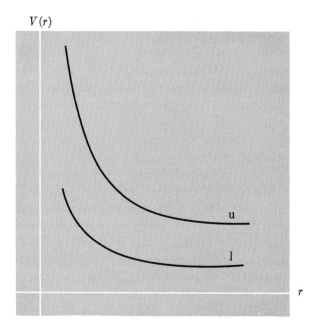

Figure 4.1. Schematic diagram to illustrate the dependence of the potential energy of the upper and the lower states of a transition on the distance r from the atom to the perturbing particle.

cases known respectively as the *quasi-static* (or *static* or *statistical*) approximation and the *impact* (or *phase shift*) approximation.

In the hope of making the following somewhat clearer, we outline the bases of these two limiting cases, detailed consideration being reserved until later.

4.3.1 The Quasi-Static and Impact Approximations

In the absence of perturbations, suppose the atom to radiate indefinitely a coherent wave of frequency ν_0. The influence of perturbers will manifest itself in amplitude, phase, and frequency variations in this emitted wave, and these in turn will destroy the coherence between two points on the wave train. As in all such problems, the Fourier spectrum of the observed wave (i.e., the line shape) will be controlled by the characteristic time τ in which the phase coherence (or the autocorrelation function of the wave amplitude) decreases by (say) e^{-1}; indeed the line width, in frequency units, is then $\sim 1/\tau$. A second important time interval is that in which a typical collision is completed. For limiting relations between these two times we obtain limiting approximate theories of line broadening.

Suppose first that the coherence time τ is much smaller than a strong collision duration t_0. Then line broadening is effected, i.e., a large phase shift occurs, while the perturber moves only a short distance and so is effectively dependent only on the instantaneous distribution of the perturbers in space. To the extent that only one perturber need be considered to be acting on a given atom at any given time, we may therefore analyze the problem as if the perturber were at rest—and so causes emission of a sharp line displaced in frequency from ν_0 by an amount depending on the strength of the interaction, i.e., on the location of the perturber according to Equation (4.44). In this case the frequency distribution of the intensity emitted by the gas *as a whole* (i.e., the line shape) follows directly from a knowledge of the probability distribution for stationary perturbers to produce a given interaction with the atom. This limiting case is the *quasi-static* approximation.

The other extreme case of the *impact* approximation occurs when, on the average, the phase of the wave is only slightly modified during a time of the order of a few collision times. There are two general conditions under which this applies. First, it will be valid if the collisions are strong enough to disrupt the phase of the wave (by the order of one radian, say) and are well separated in time from one another and occur instantaneously. Then the collision time t_0 is effectively zero while the (average) correlation time τ is the mean time between collisions. Second, the impact approximation holds if the collisions are so weak that, although they may each last for a significant time—and indeed may overlap one another—their combined effect on the wave is small in the characteristic collision time.

Quantitative validity conditions will be discussed later but it is clear that the quasi-static approximation will be better the higher the density since then the frequency of strong disrupting collisions will be greater and so τ/t_0 will be smaller. Similarly, at low temperatures when the collision duration is greater, this approximation is favored. In contrast, at low pressures the coherence time will be increased since the collision frequency will be reduced and the impact approximation will be favored; for the same reason it will apply better the higher the temperature.

The approximation to be used does not depend only on the gas conditions, however; if we followed the history of the wave radiated by a single atom we should find that some broadening collisions should be treated in the quasi-static and others in the impact approximation, depending on the relative values of the coherence and the collision duration times for the individual collisions. It is clear that the larger frequency shifts will tend to be produced during the time when a strong collision is in progress, and these will be better described by a quasi-static approximation. In terms of our definitions of these approximations, therefore, we must expect to find the line wings to be produced under the influence of quasi-static collisions while, in the same way, it may be shown that the broadening near the line center is effected by collisions for which the impact approximation applies.

With these ideas in mind we may consider some of the earlier work on line broadening as an introduction to the more recent developments.

4.3.2 Line Broadening in the Quasi-Static Approximation

THE NEAREST NEIGHBOR APPROXIMATION

Consider, with Kuhn (1934), the interaction of a *single perturber* according to the law given by Equation (4.44) when the quasi-static case is assumed.

The probability that a single particle in a volume V is at a distance between r and $r + dr$ from the emitting atom at $r = 0$ is clearly

$$p(r)\, dr = 4\pi r^2\, dr/V.$$

The corresponding frequency distribution of the line emitted by the whole gas is the probability of a frequency shift $\Delta\nu$, that is, from Equation (4.44),

$$p(\Delta\nu)\, d(\Delta\nu) = \frac{4\pi C^{3/n}}{n\,V(\Delta\nu)^{(n+3)/n}}\, d(\Delta\nu), \tag{4.45}$$

which diverges near the line center as $(\Delta\nu_{\min})^{-(n+3)/n}$, where $\Delta\nu_{\min} = C/\rho_0^n$, with ρ_0 the radius of the enclosure. This simply reflects the fact that the probability of a small shift is very large, since the (single) perturber spends most of its time far from the radiating atom.

The limitation to a single perturber was removed by Margenau (1933) by a consideration of the whole assembly of particles, again supposing in the first instance that the interactions are only due to the perturbation by the nearest neighbor. If we denote by $P(r + dr)$ the probability that the *nearest* of the N perturbers lies *outside* a sphere of radius

$r + dr$ (the emitting atom being again at $r = 0$), then $P(r + dr)$ is the probability $P(r)$ of the nearest particle being outside radius r, multiplied by the probability that no particle lies inside the shell between r and $r + dr$. Then, evidently,

$$P(r + dr) = P(r)[1 - (3r^2 \, dr/\bar{r}^3)],$$

where $\bar{r}^3 = 3V/4\pi N$, that is, $\bar{r}$ is the mean separation of the perturbers in the enclosure. It then follows from the above equation that

$$\frac{dP(r)}{dr} = -\frac{3r^2}{\bar{r}^3} P(r),$$

which may be integrated to give the probability amplitude, normalized to one particle per unit volume,

$$P(r) = e^{-(r/\bar{r})^3}. \tag{4.46}$$

The probability $p(r) \, dr$, which we seek, is that of the nearest neighbor being *inside* the shell r, $r + dr$ and so is given by the product of the probability, $P(r)$, that no particle lies inside r, and the probability that one particle lies in the shell, i.e.,

$$p(r) \, dr = \frac{3r^2}{\bar{r}^3} e^{-(r/\bar{r})^3} \, dr.$$

For the interaction law (4.44), this expression then reduces to

$$p(\Delta\nu) \, d(\Delta\nu) = \frac{3(\overline{\Delta\nu})^{3/n}}{n(\Delta\nu)^{(n+3)/n}} e^{-(\overline{\Delta\nu}/\Delta\nu)^{3/n}} \, d(\Delta\nu), \tag{4.47}$$

with $\overline{\Delta\nu} = C/\bar{r}^n$. As written, the interaction law (4.44) is one-sided and so always predicts a shift to the red or to the violet, depending on the sign of C. If the interaction can change sign (as it does, for example, for linear Stark effect when its value and sign depend on the particular Stark component considered), then the result (4.47) applies, within its limitations, for each component; if these are symmetric about the line center, the line will also be symmetrically broadened. For frequency shifts $\Delta\nu$ much greater than the mean shift $\overline{\Delta\nu}$, Equation (4.47), reduces to (4.45). This is only to be expected since such shifts correspond to particles lying closer to the atom than the mean separation distance and it is improbable that more than one such particle should do so. On the other hand, if $\overline{\Delta\nu}$ is very much greater than $\Delta\nu$, we must question the basic assumption that only the nearest neighbor interacts. Thus the line shape (4.47) could be considered as a reasonable approximation only for large shifts such that $\Delta \nu$ is much greater than $\overline{\Delta \nu}$; in that case, however, the single perturber result (4.45) applies.

GENERALIZATIONS OF HOLTSMARK AND MARGENAU

The general problem of including the simultaneous action of all the perturbers was considered first by Holtsmark (1919) in the context of linear Stark broadening and has since been developed into a sophisticated theory, largely by Margenau. The principle of the method has been indicated above; here we sketch Margenau's treatment, and represent by $V_i(x_i)$ the interaction potential at the atom due to the ith perturber located at x_i. If the action of all the perturbers is additive, the resultant interaction potential at the atom is given by

$$V(x) = \sum_i V_i(x_i),$$

where x is a configuration variable.* The probability of a particular configuration is obtained as the integral over the N perturbers

$$W(V) = [3/\rho_0^{3N}] \int_S \cdots \int \prod_i (r_i^2) \, dr_1 \ldots dr_N, \qquad (4.48)$$

and the integration is to be extended over that region, S, of the configuration space which is compatible with the production of the perturbation V at the atom; again ρ_0 represents the radius of the enclosure, and N the total number of perturbers.

Standard methods for the evaluation of such integrals have been given by Chandrasekhar (1943). For a *symmetrical* broadening—in which half the perturbations cause a frequency shift one way, half the other—Margenau (1951) finds,

$$W(V) = \frac{1}{\pi} \int_0^\infty \exp\left(-N g_n \rho^{3/n}\right) \cos \rho V \, d\rho, \qquad (4.49)$$

where

$$g_n \rho^{3/n} = \frac{4\pi}{3} (C\rho)^{3/n} \int_0^\infty t^{-3/n} \sin t \, dt. \qquad (4.50)$$

* For linear Stark effect a more detailed treatment is needed since it is the value of the electric *field* which controls the Stark splitting.

4.3.3 Early Considerations Using the Impact Approximation

The impact approximation in its original form was introduced by Lorentz (1906), who supposed that those encounters between a radiating atom and a perturber which produced line broadening were such that the radiation was instantaneously cut off at each collision. The energy emitted from the gas was thus assumed to consist of a set of truncated sine waves of basic angular frequency ω_0. In the Lorentz treatment a Fourier component of angular frequency ω in the observed radiation would therefore have amplitude

$$a(\omega) = \int_{-T/2}^{+T/2} e^{i(\omega - \omega_0)t} \, dt \tag{4.51}$$

where T is the interval between collisions. If the time between collisions was always T, the line profile would be given by

$$I_T(\omega) \propto \frac{\sin^2 [(\omega - \omega_0)T/2]}{[(\omega - \omega_0)/2]^2}.$$

Since T is, in fact, distributed according to the law $\exp(-T/\tau) \, dT/\tau$, where τ is the "mean time between collisions," the observed emission from the gas would have the frequency distribution

$$I(\omega) \propto \int_0^\infty I_T(\omega) e^{-T/\tau} \frac{dT}{\tau}$$

or, in a normalized form,

$$I(\omega) = \frac{1}{\pi\tau} \frac{1}{(\omega - \omega_0)^2 + (1/\tau)^2}. \tag{4.52}$$

The Lorentz hypothesis thus predicts a dispersion profile for the emitted line, of (half) halfwidth τ^{-1} in angular frequency units. In analogy with the case of radiation damping, we may define a collisional damping constant γ_c as the reciprocal of τ.

Since the frequency integrated absorption coefficient is an atomic constant independent of details of the broadening, the corresponding atomic absorption coefficient is simply $\pi e^2 f/mc$ times the normalized profile (4.52). The energy emitted spontaneously into all directions by an atom is normalized to the value $Ah\nu$ per second; it has the same dispersion profile provided that the distribution of excitation over the upper level is that of "natural" excitation.

Although giving a qualitative description of line broadening, and, in particular, agreeing with the experimental result that at low pressures the halfwidth is proportional to density, the Lorentz approach was unsatisfactory in the definition of a collision, since this required a complete termination of the wave train such as occurs through a superelastic collision. Such "quenching" collisions are indeed observed in the laboratory, but if the Lorentz idea were followed to its logical conclusion it would mean that increased line broadening would be accompanied by a decrease of the *intensity* of the emission, and this is not, in general, observed. Nor is the quantitative estimate of the number of such superelastic collisions in agreement with that necessary to give the observed broadening.

A different interpretation of a broadening collision was given by Lenz (1924, 1933) and by Weisskopf (1932), who showed that the complete disruption assumed by Lorentz was not necessary to produce broadening. These authors again assumed an interaction law of the form (4.44) and in a straightforward manner computed the total phase change $\Delta\phi$ due to a single straight-line transit of a perturbing particle past the radiating atom as

$$\Delta\phi = \int_{-\infty}^{+\infty} \Delta\omega \, dt = \int_{-\infty}^{+\infty} \frac{2\pi C \, dt}{(\rho^2 + v^2 t^2)^{n/2}}, \tag{4.53}$$

where ρ is the impact parameter shown in Figure 4.2. The integral is readily evaluated to give

$$\Delta\phi = \frac{2\pi C}{v\rho^{n-1}} c_n, \tag{4.54}$$

where

$$c_n = \int_{-\pi/2}^{+\pi/2} \cos^{n-2} \theta \, d\theta$$

which is a number of order unity for all cases of interest to us.

Weisskopf next assumed that, when such a collision produced a phase change $\Delta\phi$ of about unity, the subsequent wave train of the emitting atom was completely incoherent with the previous one. The effect on the wave is thus equivalent to a "collision" in the Lorentz sense without, however, being accompanied by a de-excitation of the atom. The cross section for such a collision is written as $\pi\rho_W^2$, where the "Weisskopf radius" ρ_W is such that collisions with smaller impact parameters produce phase changes greater than unity in the emitted wave. From

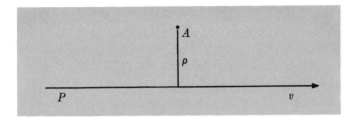

Figure 4.2. Geometry of a broadening collision: *A* represents the position of the radiating atom; the perturber *P* moves with constant velocity *v*; the impact parameter is ρ.

Equation (4.54), then,

$$\rho_{\mathrm{W}} = \left[\frac{2\pi C c_n}{v} \right]^{1/(n-1)}. \tag{4.55}$$

The Lenz-Weisskopf interpretation of a broadening collision does not, of course, alter the prediction of a dispersion shape for the absorption coefficient—in fact, a somewhat more general dispersion formula is characteristic of all treatments of the impact approximation. The only modification to the Lorentz expression occurs in the meaning to be attached to the collision "damping constant," γ_c, which is now given by $\gamma_c = 2v/\rho_{\mathrm{W}}$ and is thus dependent on the temperature of the gas— through the mean relative velocity v.

The deficiencies of the Lenz-Weisskopf theory are twofold in that it neglects (1) the main part of the close collisions and (2) the distant collisions. The neglect under (1) lies in the fact that once a unit phase change is reached, no further details of the collision are considered. Since $\Delta\phi$ is proportional to ρ^{n-1}, this involves, essentially, a neglect of the perturbation along the path inside the Weisskopf sphere; the emitted wave is considered to be chopped up into sections of mean duration τ and basic frequency ν_0, and only the Fourier components of these uncorrelated sections are assumed to be present in the emitted beam. Equivalently it is assumed that broadening accompanies only those collisions which intercept the Weisskopf sphere, and that they then occur instantaneously at the surface of the sphere. Since only single isolated collisions are considered, this treatment is an example of a pure impact approximation.

The neglect of the weak, remote collisions for which $\Delta\phi < 1$ is likely to be important simply because there is a large number of them. Their influence was first incorporated into the theory by Lindholm (1941), a treatment of this problem is considered in the following section.

4.3.4 Adiabatic Impact Theories

The method developed by Lindholm (1941) and Burkhart (1940) for including phase changes smaller than unity can be considered within the more general concept of the *correlation function* introduced by Foley (1946), and generalized by Anderson (1949).

If we assume, following Anderson, that the relative motion of the perturber and emitter may be described by a classical path (i.e., no significant uncertainties are associated with the simultaneous specification of velocity and position), a general expression associated with the Fourier component of angular frequency ω is found as,

$$I(\omega) = \frac{2e^2\omega^4}{3\pi c^3} \operatorname{Tr}\left[\rho_0 \int_{-\infty}^{+\infty} dt\, e^{i\omega t}\mu(t) \int_{-\infty}^{+\infty} dt'\, e^{-i\omega t'}\mu(t')\, dt'\right], \quad (4.56)$$

where ρ_0 is a density matrix representing the initial distribution of atoms over the atomic levels (essentially given by the Boltzmann formula for a gas near thermodynamic equilibrium), μ represents the dipole moment operator, and the symbol Tr indicates that the observable quantity $I(\omega)$ is found as the sum of diagonal elements (i.e., the trace) of the matrix in brackets.

This representation applies when $\mu(t)$ refers to the complete quantum mechanical system of atom and perturbers; the integrals over time then represent an average over the history of the emitting atom. If the motion of the perturber is assumed to be uninfluenced by the collision, the interaction is automatically prescribed as a function of time, and Equation (4.56) can be reduced to the form

$$I(\omega) \propto \operatorname{Re} \operatorname{Tr}\left[\int_{-\infty}^{+\infty} e^{i\omega t}[\rho\mu(t)\mu(0)]_T\, dt\right], \quad (4.57)$$

in which the subscript T indicates that a "thermal" average is to be taken over all possible perturber paths and now $\mu(t)$ is to be computed from the time-dependent Heisenberg equation for the Hamiltonian of an atom subject to a specified interaction. This formula is the starting point for recent studies by Kolb, Griem, and Baranger.

The expressions (4.56) or (4.57) may be simplified if we make the so-called *adiabatic assumption*. This means essentially that we assume that the perturber causes no transitions from either the initial, or the final, state. A more detailed discussion of the meaning of this assumption—together with some validity criteria—is given in Section 4.3.6;

however, it is sufficient to say here that its application permits an immediate solution for the dipole moment operator $\mu(t)$ which enables us to express Equation (4.57) in the form

$$I(\omega) \propto \left| \int_{-\infty}^{+\infty} e^{i(\omega_0 - \omega)\tau} \phi(\tau) \, d\tau \right|^2, \tag{4.58}$$

where the correlation function ϕ is given by

$$\phi(\tau) = \int_{-\infty}^{+\infty} e^{i[\eta(t+\tau) - \eta(t)]} \, dt \tag{4.59}$$

and $\eta(t + \tau) - \eta(t)$ represents the phase change of the emitted wave over the interval t to $t + \tau$. The function $\phi(\tau)$ thus measures the average degree—throughout the history of the wave—to which the phase of the emitted wave is maintained over the time interval τ. Clearly from Equation (4.58), once we know $\phi(\tau)$ we shall have solved the line-broadening problem within the assumptions of adiabaticity and classical path for the perturber.

Adopting the impact approximation, we may find a differential equation for $\phi(\tau)$ as follows. Suppose the perturber velocity, v, to be constant then, for a given interaction, the phase change is uniquely related to the impact parameter by Equation (4.54). Suppose that a phase shift η_k—which results from the passage of a perturber within an element $d\sigma_k$ of cross section—occurs in the time interval $d\tau$. The *change* in the integrand $f(t, \tau)$ of $\phi(\tau)$ resulting from such a collision is, from Equation (4.59) (see also Figure 4.3)

$$
\begin{aligned}
f(t, \tau + d\tau) - f(t, \tau) &= \exp\left\{i[\eta(t + \tau) - \eta(t)]\right\} \\
&\quad \times \left\{\exp\left[i\{\eta(t + \tau + d\tau) - \eta(t + \tau)\}\right] - 1\right\} \\
&= f(t, \tau)[\exp(i\eta_k) - 1], \tag{4.60}
\end{aligned}
$$

and the *average* change in the correlation function caused by collisions of this type during the whole history of the emitting atom is obtained by integrating over all t, that is, over all positions of T_1 in Figure 4.3, as

$$d\phi(\tau) = \phi(\tau + d\tau) - \phi(\tau) = \int_{-\infty}^{+\infty} [\exp(i\eta_k) - 1] f(t, \tau) \, dt. \tag{4.61}$$

At this stage we must appeal to the impact approximation to evaluate the time average. First, if we assume that the time $d\tau$ is short compared to the interval between collisions and yet long compared to the duration of one collision—so that the time interval $d\tau$ separates two quite uncorrelated waves—the two factors in the integrand of Equation (4.61) are independent and their time averages may be carried out separately.

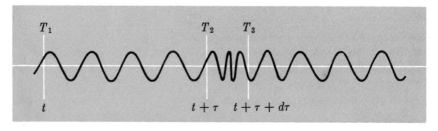

Figure 4.3. Schematic and exaggerated representation of the time variation of the emitted wave train as disturbed by collisions. The broadening contribution of the collision of type k between times T_2 and T_3 is represented by the phase change in Equation (4.62) of the text.

This average may also be taken, independently of this requirement that the collision duration be short compared to $d\tau$, provided that the collisions are weak (i.e., that η_k is small). This is in keeping with more recent definitions of the impact approximation, namely that there is only one strong collision, or a succession of weak collisions which together cause only small phase changes η_k, in a time characteristic of the relaxation time of the perturbation. Since the ergodic principle requires the time average over the phase change factor $[\exp(i\eta_k) - 1]$ to be equivalent to an average, at any given time, over all the collisions in the gas occurring at that time, the change in the correlation function due to all perturbations may be written, if the impact approximation is valid, as

$$d\phi(\tau) = [\exp(i\eta_k) - 1]_{\text{Av}}\phi(\tau). \qquad (4.62)$$

The number of collisions in time $d\tau$ producing a phase change η_k is

$$N_k = nv\,d\sigma_k\,d\tau, \qquad (4.63)$$

when n is the number density of the perturbers, so that Equation (4.62) takes the form

$$d\phi(\tau) = \left\{ nv\,d\tau \int_0^\infty [\exp(i\eta_k) - 1]\,d\sigma_k \right\}\phi(\tau). \qquad (4.64)$$

This can be immediately integrated to give

$$\phi(\tau) = e^{-nv\sigma\tau}, \tag{4.65}$$

with

$$\sigma = \sigma_r - i\sigma_i = \int_0^\infty (1 - e^{+i\eta}) \, d\sigma,$$

so that from Equation (4.58) we obtain the following normalized expression for the emitted intensity:

$$I(\omega) = \frac{nv\sigma_r/\pi}{(\omega - \omega_0 - nv\sigma_i)^2 + (nv\sigma_r)^2}. \tag{4.66}$$

The line shape is therefore a symmetrical dispersion profile having a halfwidth $\Delta\omega_{1/2} = nv\sigma_r$, whose central frequency is shifted by $\Delta\omega_s = nv\sigma_i$ from the undisturbed line center; both shift and width are proportional to the perturber density and both depend (through v) on the gas temperature.

For the basic interaction law (4.44) we have

$$\eta(\rho) = 2\pi C \int_{-\infty}^{+\infty} \frac{dt}{(\rho^2 + v^2 t^2)^{n/2}} = \frac{2\pi C c_n}{v\rho^{n-1}},$$

and so, since $d\sigma = 2\pi\rho \, d\rho$,

$$\sigma_r = 2\pi \int_0^\infty \left[1 - \cos\left\{ \frac{2\pi C c_n}{v\rho^{n-1}} \right\} \right] \rho \, d\rho \tag{4.67}$$

and

$$\sigma_i = 2\pi \int_0^\infty \sin\left(\frac{2\pi C c_n}{v\rho^{n-1}} \right) \rho \, d\rho. \tag{4.68}$$

These integrals may be evaluated using the general formula

$$\int_0^\infty (1 - e^{ix}) \frac{dx}{x^g + 1} = \frac{\pi}{\sin \pi g} \frac{e^{i\pi g/2}}{\Gamma(1 + g)}. \tag{4.69}$$

For the case of linear Stark effect ($n = 2$) this theory leads to a divergent width and shift. This failure is due to the assumption of binary encounters; for the long-range coulomb forces it is necessary to account for screening by other particles. This is usually effected by terminating the range of integration in Equations (4.67) and (4.68) at some maximum value of ρ—usually chosen as the Debye length ρ_D. The atom is assumed to be negligibly affected by perturbers lying beyond ρ_D.

Unsöld (1955) has considered the relations (4.67), (4.68) in some detail for the case $n = 4$, the quadratic Stark effect. He points out that, owing to the rapid oscillations of the integrand for $\rho < \rho_W$ in (4.68) and its monotonic behavior for $\rho > \rho_W$, the line *shift* comes from the weak collisions outside the Weisskopf sphere. These were neglected in the earlier theories which accordingly predicted no line shift. The predicted broadening, on the other hand, depends on the quadratic integrand of Equation (4.67) and is determined almost entirely by collisions intersecting the Weisskopf sphere.

4.3.5 Relationship between the Impact and Quasi-Static Theories

It is not at all clear, *a priori*, that the two theoretical descriptions used in line-broadening discussions should follow from a single formalism. Some further insight into their relationship may be obtained from the correlation function approach for adiabatic collisions which is embodied in Equations (4.58) and (4.59).

Consider the limiting case of an unperturbed wave for which $\eta(t + \tau) - \eta(t)$ is constant for all t. Here $\phi(\tau)$ is constant, and correspondingly $I(\omega)$ is nonzero only for $\omega = \omega_0$; that is, the emission is monochromatic of frequency ω_0. When the interaction is nonzero, a similar case can arise in which the emitted wave is well correlated over the collision time, but it will then have a basic angular frequency ω_0' which differs from the unperturbed frequency ω_0. In this case if the contributions to the intensity at ω_0' are sharp, the line profile will reflect the probability that a collision results in a shift $\omega_0' - \omega_0$; that is, the quasi-static approximation will hold. The condition that the contributions be "sharp" is that their width be small compared to the shift. If the collision duration is t_0 this simply requires

$$\frac{1}{t_0} \ll (\omega_0' - \omega) \equiv \Delta\omega,$$

which suggests that the shape of the extreme wings of the line (large $\Delta\omega$) can always be described by the quasi-static theory. Now for a binary collision, t_0 is of order ρ/v, while $\Delta\omega = 2\pi C/\rho^n$, so that the above condition effectively reduces to

$$\left(\frac{\rho_W}{\rho}\right)^{n-1} \gg 1,$$

or, equivalently, since $n > 1$, collision paths lying inside the Weisskopf sphere are quasi-static. Correspondingly, the quasi-static theory will hold for wavelengths much greater than $\Delta\lambda_c$ from the line center, where

$$\Delta\omega_c = \frac{2\pi c}{\lambda^2}\Delta\lambda_c = \frac{2\pi C}{\rho_W^n} = \frac{v^{n/n-1}}{(2\pi C)^{1/n-1}}. \tag{4.70}$$

The relation (4.70) was given by Unsöld (1943) and by Holstein (1950). It implies the expected result, namely that for a given line the quasi-static approximation holds closer to the line center the smaller is v, that is, the lower the temperature, or the greater the mass of the perturber.

For the applicability of the impact approximation in its strong collision form we require, as seen above, that t_0 be much shorter than the interval τ between strong collisions. Phase correlation is then, on the average, lost after a time τ and strong collisions describable by the impact approximation cannot contribute components further from the line center than $\Delta\omega$ given by $\Delta\omega \sim 1/\tau \ll 1/t_0$. Thus, the validity conditions for this form of the impact approximation are the opposite of those for the quasi-static approximation.

These effects are illustrated in Table 4.1—taken from a tabulation by Unsöld (1955)—which shows that for linear Stark broadening the ion

TABLE 4.1. The critical wavelength $\Delta\lambda_c$ (angstroms) separating the regimes of the quasi-static and impact approximations for linear Stark effect (after Unsöld (1955), Table 43)

Line	Broadening agent	Kinetic temperature		
		25000	10000	5000
Hα	Electrons	580	230	110
	Protons	0.63	0.25	0.12
Hβ	Electrons	120	48	24
	Protons	0.13	0.05	0.03
Hγ	Electrons	48	19	9
	Protons	0.05	0.02	0.01
Hδ	Electrons	32	13	6
	Protons	0.03	0.01	0.007

contribution to the broadening is described by a quasi-static theory, while that of the electrons is given by an impact theory over a large range of conditions of astrophysical interest.

4.3.6 The Adiabatic Assumption and its Removal

The simple formulation embodied in Equations (4.58) and (4.59) is valid only insofar as the perturbation causes no transitions. This (adiabatic) assumption was early recognized as a significant limitation to the theory since it neglects those changes in the emitted wave which arise when an atom is transferred under the influence of the collision from one state to another. In an extreme case the radiation could be terminated altogether (as a result of a superelastic collision) and thus contribute components to the emitted spectrum which would otherwise have been neglected. In fact, such cases are rare; however, essentially the same effect occurs when the perturbation causes transitions between states which are either degenerate or have small energy separations. It is not at all obvious that such transitions do not contribute substantially to the line broadening. In fact, their inclusion has given rise to complete revisions of earlier Stark-broadening theories.

It is convenient, following Margenau and Lewis (1959), to categorize adiabatic assumptions according to whether they suppose (1) that the interaction causes no transitions within the set of degenerate levels comprising the upper or lower state of the line transition or (2) that it causes no transitions between levels (degenerate or nondegenerate) separated by a finite energy. Under category (1) Spitzer (1940) pointed out the following fundamental difficulty in Weisskopf's treatment. Consider the broadening of a line whose upper level consists of a set of degenerate states distinguished by an angular quantum number. If we refer this quantum number to the axis defined by the line joining the atom and perturber, this axis must be conserved, in the atomic coordinates, if the collision is to be adiabatic. Hence, the atom will be swung around as the perturber passes it and—as observed in the laboratory frame—the emission at the end of the collision will therefore be 180 deg out of phase with that at the beginning. On the assumption that the collisions are adiabatic, the broadening should then be enormous since all collisions, whether inside or outside the Weisskopf sphere, would cause a phase change of π and should, accordingly, be counted as contributing to the broadening. Spitzer resolved this problem by determining the conditions under which a transition would occur (i.e., that the collision be *not* adiabatic) and showed that collisions outside the Weisskopf sphere were not in fact adiabatic in the above sense, i.e., they did *not* succeed in swinging the atom around. Weisskopf's result is thus essentially unaltered since the unjustified assumption of adiabaticity is balanced by the corresponding neglect of the possibility that the atom may rotate.

Approximate validity conditions for the adiabatic assumption may be found from the following order of magnitude arguments. Consider first those under category (1) above; the time taken for a transition to occur due to a perturber passing the atom with impact parameter ρ and velocity v is $\sim \rho/v$. This transition will contribute Fourier components of width $\Delta\omega_u \sim v/\rho$ centered about a frequency $\Delta\omega_s \sim 2\pi C/\rho^n$ from the line center. Thus, for degenerate levels nonadiabatic effects will contribute negligibly to the line broadening if $\Delta\omega_u < \Delta\omega_s$; on the other hand, for collisions such that $\Delta\omega_u > \Delta\omega_s$ the departure from adiabaticity in the collision will be significant. It follows immediately that collisions within the Weisskopf radius may be taken as adiabatic; while for those outside, this assumption will be invalid. The same conclusion was reached on the basis of uncertainty principle arguments by Unsöld (1943) and by Anderson (1949).

Validity conditions under category (2) depend on the situation. If the upper level consists of two states a and b, which are almost degenerate so that overlapping lines can be expected, the adiabatic assumption would be generally invalid except in the far wings, i.e., for frequencies much larger than that corresponding to the level separation.

Recent workers in the impact theory of line broadening have paid particular attention to the validity of the two basic approximations of adiabaticity and classical path of the perturber—the impact approximation itself is a feature common to all developments since the general problem appears quite intractable at present. The classical path approximation assumes that the position and velocity of the perturber can be specified to arbitrary accuracy and that its motion is classical. Kivel, Bloom, and Margenau (1955) have studied the validity of this assumption in some detail; their conclusions indicate that it is valid in astrophysical applications for protons, or heavier particles, but is questionable for electron collisions. The actual situation seems, however, unclear; thus Margenau and Meyerott (1955) find little difference between the predictions of the classical path approximation and a quantum mechanical description of the collision. Griem, Kolb, and Shen (1959) and Shen (1960) suggest that the use of the approximation will have little influence on predicted line broadening of H or He II by electron impacts. The question has been clarified by Baranger (1962), who has shown that a classical path approximation is always valid in practice for electron perturbers. This is essentially because the major broadening is due to weak collisions by electrons with angular momenta much exceeding $\hbar$; this is, of course, a sufficient condition for the motion to be classical.

Anderson (1949) first gave a general formulation of the line broadening problem including nonadiabatic effects for completely degenerate upper and lower levels of the line. Later, Kivel, Bloom, and Margenau (1955) considered the broadening of hydrogen lines by transitions induced by electron collisions, but they neglected the influence of ion fields in splitting the levels into their Stark components.

A consistent theory of broadening of overlapping lines in the impact approximation has been given independently by Baranger (1958) and by Kolb and Griem (1958) following earlier work of Griem (1954), and Kolb (1957). Such problems arise frequently in practice, either in the broadening of close-lying multiplet lines where the separation is fixed by the atom itself or in cases, such as linear Stark broadening by electron impact, where a degeneracy of the levels is removed under the influence of external fields, or by a quasi-static field due to the ions. In this case the electron impacts cannot be described by an adiabatic theory and the transitions induced by weak collisions in fact provide the major contribution to the line broadening under a wide range of physical conditions. The corresponding predicted line shapes are, in general, made up of a sum of dispersion curves—with different half-widths and shifts—and asymmetric curves of a type not previously predicted.

Applications of astrophysical interest have been made to the important cases of Stark broadening of H, He I and He II, we consider these in the following section.

4.4 Stark Broadening

Because a central problem in the analysis of stellar spectra lies in understanding the profiles of lines of hydrogen and helium, a great deal of attention has been devoted to understanding the mechanism of broadening of lines of these elements.   Until laboratory experiments on plasmas indicated otherwise, it was generally believed that, beyond their centers, the shapes of the hydrogen lines were due solely to the level splitting caused by the quasi-static electric field resulting from the ion configuration.   This was a prediction of the adiabatic (Lindholm) theory, but more recent theoretical work has shown this conclusion to be premature; nonadiabatic electron collisions in fact play a major role in determining the line shape.   For physical conditions compatible with the formation of hydrogen lines, it has been known for some time that over the main part of the line the heavy-ion effects are to be described in terms of the quasi-static (Holtsmark) distribution, while for the electrons the impact approximation is appropriate.   This happy circumstance allows a description of the broadening in terms of the relatively simple picture of electron impacts on a statically perturbed atom.

4.4.1 The Holtsmark Theory

In a static electric field of strength F, hydrogenic energy levels are split into many components and, correspondingly, we observe a large number of lines whose separation from the unperturbed line center is expressible as

$$
\begin{aligned}
\Delta\lambda_k &= \frac{3h}{8\pi^2 mecZ}\,\lambda^2 n_k F \\
&= 0.0192\lambda^2 n_k F/Z,
\end{aligned}
\tag{4.71}
$$

where n_k are numbers whose values depend on the principal quantum numbers of the upper and lower levels of the transition, Z is the ionic charge of the hydrogenic ion, λ and $\Delta\lambda$ are wavelengths measured in centimeters, and F is in units of esu/cm.   To each component (i.e., to each value of n_k) corresponds a certain intrinsic strength I_k—frequently normalized so that $\sum I_k = 1$.   Values of I_k, normalized to a value of 10^8, for each permitted transition in the Lyman, Balmer, Paschen, and Brackett series of hydrogen—up to the $n = 18$ line—have been given by Underhill and Waddell (1959).

In an ionized gas the field F at any point is not constant, but fluctuates as the neighboring distribution of ions changes.   The instantaneous separations $\Delta\lambda_k$ vary and, as a consequence, so does the instantaneous emission pattern.   If the conditions in the gas are

appropriate for the application of a quasi-static broadening approximation in some part of the line, then the corresponding line shape will
depend on the distribution of the electric field strength F. A limiting
form normally applicable in stellar atmospheres was obtained for this
distribution by Holtsmark. In his theory the field distribution is
expressed in terms of a "normal field strength" F_0 given, in units of
esu/cm, by

$$F_0 = 1.25 \times 10^{-9} N^{2/3}, \tag{4.72}$$

where N is the ion density in cm^{-3}; the probability distribution $W(\beta)$
for the electric field strength is then given in terms of the dimensionless
parameter $\beta = F/F_0$. A general expression for $W(\beta)$, due to Verweij
(1936), is given by Underhill and Waddell (1959) in the form

$$W(\beta) = \frac{4}{3\pi} \sum_{j=0}^{\infty} (-)^j \frac{(4j+5)!}{(2j+1)!} \beta^{2j+2}. \tag{4.73}$$

For small β, $W(\beta)$ may be found from the series expansion

$$W(\beta) = \frac{4\beta^2}{3\pi} [1 - 0.4630\beta^2 + 0.1226\beta^4 - \cdots],$$

while for large β it is usually sufficient to use the asymptotic series

$$W(\beta) = \beta^{-5/2}[1.496 + 7.639\beta^{-3/2} + 31.60\beta^{-3} + \cdots]. \tag{4.74}$$

For intermediate values, where neither limiting case is useful, one may
obtain $W(\beta)$ from expansions given in Underhill and Waddell's tables.

To relate this field distribution to the emitted line profile predicted
in the Holtsmark theory, we may use Equation (4.71) in the abbreviated
form

$$\Delta\lambda = c_k F, \tag{4.75}$$

so that

$$\beta \equiv \frac{F}{F_0} = \frac{\Delta\lambda}{c_k F_0}.$$

It is also convenient to introduce the variable α defined by

$$\alpha = c_k \beta = \frac{\Delta\lambda}{F_0}. \tag{4.76}$$

The intensity distribution $S_H(\alpha)$, summed over all components of the line, may be written

$$S_H(\alpha)\,d\alpha = \sum_k I_k W\left(\frac{\alpha}{c_k}\right)\frac{d\alpha}{c_k}, \qquad (4.77)$$

where $S_H(\alpha)$ is therefore normalized to $\sum I_k$ and the subscript H is used to indicate that the result applies to the Holtsmark approximation.

The corresponding absorption coefficient for stationary atoms is then given by

$$\alpha_H(\Delta\lambda) = \frac{\pi e^2 f \lambda^2}{mc^2}\frac{S_H(\alpha)}{F_0}. \qquad (4.78)$$

Extensive tables of $S_H(\alpha)$ are to be found in Underhill and Waddell's publication. In the line wings the asymptotic form (4.74), in conjunction with Equation (4.77), gives

$$S_H(\alpha) \sim \frac{1.50\sum I_k c_k^{3/2}}{\alpha^{5/2}},$$

which may be reduced to the form

$$S_H(\alpha) \sim 1.50 K_{ab}^{3/2}\,\alpha^{-5/2}, \qquad (4.79)$$

where K_{ab} is a constant depending on the principal quantum numbers a and b of the transition. From Underhill and Waddell's tables, Griem (1960) has derived values of K_{ab} for $a = 1, 2, 3, 4$ and for b-values up to 18. For other values of a and b the following approximate formula, given by Griem, may be used:

$$K_{ab} = \frac{(ab)^4}{(b^2 - a^2)} \times \frac{5.5 \times 10^{-5}}{Z^5}.$$

4.4.2 Electron Broadening of Hydrogenic Lines

Because of its great use in plasma diagnostics, the theory of electron broadening of hydrogenic lines has been very extensively treated in the past few years and it cannot be adequately considered here. Baranger (1962) has reviewed these developments and the reader is referred to his article and to Griem's text for a thorough discussion of the semi-classical and fully quantum mechanical theories.

In many astrophysical applications we are mainly interested in asymptotic forms for the line shape, and Griem, Kolb, and Shen (1959) have studied these in some detail. Their results, and some extensions (Griem, 1960) have been modified by Griem (1962a) following an objection by Lewis (1961) to the method adopted for limiting the influence of weak collisions by terminating the integrations (4.67) and (4.68) at the Debye radius. As Lewis pointed out, this is not necessarily valid; properly one should include in an impact approximation only those collisions which can be completed in a time of order $(\Delta\omega)^{-1}$ (otherwise they are quasi-static) and these may have impact parameters less than the Debye radius.

In place of the simple asymptotic formula derived by Griem, Kolb, and Shen (1959), namely,

$$\alpha(\Delta\lambda) \sim \alpha_{\mathrm{H}}(\Delta\lambda)[1 + R(N, T)(\Delta\lambda)^{1/2}],$$

Griem (1962a) has suggested a set of asymptotic forms giving a continuous transition to the necessary quasi-static form at very large distances from the line center. He has also studied the contribution to the broadening by strong collisions with impact parameters less than the Weisskopf radius; his final forms and the wavelength ranges to which they apply are

CASE 1: for $\Delta\lambda < \Delta\lambda_p$,

$$\alpha(\Delta\lambda) \sim \alpha_{\mathrm{H}}(\Delta\lambda)\{1 + [(\Delta\lambda_\omega)^{-1/2} + R(N, T)](\Delta\lambda)^{1/2}\}, \qquad (4.80)$$

CASE 2: for $\Delta\lambda_p < \Delta\lambda < \Delta\lambda_\omega$,

$$\alpha(\Delta\lambda) \sim \alpha_{\mathrm{H}}(\Delta\lambda)\left\{1 + \left[(\Delta\lambda_\omega)^{-1/2} + R(N, T)\frac{\ln(\Delta\lambda_\omega/\Delta\lambda)}{\ln(\Delta\lambda_\omega/\Delta\lambda_p)}\right]\Delta\lambda^{1/2}\right\}, \qquad (4.81)$$

CASE 3: for $\Delta\lambda > \Delta\lambda_\omega$, the quasi-static form

$$\alpha(\Delta\lambda) \sim 2\alpha_{\mathrm{H}}(\Delta\lambda), \qquad (4.82)$$

where

$$\Delta\lambda_\omega \simeq \frac{Z\lambda^2 kT}{chb^2} \qquad (4.83)$$

and

$$\Delta\lambda_p = \lambda^2\left[\frac{Ne^2}{\pi mc^2}\right]^{1/2}. \qquad (4.84)$$

The term $(\Delta\lambda_\omega)^{-1/2}$ in these expressions arises from strong collisions; the other modifications arise from the Lewis correction.

Tables of the function $R(N, T)$ are given by Griem, Kolb, and Shen (1959) for the first two Lyman lines and the first four Balmer lines of H I and by Griem (1962b) for the two Brackett lines ($\lambda 4686$, $\lambda 3203$) of He II. For hydrogenic lines Griem (1960, 1962a) has been able to show that the asymptotic Holtsmark law can be expressed in terms of the single function $T_H(\beta)$ defined by

$$S_H(\alpha) \simeq T_H(\beta)/K_{ab},$$

or, in view of the asymptotic relationship (4.79)

$$T_H(\beta) \simeq 1.5\beta^{-5/2}.$$

He then shows that the influence of electrons can be included by defining a generalized function

$$S^*(\alpha) = K_{ab}^{-1} T(\beta, \gamma)$$

with

$$T(\beta, \gamma) = \frac{1}{\pi} \int_{-\infty}^{+\infty} T_H(\beta') \frac{\gamma}{\gamma^2 + (\beta - \beta')^2} \, d\beta', \qquad (4.85)$$

where the electron "damping constant" γ is given by

$$\gamma = 5.6 \times 10^{-6} N^{1/3} T^{-1/2} Z^{-1}$$
$$\times \left[\log_{10} \left\{ \frac{4 \times 10^6 T Z}{b^2 N^{1/2}} \right\} \right] \frac{b^5 + a^5}{b^2 - a^2} Q(\Delta\lambda) + \gamma_s, \quad (4.86)$$

with N in cm^{-3}. In this equation the strong collision constant γ_s is represented as

$$\gamma_s = 1.5\pi\beta_\omega^{-1/2},$$

with $\beta_\omega = \Delta\lambda_\omega/F_0 K_{ab}$, while the multiplier $Q(\Delta\lambda)$ is either unity if $\Delta\lambda < \Delta\lambda_p$ or is given by the form

$$Q(\Delta\lambda) = \frac{\ln (\Delta\lambda_\omega/\Delta\lambda)}{\ln (\Delta\lambda_\omega/\Delta\lambda_p)}, \qquad \Delta\lambda_\omega > \Delta\lambda > \Delta\lambda_p$$

with $\Delta\lambda$ a representative value in the wavelength range of interest. For $\Delta\lambda > \Delta\lambda_\omega$ the Holtsmark form may be used for both electrons and ions. Griem (1960) has tabulated the function $T(\beta, \gamma)$ in the range $0 \leq \beta \leq 20$, $0 \leq \gamma \leq 10$; for larger β and γ he has suggested using the asymptotic expression

$$T(\beta, \gamma) \sim 1.5\beta^{-5/2} + \frac{\gamma}{\pi} \beta^{-2}.$$

For the high Balmer lines, or generally for lines such that $b \gg a$, Griem's formulae predict a fifth-power dependence of the electron broadening contribution on the principal quantum number b. It may be shown, however, that a fourth-power law is, in fact, the correct asymptotic form (J. W. Cooper, 1966). Griem's results were obtained by extrapolating results calculated for $b \leq 6$; for $b > 6$ an approximate correction to his *electron* broadening contribution can be obtained by multiplying this by the factor $6/b$. This correction is important in astrophysical problems where electron concentrations are frequently derived from studies of the overlapping of the high Balmer lines.

Before the more modern developments it was customary to estimate an electron density from the Inglis-Teller formula which related the principal quantum number n^* of the "last resolvable line" to the electron density n_e according to the law

$$\log n_e = 23.26 - 7.5 \log_{10} n^*.$$

Griem's original formulae led to substantial changes in this law (see, e.g., Jefferies and Orrall, 1963) in the sense that lower electron densities were needed to produce a given overlap. Vidal (1966) has shown from laboratory experiments that the approximate correction to Griem's formula suggested above gives results in essential agreement with the Inglis-Teller formula in most situations of interest in stellar atmospheres. Using Griem's original formulation, determinations of n_e for solar flares from the overlap of the high Balmer lines on the one hand, and from the variation of halfwidth with quantum number b for $b \lesssim 15$ on the other, had given conflicting results. This reduction in the contribution from electron broadening resolves this conflict in favor of the (higher) values of n_e found from the half-width variation.

4.4.3 Broadening and Shift of He I Lines

As for the hydrogen lines, nonadiabatic effects of electron-broadening collisions for nonhydrogenic lines can lead to very different predictions than the adiabatic theory. Neutral helium has been studied in detail by Kivel (1955), Vainshtein, and Sobel'man (1959) and, more satisfactorily, by Griem, Baranger, Kolb, and Oertel (1962). Much remains to be done on this important spectrum, however, particularly for the diffuse triplets which are so strong in many stellar spectra.

Computed widths and shifts for 24 lines in the wavelength range from 520 to 47000 Å are given in the last cited work. Their procedure is first to compute the nonadiabatic electron impact line shape for isolated lines—the only degeneracy being in the magnetic quantum numbers— which leads to a Lorentzian line shape as in Anderson's (1949) theory. The ion velocities are normally small enough for the adiabatic theory to hold; in the quasi-static limit of small velocities the line profile is given by

$$\alpha(x)\,dx = \frac{dx}{\pi}\int_0^\infty \frac{W_{\mathrm{H}}(\beta)\,d\beta}{1 + (x - \alpha^{4/3}\beta^2)^2},\qquad (4.87)$$

where x is the frequency, measured from the shifted line center, in units of the electron impact broadening width w; that is,

$$x = \frac{\Delta\omega - d}{w},$$

where d is the shift of the line center while

$$\alpha = \left[\frac{2\pi C}{w\rho_m^4}\right]^{3/4},$$

ρ_m being the mean separation of the perturbers ($\frac{4}{3}\pi\rho_m^3 n = 1$). In the limit of large x, Equation (4.87) takes the asymptotic forms

$$\alpha(x) \simeq \frac{1}{\pi x^2} + \frac{3\alpha}{4x^{7/4}}\qquad (4.88)$$

in the direction of the line shift and

$$\alpha(x) \simeq \frac{1}{\pi x^2}\qquad (4.89)$$

in the opposite direction. The term in x^{-2} arises from electron-impact broadening, that in $x^{-7/4}$ is the standard quasi-static limit for ion broadening and is readily shown to be equal to that given by Equation (4.45) for $n = 4$.

To apply these results we need, of course, the electron broadening width in terms of which the displacement x is measured. In their tabulation Griem *et al.* compare the predicted electron impact widths and shifts with those of the adiabatic theory—as given by Equations (4.67) and (4.68). The agreement is fair; for temperatures where He I would be strongly emitted the adiabatic width is usually too small by about 20%, though this is by no means a general rule. For astrophysical calculations on lines not included in that list, it is probably acceptable to use the adiabatic electron-impact widths reduced by a factor derivable from the tabulations. The ratios of line shift to width however, are found to be considerably smaller than the adiabatic value of $\sqrt{3}$; the error is typically a factor of 2 or more and increases with increasing temperature.

From Equation (4.67) the electron impact adiabatic width may be written

$$\Delta\omega_{1/2} = \frac{2}{3} \frac{(\pi^2)^{5/3}}{\sqrt{3}} \times \frac{1}{\Gamma(5/3)} n_e \bar{v}_e^{1/3} C^{2/3}. \tag{4.90}$$

For $n = 4, C$ is frequently expressed in units of cm^{-1} per $(100 \text{ kv/cm})^2$; the conversion to cgs units is

$$C_4 \text{ (cgs)} = 6.2 \times 10^{-14} C_4 \quad \text{(practical)}.$$

4.4.4 Stark Broadening of Lines of Other Elements

An extensive tabulation of approximate values of the shifts and widths of the Stark-broadened lines of many astrophysically important transitions has been made by Griem *et al.* (1962) and is included in Griem's monograph *Plasma Spectroscopy*, to which reference should be made for further details.

4.5 Other Pressure-Broadening Mechanisms

Although they have been discussed in much less detail than Stark broadening, other broadening mechanisms can be very significant in determining line shapes in stellar atmospheres.

It is customary in the literature to differentiate interactions between an atom and the perturbers in terms of the static interaction law (4.44) according to the following scheme:

n	Interaction
2	linear Stark
3	resonance (like particles)
4	"quadratic" Stark
6	Van der Waals

For completeness, we give in this final selection a brief summary of the pertinent results for the cases $n = 3, 4, 6$.

4.5.1 Self-Broadening ($n = 3$)

According to Weisskopf the constant C is given roughly by

$$C = \frac{e^2}{8\pi^2 mc} \lambda f. \tag{4.91}$$

In the adiabatic impact theory the width is given from Equation (4.67) as

$$\Delta\omega_{1/2} = 4\pi^3 Cn. \tag{4.92}$$

Since this is proportional to n, the number of atoms in the lower state of the transition, it is only likely to be important for hydrogen and helium lines, if it is important at all in a stellar atmosphere. For Lα we find, roughly, that $\Delta\omega_{1/2} = 5 \times 10^{-8} n_1$ while, for Hα, $\gamma \simeq 5 \times 10^{-6} n_2$. In the solar chromosphere where Lα is formed, n_1 will be too low for this mechanism to compete with the natural damping, for which $\Delta\omega_{1/2} \sim 10^8 \text{ sec}^{-1}$. Cayrel and Traving (1960) have suggested it is operative in the wings of Hα in some astrophysical situations.

4.5.2 Van der Waals Broadening ($n = 6$)

Any significant broadening by this mechanism in a stellar atmosphere will be due to perturbations by hydrogen atoms because of their overwhelming abundance. Unsöld (1955) has given the interaction constant for this case as

$$C \simeq 1.6 \times 10^{-33} n^4 / Z^2, \tag{4.93}$$

where n is the principal quantum number of the upper level of the transition. If the impact approximation is valid, the damping constant is given as

$$\Delta\omega_{1/2} \sim 20 C^{2/5} v^{3/5} N; \tag{4.94}$$

the line shift is negligible. For $C \simeq 10^{-31}$, $v = 10^6 \text{ cm-sec}^{-1}$, and $N = 10^{17} \text{ cm}^{-3}$, Equation (4.94) gives $\gamma \sim 10^9 \text{ sec}^{-1}$, a value larger than that corresponding to natural damping even of strong metal lines in the far-ultraviolet.

Unsöld and Wiedemann (1955) have compared the theoretical predictions for Van der Waals broadening with the observed widths of lines of the alkalis and other elements and report satisfactory agreement. A more recent comparison by Kusch (1958) suggests that for some Fe I lines the predicted broadening is smaller by a factor of 4 than that observed. This, if so, is undoubtedly to be ascribed to the neglected departures from adiabaticity.

4.6 Doppler Broadening

So far we have supposed that the radiating atoms are stationary. We must now incorporate the modifications introduced by the Doppler effect of the randomly moving atoms.

Consider an atom moving so that its line-of-sight velocity with respect to a fixed observer is v_l. A frequency which would be measured as v by the observer is received by the atom as v' such that

$$v' = v(1 - v_l/c).$$

For the frequency v' the atomic absorption coefficient (if Lorentzian) is

$$\alpha(v') = \frac{\pi e^2 f}{mc} \frac{\delta}{\pi} \frac{1}{(v' - v_0)^2 + \delta^2}. \tag{4.95}$$

For a Maxwellian distribution of atomic velocities the number of atoms having velocities in the range v_l to $v_l + dv_l$ is

$$dn(v_l) = \frac{n}{\sqrt{\pi} \, V} e^{-(v_l/V)^2} \, dv_l,$$

where n is the number of atoms per unit volume in the absorbing state, and $V = \sqrt{2kT/m}$ with T the kinetic temperature of the atoms. The absorption coefficient of the whole ensemble is then given by

$$\kappa_D(v) = \frac{\pi e^2 f n}{mc} \delta \int_{-\infty}^{+\infty} \frac{1}{\pi} \frac{e^{-(v_l/V)^2} \, dv_l/V\sqrt{\pi}}{[v - v_0(1 + v_l/c)]^2 + \delta^2}, \tag{4.96}$$

where we have made the replacement $v' - v_0 = v - v_0(1 + v_l/c)$. The substitution $v = (\Delta v/\Delta v_D)$, where $\Delta v_D = (v/c)\sqrt{2kT/m}$ is the *Doppler width* in frequency units, allows us to transform Equation (4.96) to the expression

$$\kappa_D(v) = \frac{\pi e^2 f}{mc} \frac{H(a, v)}{\sqrt{\pi} \, \Delta v_D} n, \tag{4.97}$$

where

$$H(a, v) = \frac{a}{\pi} \int_{-\infty}^{+\infty} \frac{e^{-y^2}\,dy}{a^2 + (v - y)^2} = \frac{1}{\sqrt{\pi}} \int_0^{\infty} e^{-ay - y^2/4} \cos vy\,dy \quad (4.98)$$

and $a = \delta/\Delta\nu_D$.

The function $H(a, v)$ has been described by Hjerting (1938); a tabulation convenient for astrophysical application is given by Harris (1948), and in more detail by Finn and Mugglestone (1965) and by Hummer (1965).

In the line core where v is small the contribution to the integral comes mainly from the region $y = v$. In this case

$$H(a, v) \simeq \frac{a}{\pi} e^{-v^2} \int_{-\infty}^{+\infty} \frac{dy}{a^2 + y^2}$$
$$\simeq e^{-v^2}. \quad (4.99)$$

In the wings, on the other hand, the main contribution arises in the region $y \ll v$. Thus, neglecting a^2, Equation (4.98) may be written

$$H(a, v) = \frac{a}{\pi} \int_{-\infty}^{+\infty} \frac{e^{-y^2}}{v^2} \left(1 + \frac{2y}{v}\right) dy$$
$$= \frac{a/\sqrt{\pi}}{v^2}. \quad (4.100)$$

The value of v_c which separates the region of applicability of these extreme forms can be found roughly from the equation

$$e^{-v_c^2} = \frac{a/\sqrt{\pi}}{v_c^2}.$$

For $a/\sqrt{\pi} = 10^{-2}, 10^{-3}, 10^{-4}$ (values in the range commonly found in practice) v_c is found as 2.7, 3.0, 3.2. Roughly, then, we can expect the absorption coefficient to be gaussian out to three Doppler widths for normal permitted lines in the visible spectrum. A detailed examination of Hummer's tables, for example, bears out this expectation.

It is important to bear the above in mind; we shall frequently refer to the line core, meaning that part of the line inside which the absorption coefficient can be well described by a gaussian law. It is equally important to note that over the first three Doppler widths the absorption coefficient decreases by a factor of about e^9, or 10^4; from there on it varies slowly. In this fact lies the essential point of analyzing line cores; they reflect in their shapes and intensities the conditions over a very large region of the atmosphere. Alternatively, a neglect of the line core is equivalent to the neglect of most of the line-forming region in its influence on the emergent radiation.

It is frequently desired to include the possibility of random motions additional to the thermal motion. We may, for example, incorporate a "microturbulent" structure by supposing the atmosphere to be made up of elements each of which contains many atoms, but also has a linear dimension small compared to the mean free path of a photon. If there are sufficient such elements in the line of sight—in practice more than about 10—and if their velocities are independent, the probability of a given velocity ξ may be expected to be described by a gaussian distribution

$$P(\xi) = \frac{1}{\sqrt{\pi}\xi_0}\, e^{-(\xi/\xi_0)^2}, \qquad (4.101)$$

where ξ_0 is a mean random velocity. The velocity broadening accompanying these random motions is superposed on the basic Doppler profile of the absorption coefficient to give an expression of the same form as given in Equation (4.97), but in which the Doppler width is given as

$$\Delta\nu_{\mathrm{D}} = \frac{\nu}{c}\left[\frac{2kT}{m} + \xi_0^2\right]^{1/2}. \qquad (4.102)$$

Since ξ_0 is presumably the same for all atomic constituents, while m is different, observations of the widths of two line profiles may often be made consistent by a suitable choice of the two parameters ξ_0 and T. This is, in fact, the reason for the consideration of such random macroscopic motions in astrophysics. For wavelengths lying beyond the line core, the atomic motion influences only slightly the line profile, since too few atoms move fast enough to take advantage of the extremely large atomic absorption coefficients at the line center. Thus, the broadening laws derived for a stationary atom, in the previous sections 4.3 to 4.5, will hold for the line wings.

REFERENCES

ANDERSON, P. W., 1949, "Pressure Broadening in the Microwave and Infra-Red Regions," *Phys. Rev. 76*, 647.

BARANGER, M., 1958, "General Impact Theory of Pressure Broadening," *Phys. Rev. 112*, 855.

BARANGER, M., 1962, *Atomic and Molecular Processes*, edited by D. R. Bates. London: Academic Press, Ch. 13.

BURKHARDT, G., 1940, " Über die Stoßverbreiterung und statistische Verbreiterung von Spektrallinien," *Z. Phys.* *115*, 592.

CAYREL, R., and G. TRAVING, 1960, "Zur Frage der Druckverbreiterung der Solaren Balmerlinien," *Z. Astrophys.* *50*, 239.

CHANDRASEKHAR, S., 1943, "Stochastic Problems in Physics and Astronomy," *Rev. Mod. Phys.* *15*, 1.

COOPER, J. W., 1966, *Private Communication.*

CORLISS, C. H., and W. R. BOZMAN, 1962, "Experimental Transition Probabilities for Spectral Lines of Seventy Elements," *Nat. Bur. Stand., Mongr. 53.*

FINN, G. D., and D. E. MUGGLESTONE, 1965, "Tables of the Line Broadening Function H(a, v)," *Mon. Not. R. Astr. Soc. 129*, 221.

FOLEY, H. M., 1946, "The Pressure Broadening of Spectral Lines," *Phys. Rev.* *69*, 616.

GLENNON, B. M., and W. L. WIESE, 1962, "Bibliography on Atomic Transition Probabilities," *Nat. Bur. Stand. Monogr. 50.*

GRIEM, H. R., 1954, "Starkeffekt-Verbreiterung der Balmer-Linien bei großen Elektronendichten," *Z. Phys. 137*, 280.

GRIEM, H. R., 1960, "Stark Broadening of Higher Hydrogen and Hydrogen-Like Lens by Electrons and Ions," *Astrophys. J. 132*, 883.

GRIEM, H. R., 1962a, "Wing Formulae for Stark-Broadened Hydrogen and Hydrogenic Lines," *Astrophys. J. 136*, 422.

GRIEM, H. R., 1962b, "Stark Broadening of Isolated Spectral Lines from Heavy Elements in a Plasma," *Phys. Rev. 128*, 515.

GRIEM, H. R., 1964, *Plasma Spectroscopy.* New York: McGraw-Hill.

GRIEM, H. R., A. C. KOLB, and K. Y. SHEN, 1959, "Stark Broadening of Hydrogen Lines in a Plasma," *Phys. Rev. 116*, 4.

GRIEM, H. R., M. BARANGER, A. C. KOLB, and G. OERTEL, 1962, "Stark Broadening of Neutral Helium Lines in a Plasma," *Phys. Rev. 125*, 177.

HARRIS, D. L., 1948, "On the Line-Absorption Coefficient Due to Doppler Effect and Damping," *Astrophys. J. 108*, 112.

HEITLER, W., 1954, *The Quantum Theory of Radiation*, Third ed. Oxford: Clarendon Press.

HJERTING, F., 1938, "Tables Facilitating the Calculation of Line Absorption Coefficients," *Astrophys. J. 88*, 508.

HOLSTEIN, T., 1950, "Pressure Broadening of Spectral Lines," *Phys. Rev. 79*, 744.

HOLTSMARK, J., 1919, "Über die Verbreiterung von Spektrallinien I," *Physik. Z. 20*, 162.

HUMMER, D. G., 1965, "The Voigt Function, An Eight-Significant-Figure Table and Generating Procedure," *Memoirs, Royal Astron. Soc. 70*, 1.

JEFFERIES, J. T., and F. Q. ORRALL, 1963, "On the Interpretation of Prominence Spectra VI. Temperature Determination and a Model for Quiescent Prominences," *Astrophys. J. 137*, 1232.

KIVEL, B., 1955, "Electron Broadening and Shift of Spectral Lines of Helium," *Phys. Rev. 98*, 1055.

KIVEL, B., S. BLOOM, and H. MARGENAU, 1955, "Electron Impact Broadening of Spectral Lines," *Phys. Rev.* 98, 495.

KOLB, A. C., 1957, *University of Michigan Engineering Research Institute*, ASTIA Document No. AD86309.

KOLB, A. C., and H. R. GRIEM, 1958, "Theory of Line Broadening in Multiplet Spectra," *Phys. Rev.* 111, 514.

KUHN, H., 1934, "Pressure Shift and Broadening of Spectral Lines," *Phil. Mag.* 18, 987.

KUSCH, H. J., 1958, "Experimentelle Untersuchung der Druckverbreiterung von Eisenlinien durch neutrale Wasserstoffatome und Wasserstoffmoleküle," *Z. Astrophys.* 45, 1.

LENZ, W., 1924, "Some Correspondence Considerations," *Z. Phys.* 25, 299.

LENZ, W., 1933, "Allgemeine Theorie der Verbreiterung von Spektrallinien," *Z. Phys.* 80, 423.

LEWIS, M., 1961, "Stark Broadening of Spectral Lines by High-Velocity Charged Particles," *Phys. Rev.* 121, 501.

LINDHOLM, E., 1941, "Zur Theorie der Verbreiterung von Spektrallinien," *Ark. f. Mat., Astr., Fys.* 28B, No. 3.

LORENTZ, H. A., 1906, "Over de absorptie-en emissiebanden van gasvormige Lichamen," *Proc. Acad. Sci. Amsterdam 8*, 591.

MARGENAU, H., 1933, "Pressure Broadening of Spectral Lines, II," *Phys. Rev.* 43, 129.

MARGENAU, H., 1951, "Statistical Theory of Pressure Broadening," *Phys. Rev.* 82, 156.

MARGENAU, H., and M. LEWIS, 1959, "Structure of Spectral Lines from Plasmas," *Rev. Mod. Phys.* 31, 569.

MARGENAU, H., and R. MEYEROTT, 1955, "Quantum Theory of Line Broadening by an Ionic Plasma," *Astrophys. J.* 121, 194.

MARGENAU, H., and W. W. WATSON, 1936, "Pressure Effects on Spectral Lines," *Rev. Mod. Phys.* 8, 22.

SHEN, K. Y., 1960, "Theory of Stark Broadening of the Spectral Lines of Ionized Helium," *Ph.D. Thesis.* College Park: University of Maryland.

SPITZER, L., 1940, "Impact Broadening of Spectral Lines," *Phys. Rev.* 58, 348.

UNDERHILL, A. B., and J. H. WADDELL, 1959, "Stark Broadening Function for the Hydrogen Lines," *Nat. Bur. Stand. Circ.*, No. 603.

UNSÖLD, A., 1943, "Über die Theorie der Druckverbreiterung und Verschiebung von Spektrallinien," *Vierteljahrschr. D. Astr. Gesellsch. 78*, 213.

UNSÖLD, A., 1955, *Physik der Sternatmosphären*, Second ed. Berlin: Springer-Verlag, p. 305.

UNSÖLD, A., and V. WEIDEMANN, 1955, *Vistas in Astronomy*, edited by A. Beer. London: Pergamon Press, Vol. 1.

VAINSHTEIN, L. A., and I. I. SOBELMAN, 1959, "Non-Stationary Theory of the Stark Broadening of Spectral Lines in Plasmas," *Opt. Spectr. 6*, 279.

VERWEIJ, S., 1936, "The Stark Effect of Hydrogen in Stellar Spectra," *Publ. Astr. Inst. Amsterdam 5*.

VIDAL, C-R., 1966, "Determination of Electron Density from Line Merging," *J. Quant. Spectrosc. Radiat. Transfer 6*, 461.

WEISSKOPF, V., 1932, "Zur Theorie der Kopplungshreite und der Stoßdämpfung," *Z. Phys. 75*, 287.

WEISSKOPF, V., and E. WIGNER, 1930, "Berechnung der natürlichen Linienbreite auf Grund der Diracschen Lichttheorie," *Z. Phys. 63*, 54.

5

The Emission Coefficient

Although ostensibly studying the profile of the line-absorption coefficient in the preceding chapter, in fact we studied the atomic emission processes. It was explicitly stated there, however, that our attention was confined to the situation of "natural" excitation. The relevance of the present chapter may perhaps be most succinctly summarized in the statement that we shall here consider the profile of the emission coefficient under conditions *departing* from those of "natural" excitation.

To clarify the meaning of this term, let us consider a volume of gas small compared to the characteristic dimension of the atmosphere (or container) but large enough to hold many atoms, and suppose that we seek the frequency distribution of the energy emitted from this volume element. An individual atom may be excited as a direct result of collisional impact or as a consequence of the absorption of radiation. If the spectrum both of the particle and photon energies is essentially constant *over the "widths" of the energy levels*, then the occupation probability for energies within the *natural width* of a given level is the same as in thermodynamic equilibrium—since over this small energy range the two situations are indistinguishable.* In order to satisfy the principle of detailed balance the profiles of the emission and absorption coefficients for a given line must be identical. This situation has been assigned the name "natural excitation."

---

* Clearly, this is not to say that the total populations of the individual discrete levels are necessarily related as in thermodynamic equilibrium.

We have agreed to assume throughout this book that the energy spectrum of the exciting particles is Maxwellian. Since this distribution function shows no fine structure over the energy range corresponding to the width of any spectral line, we must correspondingly assume that a collisional excitation to the upper state of a spectral line will result in the "natural" probability distribution for the population within the energy width of the state. Any photons emitted as a result of such collisional excitation will therefore be emitted with the frequency distribution computed in the preceding chapter.

Now let us consider the alternative excitation process of photon absorption. Clearly, we may not make the general assumption that the energy spectrum of the photon shows no structure across the line, since this very line shape is our fundamental interest. Insofar as the excitation of a level arises from photon absorption, therefore we shall not be entitled to say, *a priori*, that the frequency dependence of the emission coefficient has the same form as that for "natural" excitation, i.e., we cannot take the emission and absorption coefficients to have the same frequency shape.

The problem of determining the emission coefficient in a general case resolves into that of understanding how the line frequencies mix with one another in a process of absorption and subsequent re-emission. For example, is the frequency of a photon preserved under absorption and re-emission, or is its frequency redistributed according to some probability law?

Two extreme cases which are readily obtained, and which have been extensively treated in the literature, are those of coherent scattering—in which the line frequency is preserved—and complete redistribution—in which the absorbed and re-emitted frequencies are completely uncorrelated.

It has been known for many years that neither of these limiting descriptions is really adequate; however, the numerical difficulties in the solution of the transfer equation following from the use of a more general description of the re-emission are extreme and have, so far, not been amenable to an exact treatment—although Field (1959), Osterbrock (1962), and Hummer (1962) have made some progress.

There seems a certain value, for approximate calculations, in representing the detailed form of the redistribution in terms of a linear combination of a coherent and a completely redistributed part. Although the two limiting forms certainly do not constitute a complete set, they nevertheless embody an essential physical aspect in that we might expect a photon to be either re-emitted primarily about its absorbed frequency or to be redistributed about the line center. Such expansions have been advocated frequently in the literature in forms to be illustrated in subsequent sections of this chapter.

The following general formulation, modeled after the work of Hummer (1962, 1965a), provides a convenient basis for subsequent discussion. Consider a beam of intensity $I_\nu(\mathbf{n})$ traveling in the direction $\mathbf{n}$ and confined within the solid angle $d\Omega$ and the frequency band $d\nu$. If this is incident on a block of gas of volume dV, then the energy dE_s emitted in $d\Omega'$ in the interval $d\nu'$ by scattering of the incident radiation will be proportional to the product

$$dE_s \propto I_\nu(\mathbf{n}) \, d\nu \, d\Omega \, d\nu' \, d\Omega' \bar{\kappa} \, dV \tag{5.1}$$

where $\bar{\kappa}$ is the frequency-integrated absorption coefficient. We shall represent the constant of proportionality in this expression by the probability amplitude $4\pi R(\nu, \mathbf{n}; \nu', \mathbf{n}')$ whose normalization readily follows from first principles as:

$$\iint R(\nu, \mathbf{n}; \nu', \mathbf{n}') \, d\nu' \, d\Omega' = \frac{\phi(\nu)}{4\pi}, \tag{5.2a}$$

where $\phi(\nu)$ is the normalized profile of the absorption coefficient. Clearly, then,

$$\iiiint R(\nu, \mathbf{n}; \nu', \mathbf{n}') \, d\nu' \, d\Omega' \, d\nu \, d\Omega = 1. \tag{5.2b}$$

In order to relate the phenomenological scattering probability R to the atomic parameters, let us denote the frequencies in the reference frame of the *atom* by ξ and ξ' and again let $\phi(\xi)$ represent the normalized atomic absorption coefficient. Finally, we shall need to define a redistribution function $p(\xi, \xi')$ such that, if a $(\xi, \mathbf{n})$ photon has been absorbed, the probability that the re-emitted radiation lies in the interval $d\xi'$ about ξ' and in the direction $d\Omega'$ about $\mathbf{n}'$ is

$$p(\xi, \xi')h(\mathbf{n}, \mathbf{n}') \, d\xi' \, d\Omega', \tag{5.3}$$

where $h(\mathbf{n}, \mathbf{n}')$ is a "phase function" describing the angular distribution of the scattered radiation. The expression (5.3) must clearly be normalized to unity for integration over ξ' and Ω'. Now the energy absorbed from the $(\xi, \mathbf{n})$ beam, which is subsequently re-emitted into $d\xi'$, $d\Omega'$, is readily seen to be

$$dE_s = \bar{\kappa} \, \phi(\xi) \, I_\xi(\mathbf{n}) \, d\xi \, d\Omega \, dV \, p(\xi,\xi') \, h(\mathbf{n},\mathbf{n}') \, d\xi' \, d\Omega',$$

so that, from Equation (5.1), and the definition of R, we find that

$$R_a(\nu, \mathbf{n}; \nu', \mathbf{n}') = \phi(\xi)p(\xi, \xi') \frac{h(\mathbf{n}, \mathbf{n}')}{4\pi}. \tag{5.4}$$

This expression refers to a single atom; given its velocity $\mathbf{V}$ with respect to the rest frame, we may relate the frequencies ν and ξ to the first order through the Doppler relations

$$\nu = \xi + \frac{\nu_0}{c} \mathbf{n} \cdot \mathbf{V},$$
$$\nu' = \xi' + \frac{\nu_0}{c} \mathbf{n}' \cdot \mathbf{V}, \tag{5.5}$$

where ν_0 is the frequency at the line center.

For further progress we must study the physical basis of the mechanisms determining the form of the atomic redistribution function $p(\xi, \xi')$. In the following two sections we discuss those influences arising from radiation damping and from collisional effects which act to destroy or to limit the degree of frequency coherence for an atom at rest. In the subsequent section we shall consider the further limitations arising from the influence of the thermal Doppler effect.

5.1 Redistribution Due to the Natural Width of Levels

If we suppose, as is always done in radiation theory, that the radiation field is representable as a linear superposition of waves of perfectly definite frequencies, and if we further suppose that an atomic transition contributes a distinct frequency in accordance with the Bohr relation $E_2 - E_1 = h\nu$, then the fact that the states have definite lifetimes, i.e., that the emitted lines have finite widths, can be consistently introduced into the theory by the device of assigning an energy width to the individual levels. This width is, of course, of order $\hbar/\tau$, where τ is the level "lifetime." In these terms, let us consider an upward absorption transition by a photon of definite frequency followed by a downward emission. If the lower level has an essentially infinite lifetime, then in the absence of perturbation during the transition we would expect that the absorbed and re-emitted photons would have the same frequencies.

In other words, we would expect the scattering in a resonance line to be coherent in the rest frame of the atom.

We must approach this with a degree of caution, however. As Heitler shows, monochromatic scattering must be studied as a single-photon process; we cannot speak of a separate absorption followed by a separate emission since to do so would imply that we knew the time when the separate processes occurred. To determine this time we would have to disturb the atom (by collision or with a separate light source) at time intervals necessarily shorter than the state lifetime, and in so doing we should automatically broaden the observed line by an amount at least as great as the natural width. We may illustrate this as follows: In order to be sure that the incident and scattered photons are indeed monochromatic, i.e., that they have a width small compared to the natural width, we must measure the absorbed and scattered waves for a time $T \gg \tau$, the state lifetime. This requirement, however, automatically precludes our having any knowledge within the time τ of when the absorption and emission processes took place. Such influences of measurement time on line width have been directly observed in studies of the Mössbauer effect, cf. Frauenfelder (1962). The position is different when the incident spectrum is much broader than $1/\tau$—as, e.g., is the case for excitation by a short pulse of radiation—since then we can determine when the atom is excited to an accuracy exceeding τ and we find the expected result that the scattering process is then equivalent to two independent processes (absorption and emission) and that the shape of the emission coefficient is identical to that of the absorption coefficient.

In a case where the lower level is *not* indefinitely sharp we shall not expect that the scattering process should preserve frequency since, in a qualitative way, we can argue that the excited atom will have its choice in returning to any part of the lower level while still satisfying energy conservation within the statistical limits (i.e., within the natural widths of the states).

According to Weisskopf (1933)—see also Heitler (1954) and Rosseland (1936)—the probability of the scattering process can be written, in our notation, as

$$\phi(\xi)p(\xi, \xi') = \frac{\delta_\ell \delta_a}{\pi^2[(\xi' - \xi)^2 + \delta_\ell^2][(\xi' - \xi_0)^2 + \delta_a^2]}. \qquad (5.6)*$$

* Note that the form of this expression shows that the emission and absorption processes are not in general separable.

This distribution has two maxima, one at $\xi' = \xi$, which corresponds to coherent scattering, and one at $\xi' = \xi_0$, redistribution about the line center.   Providing that $|\xi' - \xi_0|$ is much greater than δ_u and δ_ℓ, we may roughly estimate the relative sizes of these two contributions from the areas under the two maxima when the expression on the right-hand side of Equation (5.6) is plotted as a function of ξ'.   In this way we find immediately that

$$
\begin{aligned}
p_c &\simeq \frac{\delta_u}{\delta_u + \delta_\ell}, \\
p_r &\simeq \frac{\delta_\ell}{\delta_u + \delta_\ell},
\end{aligned}
\tag{5.7}
$$

where p_c and p_r represent the coherent, and complete redistribution, contributions to the function $p(\xi, \xi')$, that is,

$$
p(\xi, \xi') \simeq p_c \delta(\xi - \xi') + p_r \phi(\xi').
\tag{5.8}
$$

In the particular case of a resonance line in a weak radiation field, for which $\delta_\ell = 0$, Equation (5.6) leads to the result that the scattering is coherent in the frame of the atom, a result which is preserved in the approximate form (5.8).   This conclusion, however, is to be used with caution, as we shall see in Section 5.4.

The extent to which the approximate representations for $p(\xi, \xi')$ are adequate can only be seen following a full solution of the transfer equation with the proper redistribution function of Equation (5.6). However, since this must be averaged over the velocity distribution of the atoms, the resulting function is so very unwieldy that its use has not been attempted, though Hummer (1965*b*) has treated the resonance-line case.

5.2 Redistribution Arising from Collisions

Perturbing atoms or ions passing sufficiently close to an excited atom will modify its state with the consequences outlined in the previous chapter.   If, on the average, the atom suffers many such collisions during the time it spends in the excited state, the history of its initial excitation will, to a greater or lesser extent, be lost.   A re-emitted photon then has correspondingly less correlation in frequency with that of the exciting photon and we should anticipate that the emission coefficient would begin to show the same frequency dependence as that of the absorption coefficient.   If, on the other hand, the chance is small that such collisions occur during the natural lifetime of the upper state, we must expect that frequency redistribution in a stationary atom would only occur through the influence of the finite radiative width of the lower level—as discussed in the preceding section.

The question has been studied by Zanstra (1941) for a classical oscillator perturbed by a sequence of random isolated collisions, as in the Lorentz-Weisskopf line broadening theory.   He was able to show that the absorption coefficient follows a dispersion profile with damping constant γ_c.   In emission, however, the wave trains were found to consist of two parts, one a coherent wave of relative intensity $\gamma_n/(\gamma_n + \gamma_c)$, the other being redistributed about the line center and having relative strength $\gamma_c/(\gamma_n + \gamma_c)$.   Holstein (1947) arrived at the same result both for a classical and a quantum-mechanical calculation. If $\gamma_c \gg \gamma_n$ the frequencies of the absorbed and re-emitted photon are quite uncorrelated—a result obtained, from general physical arguments, by Spitzer (1944).   Zanstra interpreted the constant γ_c, in accordance with the Weisskopf theory, as twice the reciprocal of the time between those collisions which produce phase shifts greater than unity.   Presumably this should be modified to incorporate the influences of weak collisions and departures from adiabaticity; however, the point is not fully clear.

Holstein (1950) has given the most satisfactory discussion of the problem in a case when the quasi-static approximation gives a valid description of the interaction between a perturber and a radiating atom. Suppose, with Holstein, that the atom is excited by a monochromatic beam of frequency ν_1, then, if the quasi-static approximation holds, absorption of this beam will occur at those times at which the perturbation produces a matching energy level shift, i.e., at times $t(r)$ when the distance r from perturber to atom satisfies the equation [see Equation (4.44)]

$$\nu_1 = \nu_0 + \frac{C}{r^n}, \tag{5.9}$$

where ν_0 is the central frequency of the unperturbed line.   Following the absorption, the atom will decay in a time τ of order $1/\gamma_n$.   Whether or not the absorbed (ν_1) and re-emitted (ν_2) frequencies are closely correlated is then clearly governed by whether or not the perturbation evolves significantly in the time τ.   If the "collision duration" is represented by t_0, the scattering should be completely redistributive if $\gamma_n t_0 \ll 1$, while if the collision is so slow that the perturbation does not effectively change in the time γ_n^{-1}, then the frequency correlation should be maintained. It is readily shown that, if the change in frequency shift in a time γ_n^{-1} is to be small compared to the frequency shift itself, we must require that

$$v \left(\frac{\Delta \nu}{C} \right)^{1/n} \ll \gamma_n. \tag{5.10}$$

Since, by assumption, any collisional broadening is quasi-static, $\Delta \nu > \Delta \nu_c$ (see Equation 4.70) so that *coherent* scattering will apply if

$$\gamma_c \ll \gamma_n. \tag{5.11}$$

If, however, the quasi-static impacts alone contribute to the wing broadening so that $\gamma_c \gg \gamma_n$, we can expect to find negligible coherent re-emission.

Zanstra's result for impact broadening follows from a similar argument. Consider an atom which, without perturbation, would re-emit coherently in its own rest frame and suppose it to be subjected to a sequence of instantaneous collisions of the Lenz-Weisskopf kind. We should expect that the fraction of coherent emission would be given by the ratio of the average time between collisions to the total radiation time $2/\gamma_n$. For a mean period $2\gamma_c^{-1}$ between collisions we recover immediately Zanstra's results:

$$p_c = \frac{\gamma_n}{\gamma_n + \gamma_c},$$
$$p_r = \frac{\gamma_c}{\gamma_n + \gamma_c}. \tag{5.12}$$

Edmonds (1955) has argued that the assignment of the collision time γ_c^{-1} for the quasi-static case is improper and that one should rather use that time characteristic of the decay of the ensemble configuration which, as is readily shown from dimensional arguments, is of order $v^{-1} n^{1/3}$, where n represents the number density of perturbers. Since in a stellar atmosphere this decay time is generally an order of magnitude smaller than that associated with the quasi-static collisions, Edmonds suggests that the Zanstra criterion (5.12), if applied to this case using the above binary collision time γ_c^{-1}, would overestimate the degree of frequency coherence by a factor of about 10. If by "coherence" we mean a very strict re-emission at the absorbed frequency, then Edmonds seems to be correct. However, the ensemble fluctuations do not normally give rise to the main broadening collisions in the quasi-static case; these are, in fact, described by binary collisions inside the Weisskopf sphere—as we saw in Section 4.3.5. The ensemble decay causes a small perturbation which destroys the *strict* coherence. However, this would not seem to argue against Zanstra's criterion if we were to allow ourselves the rather looser definition that coherent scattering corresponds to a re-emission probability which is centered about the absorbed frequency and has a width δ which is very much less than the distance $\Delta\nu$ from the line center.

5.3 Influence of the Thermal Doppler Effect on Atomic Redistribution Functions

We have seen in Section 4.6 that the random atomic motions modify the frequency dependence of the absorption coefficient, e.g., from a Lorentzian to an almost gaussian form in the line core. Similarly, the atomic redistribution functions must be averaged over the atomic velocity distribution to obtain the redistribution function appropriate to a reference frame fixed in the gas. In this section we shall discuss the form of this function in the limiting cases when the atomic scattering is completely frequency-coherent in the atom's rest frame. The opposite extreme of complete redistribution in the rest frame is briefly discussed at the end of this section.

5.3.1 Scattering Coherent in the Frame of the Atom

Hummer (1962) has analyzed the problem in detail and we shall follow his procedure here.

For an atom of mass M, the Maxwellian distribution of the dimensionless velocity components u_1, u_2, u_3 along three orthogonal axes may be written

$$df(u_1, u_2, u_3) = \pi^{-3/2} \exp\left[-(u_1^2 + u_2^2 + u_3^2)\right] du_1\, du_2\, du_3, \quad (5.13)$$

where $u_i = V_i/V_0$, and V_i is the relevant velocity component while V_0 is the mean velocity $(2kT/M)^{1/2}$. The averaged redistribution function then follows from Equation (5.4) as

$$R(v, \mathbf{n}; v', \mathbf{n}') = \frac{h(\mathbf{n}, \mathbf{n}')}{4\pi^2} \int_{-\infty}^{+\infty} du_1 \int_{-\infty}^{+\infty} du_2 e^{-(u_1^2+u_2^2)}\phi(\xi)p(\xi, \xi'), \quad (5.14)$$

where the frequencies ξ, ξ' are related to ν, ν' through Equations (5.5); the dimensionless frequency shifts from the line center (v, v') are expressed in terms of the Doppler width. The integration over the variable u_3 is immediate if we suppose the scattering to take place in the (1, 2) plane. Henyey (1940) demonstrated that the above integrals can be made tractable by a suitable choice of the coordinate system—this point is further discussed by Hummer and need not be considered here. For isotropic scattering $h(\mathbf{n}, \mathbf{n}')$ is $1/4\pi$ and the integration over $\mathbf{n}, \mathbf{n}'$ can immediately be carried out to give, with the proper normalization, the more convenient function

$$R(v, v') \equiv 4\pi \int R(v, \mathbf{n}; v', \mathbf{n}') \, d\Omega. \tag{5.15}$$

According to the definition of the function R the component of the emission coefficient which is due to direct scattering* may be written

$$\varepsilon_s(\nu') = 4\pi \int_{4\pi} \int_{-\infty}^{+\infty} I_\nu(\mathbf{n}) R(v, \mathbf{n}; v', \mathbf{n}') \bar{\kappa} \, dv \, d\Omega, \tag{5.16}$$

with $I_\nu(\mathbf{n})$ representing the specific intensity, and with $\bar{\kappa}$ defined by the equation

$$\bar{\kappa} = \int_{-\infty}^{+\infty} \kappa(v) \, dv.$$

If the intensity I_ν and the re-emission are taken as isotropic, the corresponding component of the source function then may be written in terms of the mean intensity J_ν:

$$S_s(v') = \int_{-\infty}^{+\infty} J_\nu g(v, v') \, dv, \tag{5.17}$$

where

$$g(v, v') = \frac{R(v, v')}{\phi(v')}. \tag{5.18}$$

Some normalization requirements follow from the definition of the quantity R. Since if a photon is scattered it must be scattered at some frequency, the integral of $R(v, v')$ over all v' is just the absorption probability,

$$\int_{-\infty}^{+\infty} R(v, v') \, dv' = \phi(v). \tag{5.19}$$

* The remaining emission arising from other processes which populate the upper level.

Again, since an incident "white" spectrum can only produce emission having the same frequency dependence as the absorption coefficient, it follows at once that

$$\int_{-\infty}^{+\infty} R(v, v')\, dv = \phi(v'). \tag{5.20}$$

Clearly, therefore, $R(v, v')$ is normalized to unity and so the function $g(v, v')$ must be normalized in accordance with the relationship

$$\int_{-\infty}^{+\infty} g(v, v')\, dv = 1. \tag{5.21}$$

In his discussion Hummer distinguishes the two cases of zero and finite natural width a. For the first case, $a = 0$, he finds Unno's (1952a) result

$$R_{\mathrm{I}}(v, v') = \tfrac{1}{2}\, \mathrm{erfc}\, (|\bar{v}|), \tag{5.22}$$

where the complement to the error function is defined as

$$\mathrm{erfc}\, (x) = \frac{2}{\sqrt{\pi}} \int_{x}^{\infty} e^{-t^2}\, dt \tag{5.23}$$

and $|\bar{v}|$ is the larger of $|v|$ and $|v'|$. For a nonzero we have the result, also due to Unno (1952b),

$$R_{\mathrm{II}}(v, v') = \pi^{-3/2} \int_{(\bar{v}-\underline{v})/2}^{\infty} e^{-u^2}\left[\tan^{-1}\left(\frac{v+u}{a}\right) - \tan^{-1}\left(\frac{\bar{v}-u}{a}\right) \right] du, \tag{5.24}$$

where now $\bar{v}$ and $\underline{v}$ are respectively the larger and smaller of v and v'.

The unusual arguments $\bar{v}$ and $\underline{v}$ in these expressions arise because, by assumption, the scattering is coherent in the frame of the atom and only a restricted range of v' is therefore possible for a given absorbed frequency v, and a given atomic velocity. In this respect the problem differs from that of complete redistribution in the atom's frame, for which any frequency v' may be emitted following absorption of a given frequency v.

The function $g_{\mathrm{I}}(v, v')$, defined through Equations (5.18) and (5.22) is illustrated in Figure 5.1, while Figure 5.2, due to Jefferies and White (1960), shows $g_{\mathrm{II}}(v, v')$ for the case $a = 10^{-3}$.

It is instructive to compare the results shown in these two figures. In the line core g_{I} and g_{II} are much the same. In the wings, however,

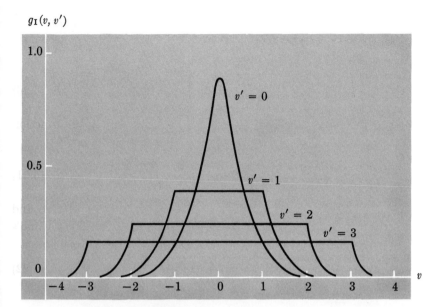

$g_{\mathrm{I}}(v, v')$

Figure 5.1. The redistribution function $g_{\mathrm{I}}(v, v')$ for the case of zero natural line width (see Equations (5.18) and (5.22) of the text); v and v' are respectively the incident and scattered dimensionless frequencies.

the difference is very marked, the case of nonzero damping produces a redistribution function $g_{\mathrm{II}}(v, v')$ which is decidedly centered on $v = v'$, and which thus shows the physical characteristic of coherent scattering. The explanation of these features is straightforward: in the core ($v, v' \lesssim 3$) absorption will be mainly—entirely if $a = 0$—due to those atoms moving with such a velocity as to "see" the photon at their own line center since the atomic absorption coefficient is enormously larger there than at neighboring frequencies.   The re-emission at frequency v' is supposed isotropic and so in the rest frame of the atmosphere it is distributed between the frequencies $\pm v$ ($\equiv \pm \Delta\nu/\Delta\nu_{\mathrm{D}}$). A closer analysis shows that the distribution is equally probable between these frequencies.

As the incident frequency moves further into the line wings, however, the number of atoms able to absorb in the line center falls rapidly—in fact, like $\exp(-v^2)$. If a were zero, the atom would have no choice but to accept this since in that case its absorption coefficient is zero except at the central frequency.   In the practical case where $a \neq 0$ a frequency v_c will be reached in the wings such that beyond v_c the small

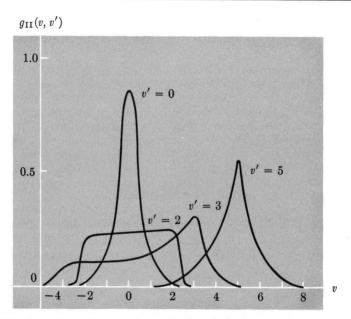

$g_{\mathrm{II}}(v, v')$

Figure 5.2. The redistribution function $g_{\mathrm{II}}(v, v')$ for the case of finite natural line width $a = 10^{-3}$ (see Equations (5.18) and (5.24) of the text); v and v' are respectively the incident and scattered dimensionless frequencies.

residual wing absorption coefficient overbalances that due to atoms moving so as to absorb at the line center; in practice, for allowed lines in the visible, v_c is well known to be of order 3. For such wing frequencies, therefore, the predominant absorption will be due to the atoms having small line-of-sight velocities since they are the most numerous. The frequency v' of the re-emitted radiation is therefore more or less equal to that absorbed in this case when the atom itself scatters coherently. In fact, for large v we would expect to find that the probability distribution for v' was centered on v and had a width of the order of one Doppler width.

To summarize, then, we see in Figures 5.1 and 5.2 what we must expect physically, namely that in the line core the redistribution is about the line center while in the wings redistribution is approximately coherent in the observer's reference frame since then the absorption in the wings is predominantly due to the slowly moving atoms.

Evidently the redistribution functions of Figures 5.1 or 5.2 would be difficult to incorporate in a transfer equation and it is, therefore, desirable to look for a physically reasonable representation in terms of the limiting forms of coherent scattering and complete redistribution. In either figure, strict coherent scattering would be represented for a given (v, v') as the delta function $\delta(v - v')$, while complete redistribution would be indicated by the single curve $g(v, v') = H(a, v)$. While neither of these limiting forms, separately or in combination, can reproduce the curves shown in the figures, there are strong elements of similarity.

In the line core $|v| \lesssim 3$, $g(v, v')$ is symmetric about $v = 0$; in the wings it is centered about $v = v'$. Thus, the *physical characteristics* of the two limiting forms are reflected in our figures even if the mathematical details are not, and we may reasonably anticipate that the physical consequences of the actual redistribution will be, at least qualitatively, reflected in any theoretical predictions following on the replacement

$$g(v, v') = a(v')\delta(v - v') + [1 - a(v')]\phi(v), \qquad (5.25)$$

where again $\phi(v)$ is the profile of the absorption coefficient.

The function $a(v')$ appropriate to the redistribution shown in Figure 5.2 was obtained by Jefferies and White (1960) from a simple measurement of the areas under the curves centered on $v = v'$ and on $v = 0$; the result is illustrated in Figure 5.3 and clearly indicates a rapid

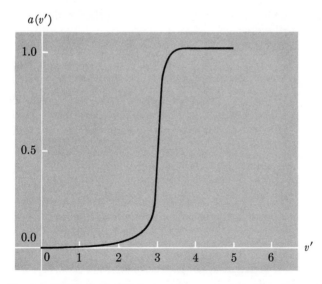

Figure 5.3. The fraction $a(v')$ of effectively coherent scattering as deduced from the redistribution function illustrated in Figure 5.2.

transition from effectively complete redistribution in the line core to "coherence" in the wings. Spitzer's (1944) conclusion that the scattering in the wings would be $\frac{1}{3}$ essentially coherent and $\frac{2}{3}$ noncoherent is not in conflict with this result since his argument referred to the case of zero damping width ($a = 0$) where the photons can only be absorbed at the line center (as seen by the atom).

5.3.2 Scattering Completely Redistributed in the Frame of the Atom

It must be emphasized that the above arguments only apply to that fraction of the scattering which is coherent in the frame of the atom. To the extent that the atom scatters with complete redistribution in its own frame the function $g(v, v')$ follows from Hummer's analysis, and in his notation is given as,

$$R_{\mathrm{III}}(v, v') \equiv \phi(v')g_{\mathrm{III}}(v, v')$$

$$= \pi^{-5/2} \int_0^\infty e^{-u^2} \left[\tan^{-1}\left(\frac{v + u}{a}\right) - \tan^{-1}\left(\frac{v - u}{a}\right) \right]$$

$$\times \left[\tan^{-1}\left(\frac{v' + u}{a}\right) - \tan^{-1}\left(\frac{v' - u}{a}\right) \right] du. \quad (5.26)$$

This does *not* correspond to complete redistribution in the frame of reference in which v, v' are measured; in other words, a residual coherence appears, which may at first sight seem surprising. It arises, of course, from the fact that no velocity change occurs in the atom during the scattering process so that the absorbed and emitted frequencies—as measured in a stationary frame—must reflect the uniformity of the atom's velocity in this frame. In other words, if an atom absorbs in the red, its re-emission will tend to be centered to the red of the line center even though it redistributes the frequency completely over its absorption coefficient in its own reference frame.

Hummer has given the following expansion for the integral (5.26):

$$R_{\mathrm{III}}(v, v') = \frac{2}{\pi^2} \sum_{n=0}^\infty [2^{2n+1}(2n + 1)!]^{-1} K_{2n}(a, v) K_{2n}(a, v'), \quad (5.27)$$

with

$$K_n(a, v) \equiv \int_0^\infty t^n e^{-at - t^2/4} \cos vt \, dt. \quad (5.28)$$

In the line wings the first term of the expansion (5.27) constitutes a sufficient representation for the integral and it then follows at once from Equation (4.98) that

$$R_{\mathrm{III}}(v, v') = \phi(v)\phi(v')$$

or

$$g_{\mathrm{III}}(v, v') = \phi(v), \tag{5.29}$$

which corresponds to complete redistribution in the rest frame. So far as is known, numerical values for $R_{\mathrm{III}}(v, v')$ have not been computed and it has been customary to assume that if redistribution is complete in the frame of the atom, it is also complete in the frame of the observer. Since Equation (5.27) shows that this is not so—except in the line wings—it remains a question of some importance to determine just what form the redistribution function does take.

5.3.3 The Influence of Recoil

In stellar atmospheres we can normally neglect the recoil experienced by an atom in the scattering process. This influence has been studied quantitatively by Field (1959) in the general context of the escape of Lα radiation from a dilute, but optically very thick, gas. Field shows that for zero natural damping the influence of recoil on the redistribution function is to modify it from Unno's form (5.22) to the relation

$$R'_{\mathrm{I}}(v, v') = \frac{1}{\sqrt{\pi}} e^{2\gamma v + \gamma^2} \int_{|v + \gamma|}^{\infty} e^{-y^2} \, dy, \tag{5.30}$$

where $\gamma = h v_0 / M V_0 c$, with V_0 the Doppler velocity.

Complete solutions of the equations of radiative transfer with redistribution according to the various laws discussed in this section have generally not been obtained—except in the limiting forms of coherent scattering or complete redistribution. Field (1959), and Osterbrock (1962), have given illuminating discussions and clarified essential points, while Hummer (1965b) has obtained solutions for redistribution according to his case I ($a = 0$). His procedure permits the solution for more complicated cases.

5.4 Influence of Interlocking on the Redistribution Functions

As mentioned earlier, we must interpret with care the conclusion that the scattering is coherent in the frame of the atom for a line whose lower level has an infinite lifetime. To illustrate, let us consider the scattering of the Lyman β line in the sun. Since the upper level of Lβ is $3p$, the outcome of an Lβ absorption may be either the re-emission of Lβ or the emission of an Hα photon through the $3p$–$2s$ transition. The directly scattered Lβ photons should preserve their coherence; however, following a $3p$–$2s$ transition the subsequent absorption of an Hα photon will raise the atom back to $3p$, and if this is followed by a re-emission of Lβ, its frequency will in general be uncorrelated with that originally absorbed. Depending on the degree of reabsorption of the Hα line, the fraction of the Lyman β scattering which is coherent in the atom's frame could drop from the value unity which might be uncritically adopted, to a value $\simeq \frac{2}{3}$ and this would lead to a dramatic change in the predicted line profile—cf. Jefferies and White (1960).

In Lyman α, on the other hand, the influence is likely to be much less since the probability of a transition upward is, in general, much smaller than for the direct re-emission. The influence of the higher degree of coherent re-emission in Lα may conceivably be the origin of the greatly different extent of the wings of Lα and Lβ observed in the solar spectrum.

5.5 Summary

Until better theoretical calculations and laboratory spectroscopy can give us a guide, we can probably do nothing but adopt the results given above. In general, we may suppose that the line cores, at least, of resonance lines are formed by a mechanism approaching that of complete redistribution, while the wings of the first resonance line in a series may have a significant degree of essentially coherent scattering; for the later resonance lines we shall find less coherence. If the line is collisionally broadened it seems legitimate to suppose it to be formed in complete redistribution in the core and the wings.

REFERENCES

EDMONDS, F. N., 1955, "Noncoherent Scattering Due to Collisions; I, Zanstra's Ratio of Coherent to Uncorrelated Noncoherent Scattering," *Astrophys. J. 121*, 418.

FIELD, G. B., 1959, "The Time Relaxation of a Resonance-Line Profile," *Astrophys. J. 129*, 551.

FRAUENFELDER, H., 1962, *The Mössbauer Effect, a review, with a collection of reprints.* New York: W. A. Benjamin.

HEITLER, W., 1954, *The Quantum Theory of Radiation*. Oxford: Clarendon Press.

HENYEY, L. G., 1940, "The Doppler Effect in Resonance Lines," *Proc. Nat. Acad. Sci. 26*, 50.

HOLSTEIN, T., 1947, "Imprisonment of Resonance Radiation in Gases," *Phys. Rev. 72*, 1212.

HOLSTEIN, T., 1950, "Imprisonment of Resonance Radiation in Gases; II," *Westinghouse Res. Lab. Sci. Paper No. 1501*.

HUMMER, D. G., 1962, "Non-Coherent Scattering; I, The Redistribution Functions with Doppler Broadening," *Mon. Not. R. Astr. Soc. 125*, 21.

HUMMER, D. G., 1965*a*, "The Emission Coefficient," *Proceedings, Second Harvard–Smithsonian Conference on Stellar Atmospheres*, p. 13.

HUMMER, D. G., 1965*b*, "Discrete Ordinate Analysis of Complete Redistribution with Continuous Absorption," *Final Report, AFSWC Contract No. AF 29(601)-6013*, Section II*b*.

JEFFERIES, J. T., and O. R. WHITE, 1960, "Source Function in a Non-Equilibrium Atmosphere; VI, The Frequency Dependence of the Source Function for Resonance Lines," *Astrophys. J. 132*, 767.

OSTERBROCK, D. E., 1962, "The Escape of Resonance-Line Radiation from an Optically Thick Nebula," *Astrophys. J. 135*, 195.

ROSSELAND, S., 1936, *Theoretical Astrophysics*. Oxford: Clarendon Press.

SPITZER, L., 1944, "Notes on the Theory of Noncoherent Scattering," *Astrophys. J. 99*, 1.

UNNO, W., 1952*a*, "On the Radiation Pressure in a Planetary Nebula; II," *Publ. Astr. Soc. Japan 3*, 158.

UNNO, W., 1952*b*, "Note on the Zanstra Redistribution in Planetary Nebulae," *Publ. Astr. Soc. Japan 4*, 100.

WEISSKOPF, V. F., 1933, "The Intensity and Structures of Spectral Lines," *Observatory 56*, 291.

ZANSTRA, H., 1941, "On the Weakening of the Polarisation Effect by Collision Damping," *Mon. Not. R. Astr. Soc. 101*, 273.

6

The Equations of Statistical Equilibrium

It was emphasized in Chapter 3 that our fundamental problem lies in the specification of the emission and absorption coefficients ε_ν and κ_ν for the material in the radiating atmosphere, since in their ratio—the line source function—we obtain the most basic description of the spectroscopic state of the gas. Our present understanding of the frequency dependence of this ratio has been discussed in Chapter 5; while we were not led there to a definitive picture, we may yet have some confidence that physically significant predictions can be made on the basis of the approximate redistribution functions which were derived there.

The coefficients ε_ν and κ_ν introduced into the transfer equations are macroscopic quantities; the first referring to the emission per unit volume, the second to the absorption per unit length. Our specification, therefore, must reflect the populations per unit volume of the levels between which the line is formed; in fact, it follows readily that, apart from a possible frequency dependence, S_l is determined by the ratio of the two populations. This ratio is itself determined through a set of equations which specify the time independence, on the average, of the population of each level at each location in the gas. In this chapter we shall discuss this system of statistical equilibrium equations and, in particular, the determination of the rates of the individual

110

transitions; the transition rates per atom constitute, of course, the coefficients of the equilibrium equations.

Among the transitions which determine the equilibrium populations are two—those of radiative excitation and stimulated emission—which depend on the radiation intensity in the relevant line or continuum. In general, we shall not be able to specify these self-consistently, i.e., so that they satisfy simultaneously the equations of transfer and the conditions of statistical equilibrium; rather we can in general obtain a full solution only through a simultaneous discussion of both sets of equations. The solution of this general problem leads to a theory of the line source function which we shall discuss in Chapters 7 and 8.

As we shall see, however, there exist certain degenerate cases where we may be justified in assuming a solution to the transfer equations in each relevant spectral region, and in this case the equilibrium equations may be solved at once for a gas of given composition and structure. In this chapter, therefore, we first discuss the character of the statistical equilibrium equations and their formal solution. Following this, we derive relations giving the rates of the various upward and downward transitions for collisional and radiative processes. In Section 6.3 we shall consider some special solutions of the equations which follow from assumptions of the strength of the radiation field, or equivalently of the solutions of the radiative transfer equations.

6.1 Formulation and Solution of the Equations

Let us consider a gaseous atmosphere in a statistically time-independent state and in which there is no divergence in any macroscopic flow velocities. In each volume element, transitions occur between any given level, and any other, of a given atomic species. The equilibrium distribution of populations is then expressed by the solution of the statistical equilibrium equations

$$\left(\int_j + \sum_j\right) P_{ij} n_i = \left(\int_j + \sum_j\right) P_{ji} n_j \qquad (\text{all } j \neq i), \qquad (6.1)$$

$$\left(\int_j + \sum_j\right) n_j = N, \qquad (6.2)$$

where N is the total number of atoms, per unit volume, of the species whose excitation is to be studied; the integrations are over the continuum states, and the sums refer to the bound-state transitions. The term P_{ij} represents the rate of the transition which transfers an atom from level i to level j, while n_i is the number density of atoms in the level i. The set (6.1) is singly degenerate and so may only be solved for population ratios; the individual n_i may be obtained from the auxiliary equation (6.2).

The transition rates P_{ij} consist, in general, of two terms, corresponding to a collisional rate, denoted C_{ij}, and a radiative rate, denoted R_{ij}; the C_{ij} are proportional to the density of the particles causing the transition—normally these are electrons, though in special cases protons or other heavy particles may be important.

6.1.1 Solution of the Equations for the Continuum States

We have already agreed to suppose the atomic and electron velocity distribution functions to be Maxwellian and to be characterized by a common temperature T. For consistency, therefore, we must accept the solutions of Equations (6.1) *within the continuum states* to be in accordance with this distribution. Equivalently, we must say that free–bound transitions occur infrequently in comparison with the free–free collisions which redistribute the velocities of the ions or electrons among their kinetic degrees of freedom. We can therefore perform the integrations over continuum states at once and need to consider only the *total* number n_κ of ions of each particular type as an unknown in the equilibrium equations.

6.1.2 An Alternative Formulation of the Equations

Much astronomical literature on the solutions of the Equations (6.1) begins by reformulating them in terms of parameters b_j defined by the modified Saha-Boltzmann relation which may be written, in a standard notation, as

$$n_j = \left(\frac{h^2}{2\pi m k T_e}\right)^{3/2} \frac{n_e n_\kappa}{2U_+} g_j e^{X_j/kT} b_j. \tag{6.3}$$

Thus, b_j is a number measuring the ratio of the population n_j to its value in thermodynamic equilibrium at the same values of T, n_e, and n_κ.

For the most part we shall be more interested in the actual populations n_j than in their departures from LTE; nevertheless, the b_j formulation is a very convenient one, especially in discussions of the relative behavior of the populations of different levels, and in the study of the asymptotic approach to LTE at high depths, or at high quantum members.

6.1.3 A Formal Solution

Following Section 6.1.1 above, we may write the Equations (6.1) in the form

$$\sum_j P_{ij} n_i = \sum_j P_{ji} n_j, \tag{6.4}$$

and these comprise a set of n equations (one for each of the $n - 1$ bound levels, one for the continuum) which are to be solved in some parametric form, e.g., in the population ratios. The single degeneracy allows the solutions to be written in a large variety of ways; for any given choice of a set of $n - 1$ equations the solution could be expressed in determinantal form in the usual manner. This freedom has shown itself in the literature in the appearance of various equivalent solutions—see, e.g., White (1961). Our problem is a physical one, however, and as such it is desirable, if possible, to select the form of the solution so that the terms entering should not be merely fortuitous algebraic arrangements of transition rates, but should themselves emphasize the various physical processes which maintain the populations. Such a solution should be obtainable from the general considerations of the processes maintaining the populations of any two states i and j.

With this in mind, let us consider the equivalent problem of determining the fraction of time which an individual atom spends in any one state, in terms of the various possible chains of transitions which transfer an atom from state i to state j. The equations of statistical equilibrium are then embodied in the statement that the total probability for transfer of an atom from state i to j by all of these possible chains is equal to the corresponding probability of the reverse processes.

In a time interval dt the probability that an atom leaves the state i on a path which subsequently reaches j before returning to i can be written

$$p_i T_i \, dt \sum_k p_{ik} q_{kj,i}, \tag{6.5}$$

where p_i is the probability that the atom is in state i at the time, T_i is the number of transitions per atom out of i per unit time, p_{ik} is the probability of the transition $i \rightarrow k$ and $q_{kj,i}$ is the probability that a transition from k arrives in j before i. For equilibrium we therefore require

$$\frac{n_i}{n_j} = \frac{p_i}{p_j} = \frac{T_j \sum_k p_{jk} q_{ki,j}}{T_i \sum_k p_{ik} q_{kj,i}} \qquad (6.6)$$

or, since $T_j p_{jk} = P_{jk}$,

$$\frac{n_i}{n_j} = \frac{\sum_k P_{jk} q_{ki,j}}{\sum_k P_{ik} q_{kj,i}}, \qquad (6.7)$$

where the sums are over all states k and we require that $q_{ii,j} = 1$, $q_{ij,i} = 0$.

The solution so far is purely formal, but it has the specific advantage that it may be written down at once in a way which allows an immediate interpretation of the terms in the numerator and denominator of the right-hand side. It is, consequently, often possible to approximate the q-probabilities using simple physical arguments, rather than by the lengthy numerical evaluation which other formulations entail.

An important relationship follows from the fact that paths from states k to j either do or do not pass through state i. In terms of the q-factors, this may be expressed

$$q_{ki,j} + q_{kj,i} = 1, \qquad (6.8)$$

and this has the definite practical advantage of halving the number of probabilities to be determined. In practice it often happens that one of the conjugate pair in this equation is close to unity, in which case it is, of course, wise to evaluate the smaller one.

A procedure for determining the q's may be readily obtained as follows. A little consideration shows that the probability $q_{ij,k}$ may be represented as a linear combination of all $q_{lj,k}$ (for $l \neq i$) through the relationship

$$q_{ij,k} = \sum_l p_{il} q_{lj,k} \qquad \text{(all } l \neq i\text{)}. \qquad (6.9)$$

By permitting i to take all values other than j and k, the representation of the q-factors in terms of the basic probabilities p_{rs} is then given from the solutions of the nondegenerate system (6.9).

When the number of states is relatively small, expressions for the q-probabilities may be written down from first principles. Consider, for example, a four-level atom and suppose that we seek the ratio n_2/n_1 given by Equation (6.7) as

$$\frac{n_2}{n_1} = \frac{P_{12} + P_{13}q_{32,1} + P_{14}q_{42,1}}{P_{21} + P_{23}q_{31,2} + P_{24}q_{41,2}}. \tag{6.10}$$

The paths whose probabilities contribute to $q_{32,1}$, for example, can be enumerated as the infinite sequences

$$3 \rightarrow 2,$$
$$3 \rightarrow 4 \rightarrow 3 \rightarrow 2,$$
$$3 \rightarrow 4 \rightarrow 3 \rightarrow 4 \rightarrow 3 \rightarrow 2,$$
$$\vdots$$

and

$$3 \rightarrow 4 \rightarrow 2,$$
$$3 \rightarrow 4 \rightarrow 3 \rightarrow 4 \rightarrow 2,$$
$$3 \rightarrow 4 \rightarrow 3 \rightarrow 4 \rightarrow 3 \rightarrow 4 \rightarrow 2,$$
$$\vdots$$

so that

$$q_{32,1} = \frac{p_{32} + p_{34}p_{42}}{1 - p_{34}p_{43}}; \tag{6.11}$$

results for the other q-factors are obtained from an appropriate permutation of indices.

The linear system (6.9) for this case can be written

$$q_{32,1} - p_{34}q_{42,1} = p_{32},$$
$$-p_{43}q_{32,1} + q_{42,1} = p_{42}, \tag{6.12}$$

which, evidently, leads to the same solution (6.11). For a five-level atom the q-factors become quite unwieldy; specific examples are given by Zirker (1959), and by Jefferies and Pottasch (1959); in more complex structures it is preferable to use the linear systems (6.9), or perhaps to go back to the original equations (6.4).

The equivalence of the formal solution (6.7) to the determinantal solution of the original system (6.4) is simply demonstrated via the system (6.9) and will not be justified here.

In certain special cases the solutions (6.7) take simple forms; before looking at these, however, we shall consider the evaluation of the rate coefficients P_{ij}.

6.2 The Coefficients of the Statistical Equilibrium Equations

In this section we shall discuss separately the contributions of collisional and radiative transitions to the total transition rate P_{ij}; it is also found convenient to study separately the rates of excitation and ionization.

6.2.1 Collisional Excitation and De-excitation

The rate of electron collision excitation to an upper state u, per atom in the lower state ℓ is given by the expression

$$C_{\ell u} = n_e \int_{\eta_0}^{\infty} Q_{\ell u}(\eta) \sqrt{\frac{2\eta}{m}} f(\eta)\, d\eta, \qquad (6.13)$$

where $Q(\eta)$ is the relevant cross section for excitation by electrons with kinetic energy η, $f(\eta)\, d\eta$ represents the fraction of electrons with energies in the range η to $\eta + d\eta$, and η_0 is the threshold energy of the transition $\ell \to u$. The factor $\sqrt{2\eta/m}$ is the relative velocity of the electron, m being the electron mass. For a Maxwellian distribution at temperature T,

$$f(\eta) = \frac{2\pi}{(\pi kT)^{3/2}} \sqrt{\eta} \exp\left(\frac{-\eta}{kT}\right), \qquad (6.14)$$

so that

$$C_{\ell u} = \frac{1}{\sqrt{\pi m}} \left(\frac{2}{kT}\right)^{3/2} n_e \int_{\eta_0}^{\infty} Q_{\ell u}(\eta)\eta e^{-\eta/kT}\, d\eta. \qquad (6.15)$$

The corresponding rate of de-exciting (or superelastic) collisions $u \to \ell$ may be obtained, as follows, from general considerations given by Klein and Rosseland (1921) and by Fowler (1955). Consider the excitation scheme, shown in Figure 6.1, in which an electron with kinetic energy η excites the atom A, so losing energy η_0. The number of such collisions per unit volume per second due to electrons in the energy range $d\eta$ about η is

$$n_\ell n_e f(\eta) \sqrt{\frac{2\eta}{m}}\, Q_{\ell u}(\eta)\, d\eta, \qquad (6.16)$$

while the rate for the corresponding de-excitations, in which the electron follows the reverse path (CAB), is

$$n_u n_e f(\eta - \eta_0) \sqrt{\frac{2(\eta - \eta_0)}{m}}\, Q_{u\ell}(\eta - \eta_0)\, d(\eta - \eta_0). \qquad (6.17)$$

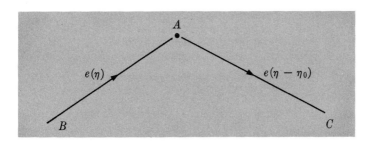

Figure 6.1. Geometry of an exciting collision in which an electron of energy η moving along BA excites an atom at A and moves off along AC with energy $\eta - \eta_0$.

If the atoms formed part of a system which was in thermodynamic equilibrium, the principle of detailed balance would require that the rates (6.16) and (6.17) should be equal, while the distributions $f(\eta)$ would then be given by the form (6.14), and the population ratios by the Boltzmann formula

$$\frac{n_u}{n_\ell} = \frac{g_u}{g_\ell} \exp\left(\frac{-\eta_0}{kT}\right). \tag{6.18}$$

Hence, for all $\eta \geq \eta_0$, we conclude that for atoms in a system which is in thermodynamic equilibrium;

$$\eta Q_{\ell u}(\eta) = \frac{g_u}{g_\ell}(\eta - \eta_0)Q_{u\ell}(\eta - \eta_0). \tag{6.19}$$

This equation, however, expresses the relative energy dependences of two purely atomic parameters; and such a relationship cannot depend on the state of the gas as a whole and so, while derived for the limiting state of TE, it must hold under arbitrary conditions. We may state this another way: We know that in TE certain energy distributions hold independently of the mechanisms establishing the equilibrium; if we did not relate the forward and backward atomic transition cross sections through Equation (6.19) we would not establish the TE distributions in that limiting case.

With the specific energy distribution (6.14) we therefore find;

$$C_{u\ell} = \frac{1}{\sqrt{\pi m}} \left(\frac{2}{kT}\right)^{3/2} n_e \int_{\eta_0}^{\infty} (\eta - \eta_0)Q_{u\ell}(\eta - \eta_0)e^{-(\eta - \eta_0)/kT} \, d\eta, \tag{6.20}$$

so that

$$C_{u\ell} = \frac{g_\ell}{g_u} \exp\left(\frac{\eta_0}{kT}\right) C_{\ell u}, \tag{6.21}$$

a relation owing its simple form to the assumption of a Maxwellian velocity distribution—and one which is, of course, less general than (6.19) which applies independently of the form of any velocity distributions of the gas constituents.

Over the past few years experimental and theoretical work has greatly increased our knowledge of collision cross sections. Detailed accounts are contained in review articles, and special publications, of a number and variety too great to review here. A comprehensive and continuing bibliography of work on atomic collision excitation and ionization cross sections is maintained at the Joint Institute for Laboratory Astrophysics, University of Colorado, Boulder, Colorado—cf. Kieffer (1964)—to whom requests for specific data may be addressed. A succinct statement of the current (1965) situation in this rapidly evolving field is given by Seaton (1965).

Because of their versatility and ease in use, however, we should refer specifically to some semi-empirical representations for $Q(\eta)$. The first of these, given by Seaton (1962a) and van Regemorter (1962), is the so-called dipole approximation and originated in a comparison of a limiting theoretical form with the best experimental data, to yield the approximation

$$Q_{\ell u}(\eta) \simeq \frac{8\pi}{\sqrt{3}} \frac{I_{\mathrm{H}}^2}{\eta \eta_0} f \bar{g} \pi a_0^2, \qquad (6.22)$$

in which I_{H} ($= 13.6$ ev) is the ionization potential of hydrogen, f is the absorption oscillator strength for the corresponding optical transition, and $\bar{g}$ is a factor depending only on the energy ratio η/η_0 and on the charge of the ion; to a first approximation, therefore, $\bar{g}$ is independent of the particular transition. By comparison of the form (6.22) with experimental data, van Regemorter (1962) has derived values of $\bar{g}$ which, for optically permitted transitions in *neutral* atoms may be fitted with the formula—Zirker (1962)—

$$\bar{g} = 0.12(\eta/\eta_0 - 1)^{0.68}. \qquad (6.23)$$

The corresponding excitation rate is then found, in cgs units (cm^{-3}-sec^{-1}), as

$$C_{\ell u} = 2.16\alpha^{-1.68}e^{-\alpha}T^{-3/2}fn_e, \qquad (6.24)$$

with $\alpha = \eta_0/kT$, n_e in cm^{-3}. An essentially equivalent result has been given by Hummer (1963).

The cross section for electron excitation of *positive ions* differs in being nonzero at the threshold.* A good representation then seems to be to take $\bar{g} = 0.2$ in Equation (6.22), in which case we find, for cgs units,

$$C_{\ell_a} = 3.9\alpha^{-1}e^{-\alpha}T^{-3/2}fn_e.\qquad (6.25)$$

The formulas (6.24) and (6.25) are said to be unreliable when f is small —Tait (1964).

An improved procedure is given by Seaton (1962b) in terms of an impact parameter formulation such that the cross section $Q(\eta)$ for the collision transition $n \to n'$ is represented in the integral form

$$Q(\eta) = 2\pi \int_0^\infty P_{n'n}(R, \eta)R \, dR,\qquad (6.26)$$

where $P_{n'n}(R, \eta)$ is the probability that a collision of an electron with energy η and impact parameter R will cause the atomic transition $n \to n'$. In the dipole approximation Seaton derives the expression

$$P_{n'n}(R, \eta) = \frac{4I_{\mathrm{H}}^2}{\eta\eta_0}\frac{a_0^2}{R^2}f\zeta\left(\frac{\alpha_{n'n}R}{a_0}\right),\qquad (6.27)$$

where a_0 is the radius of the first Bohr orbit of hydrogen and

$$\alpha_{n'n} = \frac{1}{2}\frac{\eta_0}{\sqrt{I_{\mathrm{H}}\eta}},\qquad (6.28)$$

while $\zeta(x)$ is a function tabulated by Seaton.

Seaton distinguishes two forms, designated as the strong or weak coupling approximations depending on the values of the impact parameters R which contribute most strongly to the integral (6.26). In the *weak coupling* case the integration range extends from a certain value R_0 to infinity, where R_0 is the effective radius of the atom in the lower state of the transition, i.e., for a hydrogen orbit,

$$R_0 \simeq \frac{(5n^2 + 1)a_0}{4},\qquad (6.29)$$

while, more generally, one presumes that the effective principal quantum number may be used in place of n. In the weak coupling form, therefore,

$$Q^W(n \to n') = \frac{8I_{\mathrm{H}}^2}{\eta\eta_0}f\phi(\beta_0)\pi a_0^2,\qquad (6.30)$$

---

* However, for the hydrogen 1s–2p transition Chamberlain, Smith, and Heddle (1964) found a nonzero threshold cross section implied from their measurements. This peculiarity seems to belong to hydrogen alone and to be a product of the degeneracy of the levels.

with $\beta_0 = \alpha_{n'n} R_0/a_0$,

$$\phi(\beta_0) = \int_{R_0}^{\infty} \zeta(\beta)\, \frac{dR}{R} \tag{6.31}$$

and $\beta = \alpha_{n'n} R/a_0$.

In the strong coupling form the integral is more difficult to estimate; Seaton suggests that the cross section should be written

$$Q^S(n \to n') = \frac{8I_{\rm H}^2}{\eta\eta_0} f\{\tfrac{1}{2}\zeta(\beta_1) + \phi(\beta_1)\}\pi a_0^2, \tag{6.32}$$

where $\beta_1 = \alpha_{n'n} R_1/a_0$ and the radius R_1 is chosen such that

$$P_{n'n}(R_1) = \tfrac{1}{2},$$

that is,

$$\left(\frac{\eta}{\eta_0}\right)^2 = \frac{2I_{\rm H}}{\eta_0} f \frac{1}{\beta_1^2}\, \zeta(\beta_1). \tag{6.33}$$

Seaton has also tabulated $\phi(x)$ and has given the limiting forms:

$$\begin{aligned} \phi(x) &\simeq \ln(1.12/x) \\ \zeta(x) &\simeq 1 \end{aligned} \qquad x \ll 1, \tag{6.34}$$

$$\begin{aligned} \phi(x) &\simeq (\pi/2)e^{-2x} \\ \zeta(x) &\simeq \pi x e^{-2x} \end{aligned} \qquad x \gg 1. \tag{6.35}$$

In practice, one adopts the smaller of the cross sections given by (6.30) or (6.32).

These results have been applied by Saraph (1964) in a study of the $n \to n + 1$ collision transitions of hydrogen for which he showed that the strong coupling form was most appropriate for energies near threshold and yielded cross sections of the order of the Bohr radius for the level of principal quantum number n; more specifically,

$$Q^S(n \to n + 1) = \frac{4I_{\rm H}^2}{\eta\eta_0} \pi a_0^2 f, \tag{6.36}$$

and this differs relatively little (a factor of about 2) from the result (6.22).

The dipole approximation can only be applied to transitions which would be optically permitted; collision excitation of optically forbidden transitions can be studied by a classical approximation which treats the electron–atom collision as a binary encounter between two electrons, cf. Burgess (1964a), Gryzinski (1959, 1965). Their procedure is too detailed to study here; in the nature of the case the cross section must depend on the estimated orbital velocity of the bound electron —since the cross section depends on the *relative* velocity—and some skill must be exercised in choosing this parameter.

Rates of the reverse de-exciting collisions follow at once from the reciprocal relation (6.21); since the exponential factor does not appear in the de-excitation rate, it is relatively insensitive to temperature.

6.2.2 Collisional Ionization and Three-Body Recombination

The rate, per atom in state ℓ, of collisional ionization by electrons having a Maxwellian distribution of velocities, may be written [cf. Fowler (1955)]

$$C_{\ell\kappa} = \frac{1}{\sqrt{\pi m}} \left(\frac{2}{kT}\right)^{3/2} n_e \int_{\eta_0}^{\infty} d\eta \int_0^{\eta-\eta_0} S_{\ell\kappa}(\eta, \zeta) \eta e^{-\eta/kT}\, d\zeta, \quad (6.37)$$

where $S_{\ell\kappa}(\eta, \zeta)$ is the cross section for the process in which an electron of energy η produces an ion, together with a pair of electrons of energies ζ and $\eta - \eta_0 - \zeta$, where η_0 is the ionization potential for an atom in the state ℓ.

Seaton (1962a) has given a dipole approximation for the quantity $Q_{\ell\kappa}$ in the form

$$Q_{\ell\kappa} \equiv \int_0^{\eta-\eta_0} S_{\ell\kappa}(\eta, \zeta)\, d\zeta$$

$$= \frac{2}{\sqrt{3}} \frac{\bar{g}_i}{\alpha_f} \frac{I_H}{\eta} \frac{\eta - \eta_0}{\eta_0} a(0), \quad (6.38)$$

where α_f ($= 1/137$) is the fine structure constant, $a(0)$ is the photo-ionization absorption cross section at threshold, and $\bar{g}_i$ is a scaling factor whose value is found to depend on the charge Z of the ion; for $Z = 1, 2, > 2$ the suggested values for $\bar{g}_i$ are 0.1, 0.2, 0.3, respectively. The cross section (6.38) yields the collisional ionization rate, for cgs units,

$$C_{\ell\kappa} = 1.55 \times 10^{13} T^{-1/2} \bar{g}_i a(0) e^{-\alpha} \alpha^{-1} n_e, \quad (6.39)$$

with $\alpha = \eta_0/kT$.

For hydrogenic ions, the consistency of expression (6.38) with an extrapolated form of (6.22) may be shown as follows: The total collision cross section from level ℓ to all bound levels $j \geq u$ follows from the expression (6.22) as

$$\sum_{j=u}^{\infty} Q_{\ell j} = \frac{8\pi}{\sqrt{3}} \frac{I_{\mathrm{H}}^2}{\eta} \pi a_0^2 \sum_{j=u}^{\infty} \bar{g} \frac{f(\ell, j)}{\eta_0(\ell, j)}. \tag{6.40}$$

The asymptotic form for the oscillator strength is

$$f(\ell, j) = \frac{\eta_0(\ell, j)}{Z^2 I_{\mathrm{H}}} \frac{32}{3\pi\sqrt{3}} \frac{1}{\ell^5 j^3 \left(\dfrac{1}{\ell^2} - \dfrac{1}{j^2}\right)^4}, \tag{6.41}$$

while

$$\eta_0(\ell, j) = I_{\mathrm{H}} Z^2 \left[\frac{1}{\ell^2} - \frac{1}{j^2}\right]. \tag{6.42}$$

If we replace the sum in Equation (6.40) by an integral over j and make the obvious transformation

$$y = \left(\frac{1}{\ell^2} - \frac{1}{j^2}\right), \tag{6.43}$$

we obtain the result

$$\sum_{j=u}^{\infty} Q_{\ell j} = \frac{128\bar{g}}{27\eta} \frac{\pi a_0^2 I_{\mathrm{H}}}{Z^2 \ell^5} \left\{ \frac{1}{\left(\dfrac{1}{\ell^2} - \dfrac{1}{u^2}\right)^3} - \frac{1}{\left(\dfrac{1}{\ell^2}\right)^3} \right\}. \tag{6.44}$$

For continuity over the bound into the free states we must therefore require

$$Q_{\ell \kappa} = \frac{128\bar{g}}{27} \frac{\pi a_0^2}{Z^2} \frac{I_{\mathrm{H}}}{\eta} \ell. \tag{6.45}$$

For hydrogenic ions, Kramer's formula is

$$a(0) = 7.91 \times 10^{-18} \ell / Z^2 \tag{6.46}$$

and, on substituting numerical values, we find that the expressions (6.45) and (6.38) are equivalent provided we choose $\bar{g}$ and $\bar{g}_i$ to satisfy the relationship

$$\frac{\bar{g}}{\bar{g}_i} \simeq 3\left(\frac{\eta - \eta_0}{\eta}\right). \tag{6.47}$$

It seems that it would be important to preserve in this way the continuity of the cross section across the series limit if one were interested in studying the approach of the populations of the high-lying states to their LTE values. The fact that the corresponding continuity holds for the radiative processes is simply demonstrated, from Equations (6.41) and (6.46), by a similar argument which need not be given here. We should bear in mind, however, that the simple dipole forms for the collision cross sections are meant for approximate calculations; for any specific problem, continuity of the cross sections across the series limit is assured through basic quantum mechanical properties of the wave functions describing the states.

An alternative form for the collision ionization cross section, which has been given by Seaton (1964a) and has been extensively applied by him to discussions of the coronal ionization, is

$$Q_{\ell k} \simeq \frac{2.2\zeta I_{\mathrm{H}}^2}{\eta\eta_0}\left(\frac{\eta - \eta_0}{\eta_0}\right)\pi a_0^2, \qquad (6.48)$$

where ζ is the number of electrons in the shell from which the ionization takes place. For small values of the principal quantum number ℓ, the cross section (6.48) is essentially equivalent to that of expression (6.38). The corresponding rate of collisional ionization is found to be

$$C_{\ell k} \simeq 2.7\zeta T^{-3/2}\alpha^{-2}e^{-\alpha}n_e. \qquad (6.49)$$

The process inverse to collision ionization—three-body recombination—occurs when two electrons of energies $\eta - \eta_0 - \zeta$ and ζ interact with an ion of charge Z to produce an ion of charge $Z - 1$, in a state ℓ whose ionization potential is η_0, while the remaining electron moves off with energy η. A relationship between the recombination and ionization rates follows, as for the excitation–de-excitation case above, from the application of the principle of detailed balance to determine the relative values of the forward and inverse processes which are necessary to preserve the distribution laws for the state of thermodynamic equilibrium. It is readily shown—cf. Fowler (1955)—that we require

$$\eta S_{\ell\kappa}(\zeta, \eta) = \frac{16\pi U_+}{h^3 g_\ell}\, m\zeta\xi S_{\kappa\ell}(\zeta, \xi), \qquad (6.50)$$

with $\xi = \eta - \eta_0 - \zeta$, and U_+ the partition function of the ion with charge Z. In particular, when the velocity distribution is Maxwellian,

$$C_{\kappa\ell} = 2.06 \times 10^{-16}(g_\ell/U_+)e^\alpha T^{-3/2}C_{\ell\kappa}n_e \qquad (6.51)$$

or, if we use Equation (6.39), the rate of three-body recombination is found as

$$C_{\kappa\ell} = 3.19 \times 10^{-3}(g_\ell/U_+)T^{-2}\bar{g}_i a(0)\alpha^{-1}n_e^2 \qquad (6.52)$$

in units of $cm^{-3}\text{-}sec^{-1}$. Note that because of the statistical weight factor g_ℓ, $C_{\kappa\ell}$ becomes very large near the series limit.

6.2.3 Radiative Excitation Rates

In Chapter 4 we introduced and discussed the Einstein transition probabilities $A_{u\ell}$, $B_{\ell u}$, $B_{u\ell}$. Their relationship to the coefficients occurring in the equilibrium equations is as follows:

$$R_{u\ell} = A_{u\ell} + 4\pi B_{u\ell}\int J_\nu \chi_\nu \, d\nu, \qquad (6.53)$$

$$R_{\ell u} = 4\pi B_{\ell u}\int J_\nu \phi_\nu \, d\nu, \qquad (6.54)$$

where, again, ϕ_ν and χ_ν are the frequency profiles of the absorption and stimulated emission coefficients respectively—we shall normally take these to be the same. Equation (6.54) may be written in the equivalent form:

$$R_{\ell u} = 4\pi \int \frac{J_\nu \alpha_\nu \, d\nu}{h\nu}, \qquad (6.55)$$

where α_ν is the atomic absorption coefficient.

If the radiation field across the line frequencies is constant, it may be represented as Planckian at some "radiation" temperature T_r, perhaps diluted by a factor W, so that

$$J_\nu = W\frac{2h\nu^3}{c^2}\left[\exp\left(\frac{h\nu}{kT_r}\right) - 1\right]^{-1}, \qquad (6.56)$$

in which case

$$R_{u\ell} = A_{u\ell}\left[1 + W\left\{\exp\left(\frac{h\nu}{kT_r}\right) - 1\right\}^{-1}\right] \qquad (6.57)$$

and

$$R_{\ell u} = A_{u\ell}\frac{g_u}{g_\ell}W\left[\exp\left(\frac{h\nu}{kT_r}\right) - 1\right]^{-1}. \qquad (6.58)$$

In particular for thermodynamic equilibrium $W = 1$, $T_r = T$; more commonly, however, we shall be interested in deriving these rates for a gas which is optically thin to the (u, ℓ) transition and which, like a chromosphere, immediately overlies a stellar photosphere so that $W = \frac{1}{2}$, or which lies at some distance R from a star of radius R^*, in which case W is of order $\frac{1}{2}(R^*/R)^2$. If the atmosphere is optically thick to the (u, ℓ) line, this procedure, of course, is of no interest to us since we shall then not be able to specify the radiation intensity in advance and furthermore its intensity will usually vary across the line.

6.2.4 Photoelectric Ionization and Recombination Rates

The rate, per atom in state ℓ, of photoelectric ionization may be written

$$R_{\ell\kappa} = 4\pi \int_{\nu_0}^{\infty} \frac{J_\nu \alpha_\nu \, d\nu}{h\nu}, \qquad (6.59)$$

where α_ν is the relevant atomic absorption coefficient. The rates of the reverse processes of stimulated and spontaneous recombination again follow from detailed balance arguments as shown, e.g., by Fowler (1955). If we define cross sections $F(\eta)$ and $I_\nu G(\eta)$ respectively for the spontaneous and stimulated recombination rates, we find that the requirement for preservation of a Planck distribution in the limiting case of thermodynamic equilibrium becomes

$$\alpha_\nu = \frac{8\pi U_+}{g_\ell} \frac{mc^2}{(h\nu)^2} \, \eta F(\eta) \qquad (6.60)$$

and

$$F(\eta) = \frac{2h\nu^3}{c^2} \, G(\eta), \qquad (6.61)^{\dagger}$$

where $\eta + \eta_0 = h\nu$. The rate, per ion, of recombinations which give photons into unit solid angle and which involve electrons in the energy range $d\eta$ about η is then

$$dR_{\kappa\ell} = \frac{d\eta}{\sqrt{\pi m}} \left(\frac{2}{kT}\right)^{3/2} \eta e^{-\eta/kT}[F(\eta) + I_\nu G(\eta)]n_e, \qquad (6.62)$$

and the total recombination rate, per ion, into state ℓ follows as

$$R_{\kappa\ell} = \frac{4\pi}{c^2} \left(\frac{h^2}{2\pi mkT}\right)^{3/2} n_e \frac{g_\ell}{U_+} \int_{\nu_0}^{\infty} \nu^2 \alpha_\nu e^{-h(\nu - \nu_0)/kT}\left[1 + \frac{J_\nu c^2}{2h\nu^3}\right] d\nu. \qquad (6.63)$$

Seaton (1958) and Burgess and Seaton (1960) have developed a general "quantum defect" procedure for evaluating the continuous absorption coefficients as functions of frequency. The tables presented by these authors allow a ready estimate of the absorption coefficient from a knowledge of the difference between the principal quantum number and the effective quantum number (i.e., the quantum defect) as extrapolated to the series limit. The procedure need not be reviewed here; the reader is referred to the original papers for details of the method and for the impressive agreement which it gives with much more elaborate theoretical calculations.

In many cases α_ν may be represented adequately by a simple hydrogenic formula due to Gaunt (1930) which, for cgs units, becomes

$$\begin{aligned}
\alpha_\nu &= 2.81 \times 10^{29} g(\nu) Z^4 / n^5 \nu^3 \\
&= 1.02 \times 10^{-2} \lambda^3 g(\nu) Z^4 / n^5,
\end{aligned} \qquad (6.64)$$

for ionization from level n; the multiplier $g(\nu)$ is the Gaunt factor and is a number of order unity for radiation in the visible and near-visible wavelength range.

6.2.5 Dielectronic Recombination

Burgess (1964b, 1965a, b) has recently drawn attention to the fact that the mechanism of dielectronic recombination can play an important role, in astrophysical situations, in determining the equilibrium degree of ionization. Indeed, he has been able to demonstrate that the inclusion of this process accounts for a long-standing anomaly between the coronal temperature as deduced from line widths, and that obtained from considerations of the ionization equilibrium. This process has been well known for many years, but previous investigators had underestimated its importance.

The process may be discussed, following Burgess, in the simplified context of the pair of transitions

$$X^{+(z)}(nl) + e(E, l'' + 1) \rightleftarrows X^{+(z-1)}(n'l + 1; n''l''), \qquad (6.65)$$

$$X^{+(z-1)}(n'l + 1; n''l'') \rightleftarrows X^{+(z-1)}(nl; n''l'') + h\nu, \qquad (6.66)$$

through which an ion of species X and charge z, which has a single (nl) electron in its ground state, recombines with a free electron to produce an ion of charge $z - 1$ in which both electrons are excited; this ion then decays spontaneously with emission of a photon to a singly excited state.

To contribute significantly, the pair of processes (6.65) and (6.66) must occur with high probability, in particular the density must not be so high that the doubly excited state of $X^{+(z-1)}$ is destroyed by collisional ionization before it can spontaneously decay. High densities also limit the number of effective levels n'' contributing to the total recombination—this influence is substantial, as shown by Burgess (1956b) and

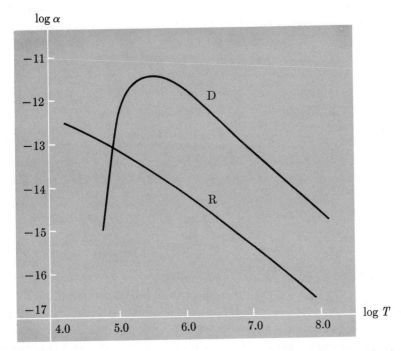

Figure 6.2. The temperature variations of the radiative and dielectronic recombination rates, α_D and α_R, in units of cm³-sec⁻¹ for the recombination He⁺ + e. Logarithms are to base 10. (After Burgess, 1964, *Astrophys. J. 139*, 779, Figure 1.)

leads him to the conclusion that the mechanism is unlikely to be important at chromospheric densities. Furthermore, the process will be ineffective in repopulating the *lower* states of the $z - 1$ ion unless the rate of downward cascade exceeds the rate of collisional ionization from the $(nl; n''l'')$ state. In summing over all values of n', n'', l'' to obtain the total recombination rate the influence of large values of n'' is important; the corresponding doubly excited levels of the $z - 1$ ion thus lie close in energy to their series limit, i.e., to the $(n'l + 1)$ state of the ion of charge z. The process is, therefore, unlikely to compete with radiative recombination unless a sufficient number of electrons possess the energy required to excite the z ion from the state (nl) to $(n'l + 1)$.

For example, let us consider the dielectronic recombination of He^+ ions in their ground $(1S)$ state. Burgess has found that the main contribution arises from the recombination in which the doubly excited He atom is in the $(2p, n''p)$ or $(2p, n''d)$ states with n'' taking a wide range of values. The decay is to the singly excited $He(1s, n''p)$ or $He(1s, n''d)$ with emission of a photon of energy (for n'' large) quite closely equal to that of the $He^+(2P) \rightarrow He^+(1S)$, transition. The electron energy E, required for efficient dielectronic recombination, is of order 41 ev and the temperature must be correspondingly high if the process is to be important. The case of He^+, as computed by Burgess, is illustrated in Figure 6.2.

The parallel emission of a photon in the dielectronic recombination process led to the suggestion, by Goldberg (1964), that this may be important as an emission source for such lines as Ca II H and K. A quantitative study by Noyes (1965), however, has demonstrated that it is of essentially no importance, at least in the solar atmosphere.

6.3 Some Special Solutions

Although the general problem of the solution of the equilibrium equations is formidably complicated by the need to solve, simultaneously, the radiative transfer equations, solutions may be obtained in certain limiting cases. Because many of these have been extensively treated in the literature, and because they illustrate important points, we shall discuss them in some detail.

6.3.1 The Collision-Dominated Case

This simplest of the special cases applies when the density is so high that radiative emission and absorption processes occur at a rate negligible in comparison with the corresponding collisional processes. Under such circumstances we should expect to find that the level populations at any given location in the gas are given by the LTE distributions. This may be very simply proved from the solution (6.7) of the equilibrium equations. Consider, for definiteness the ratio

n_2/n_1. If we expand the probabilities q we may write Equation (6.7) in the form

$$\frac{n_2}{n_1} = \frac{T_1}{T_2} \left[\frac{p_{12} + \sum p_{1j}p_{j2} + \sum\sum p_{1j}p_{jk}p_{k2} + \cdots}{p_{21} + \sum p_{2j}p_{j1} + \sum\sum p_{2j}p_{jk}p_{k1} + \cdots} \right], \qquad (6.67)$$

where the summations are over all j, k, etc., not equal to 1 or 2. Any term in the numerator describes the probability of a specific path connecting states 1 and 2 and to this term there corresponds one in the denominator describing the reverse path. If only collision processes are important, then the forward and backward transition rates are governed by Equation (6.21) or (6.51) and it is then trivial to show that the ratio of any two corresponding terms in the numerator and denominator of Equation (6.67) is just $(g_2/g_1) \exp(-E_{12}/kT)$ so that the ratio n_2/n_1 is given by the same expression. It is important to realize that this result follows from the assumption of a Maxwellian velocity distribution for the electrons and not merely from the predominance of collisions—although in general the one will imply the other.

We may quite simply estimate the conditions for validity for this special case as follows. For a typical situation, the collision cross section is of order 10^{-16} cm^2 and the electron velocity is of order 10^8 cm-sec^{-1}, so that the collisional de-excitation rate per atom is about $10^{-8}n_e$ sec^{-1}. Compared with a typical A-value of 10^8 sec^{-1}, this requires $n_e > 10^{16}$ cm^{-3} before collisions predominate.* Such electron densities are not reached in the solar atmosphere until about optical depth unity in the continuum, so that LTE is not *a priori* applicable. At the same time the predominance of collisions is not a *necessary* condition for LTE—consider, for example, a very tenuous gas in equilibrium inside an enclosure.

6.3.2 Optically Thin Irradiated Atmospheres†

A degenerate case frequently discussed in the literature is that in which the radiation intensity J_ν everywhere inside the atmosphere is taken equal to that incident. This situation, which is known as the

---

* This limit would have to be raised for highly stripped atoms radiating in the UV or X-ray regions since the resonance transitions increase by a factor $\sim Z^4$ while the cross sections decrease at a similar rate. See Griem, *Plasma Spectroscopy*, p. 151, for further details.

† This section is included here for completeness, its proper understanding will follow better after reading Chapter 7.

optically thin case, is characterized therefore by the assumption that the atmosphere produces no sensible modification to the incident beam. To obtain a rough criterion for its applicability, consider a slab of gas irradiated from below by a collimated beam of flux $4\pi F$. If the emission arising directly from collisions is denoted ε', and if the total optical depth of the slab at the line center is represented by τ_1 (assumed less than unity) the mean diffuse intensity J_D produced in the gas will be independent of depth and equal to

$$J_D \sim \tau_1(b + \varpi_0 F),\tag{6.68}$$

where $b = \varepsilon'/\kappa_0$ and κ_0 represents the line center absorption coefficient, while ϖ_0 is the albedo for single scattering. The criterion for the validity of the "thin atmosphere" assumption is then that J_D be small compared to the externally incident flux F. That is, we require

$$F > b\tau_1.\tag{6.69}$$

We can make this condition stronger. Suppose that in fact the condition (6.69) were violated, as it would be if there were no flux incident. Then, neglecting stimulated emission, the population ratio for a two-level atom would be given as

$$\frac{n_2}{n_1} = \frac{4\pi \int J_D(\nu)\alpha_\nu \, d\nu/h\nu + C_{12}}{A_{21} + C_{21}}\tag{6.70}$$

or using the result (6.68),

$$\frac{n_2}{n_1} \simeq \frac{b\tau_1}{\rho_\nu} + \frac{C_{12}}{A_{21} + C_{21}}\tag{6.71}$$

with $\rho_\nu = (2h\nu^3/c^2)g_1/g_2$. From its definition, however,

$$b = \rho_\nu\left(\frac{C_{12}}{A_{21} + C_{21}}\right),$$

so that

$$\frac{n_2}{n_1} \simeq \frac{C_{12}}{A_{21} + C_{21}}(1 + \tau_1)$$

$$\simeq \frac{C_{12}}{A_{21} + C_{21}},\tag{6.72}$$

since τ_1 is assumed small.

We may conclude, therefore, that, if the optical thickness near the line center is small, we may neglect the self-radiation of the gas, and the equilibrium equations may be solved using the incident flux to compute the rate of radiative excitations—even in the limiting case when the incident flux is zero. The validity condition for the "thin atmosphere" approximation is thus simply $\tau_1 \ll 1$.

The approximation was adopted first by Rosseland in his theory of cycles discussed in Chapter 3. Essentially similar studies which did not, however, neglect collision excitation, were made by Giovanelli (1948, 1949) and by Thomas (1948) in efforts to account for the hydrogen spectrum of the solar chromosphere. These authors supposed initially that the chromospheric excitation arose directly from collisions, together with absorption of the incident photospheric flux. It soon became evident, however, that these analyses were not applicable since the predicted populations and the observed scale height and electron density would result in chromospheric optical thicknesses which were, in fact, not at all small in the Lyman lines or even in Hα.

These authors attempted, therefore, to include the influence of the radiation produced by the chromosphere itself and so encountered a problem of a much more difficult character.

A point of confusion to some workers seems to lie in the role played by collisions. If the radiative transition rates are controlled by incident radiation—as they are in the thin atmosphere case—they are obviously independent of the collision rates, and the two may be immediately added to give a total transition rate. So far as $R_{ij} > C_{ij}$, the collisions may be entirely neglected, *providing that the atmosphere is optically thin in the (ij) radiation*. If the atmosphere is optically thick in this line, however, the collisions can under no circumstances be neglected since, in general, they provide the ultimate source of the radiation.

6.3.3 Optically Thick Atmospheres

A second general situation in which the solution of the transfer equation is immediate is found for atmospheric regions far enough from a boundary that a photon has a negligible chance of escaping before its energy is converted to thermal energy, or to a photon in an optically thin spectral range. The detailed situation is not entirely clear in a general case where interlocking of photons in different lines or continua occurs, but in certain circumstances it seems legitimate to suppose that upward and downward radiative transitions in the optically thick lines will balance in detail—this limiting case is the opposite of that discussed above and is designated the "thick atmosphere" assumption. Here we do not actually determine the radiation intensity, rather we suppose it to be such that the transition rates $R_{ij}n_i$ and $R_{ji}n_j$ are equal in certain transitions* so that these terms disappear from the equilibrium equations. The approximation must be made with care. In general the radiation field in an optically thick line may build up to values such that the radiative absorption and emission rates far exceed those of the corresponding collisional transitions so that, in a simple two-level case we could say $R_{12}n_1 \simeq R_{21}n_2$. Since the collisions provide the ultimate source of the radiation, however, the radiative rates must balance to the order of the collision rates before detailed balance can be assumed.

This point may be exemplified for a two-level atom, for which the equilibrium equation may be written,

$$R_{21}n_2 - R_{12}n_1 = C_{12}n_1 - C_{21}n_2. \qquad (6.73)$$

The assumption of radiative detailed balance in this simple case leads to the immediate conclusion that

$$\frac{n_2}{n_1} = \frac{C_{12}}{C_{21}} = \frac{g_2}{g_1} \exp\left(\frac{-E_{12}}{kT}\right), \qquad (6.74)$$

which in turn requires $S_\nu = B_\nu(T)$ by Equation (3.33). As we shall see in the following chapter, however, the source function S_ν does not saturate to $B_\nu(T)$ until optical depths τ_0 at the line center of order $1/(1 - \varpi_0)$ (that is, $\simeq A_{21}/C_{21}$) because on the average the photon is scattered $(1 - \varpi_0)^{-1}$ times before being degraded into thermal energy.

Near the surface detailed calculations show that $S_\nu = \sqrt{\lambda}\, B_\nu(T)$, where $\lambda = 1 - \varpi_0$. Now suppose $\lambda = 10^{-4}$, then $R_{21} = 10^4 C_{21}$, while some consideration would show that near the surface, $R_{12} \simeq 10^2 C_{12}$ so that both R_{21} and R_{12} are much greater than their collisional counterparts. Nevertheless, the condition of radiative detailed balance, if assumed near the surface, would lead to an overestimate of order 10^2 in the population ratio (n_2/n_1). Thus, it might be anticipated that the condition of radiative detailed balance will hold only at optical depths substantially greater than unity and, as we shall in Chapter 7, this is indeed the case. Thus, in this context "optically thick" must

---

* Clearly, we do not envisage application of this approximation to *every* spectral line and continuum formed by the atom since that leads only to the degenerate case of local or complete thermodynamic equilibrium.

usually be read to mean that the optical depth must be *very* much greater than unity.

6.3.4 Summary on the Thick and Thin Atmosphere Assumptions

If the atmosphere is either optically very thick, or is thin, in the spectral lines or continua formed by an atom, we may obtain solutions to the equilibrium equations quite simply. Such a procedure has been extensively applied to discussions of the excitation and ionization of hydrogen and helium in the solar chromosphere with a view to interpreting the eclipse spectrum in the optically thin lines. These approximations are clearly not applicable to the case of an opacity only marginally fulfilling the requirements (for example, $\tau_1 \simeq 10^4$ in our simple example in Section 6.3.3); for such situations, as well as for a discussion of the emergent radiation from an opaque atmosphere, there seems no escaping the detailed solution of the transfer equation.

6.3.5 The General Case—the Net Radiative Bracket

The two limiting cases discussed above may be incorporated into a general framework which, though formal at this stage, will prove extremely useful in practice. This net radiative bracket (NRB) formulation was introduced by Thomas (1960) as follows: If we define a quantity $Z_{u\ell}$ for a line formed between levels u and ℓ by the equation

$$R_{u\ell}n_u - R_{\ell u}n_\ell = A_{u\ell}n_u Z_{u\ell}, \qquad (6.75)$$

then in terms of the result, valid for complete redistribution,

$$S_l = \frac{2h\nu^3}{c^2}\left(\frac{g_u}{g_\ell}\frac{n_\ell}{n_u} - 1\right)^{-1}, \qquad (6.76)$$

the net radiative bracket, $Z_{u\ell}$, in the line can be expressed as

$$Z_{u\ell} = 1 - \frac{\int J_\nu \phi_\nu \, d\nu}{S_l}. \qquad (6.77)$$

We may define a corresponding quantity $Y_{u\ell}$ through the equation

$$R_{u\ell}n_u - R_{\ell u}n_\ell = A_{u\ell}n_u Y_{u\ell}, \qquad (6.78)$$

so that

$$Y_{u\ell} = \frac{g_u}{g_\ell}\left\{\frac{S_l - \int J_\nu \phi_\nu \, d\nu}{S_l + 2h\nu^3/c^2}\right\}. \qquad (6.79)$$

The terms $R_{u\ell}n_u$ and $R_{\ell u}n_\ell$ must obviously always appear on opposite sides in the equilibrium equations so that the equations, or their formal solutions, must remain unchanged if we make the dual replacement

$$R_{u\ell} = A_{u\ell}Z_{u\ell}, \qquad R_{\ell u} = 0 \qquad\qquad (6.80)$$

or

$$R_{u\ell} = 0, \qquad R_{\ell u} = -A_{u\ell}Y_{u\ell}. \qquad\qquad (6.81)$$

The thick atmosphere case for the u–ℓ transition corresponds to $Z_{u\ell}$ or $Y_{u\ell} = 0$; the thin atmosphere case, with no incident radiation, is obtained by putting $Z_{u\ell} = 1$ or

$$Y_{u\ell} = \frac{g_u}{g_\ell} \frac{S_l}{S_l + 2h\nu^3/c^2}. \qquad\qquad (6.82)$$

For example, for a two-level atom,

$$\begin{aligned}
\frac{n_2}{n_1} &= \frac{P_{12}}{P_{21}} = \frac{R_{12} + C_{12}}{R_{21} + C_{21}} \\
&= \frac{C_{12}}{A_{21}Z_{21} + C_{21}} = \frac{-A_{21}Y_{21} + C_{12}}{C_{21}}.
\end{aligned} \qquad\qquad (6.83)$$

The formulation in terms of $Y_{u\ell}$ has been little used, though it appears to have advantages in certain circumstances—cf. Jefferies (1960).

The net radiative brackets are introduced purely formally; they cannot be evaluated, except in the limiting cases above, without a parallel solution of the transfer equations. Nevertheless, they are useful in practice since they permit the formal cancellation of some very large terms in the equilibrium equations. As mentioned above, the radiative terms may separately be much larger than their collisional counterparts which ultimately control the radiation strength. We may, therefore, make serious errors in estimating the excitation state of the gas if the radiative transition rates are inaccurate.

6.3.6 The Recombination Spectrum

The special case of the recombination spectrum has received a great deal of attention in the literature and will not be reviewed here in detail. Formally it can be characterized as one in which each bound state is populated only from above, so that ultimately a given state owes its population to recombination. The equilibrium is supposed maintained by ionization from the ground state, for example through the absorption of ionizing radiation from a neighboring star.

In outline the problem amounts to this: We are given a gas of specific electron temperature and density, both of which are maintained constant by some process which lies outside our consideration. We seek the populations of the various states under the assumptions that (1) collisions are negligible, and either (2) the gas is optically thin to all the lines and continua emitted by it so that the levels are maintained through recombination and cascade, or (3) the gas is sufficiently optically thick to the resonance lines that the emission and absorption transitions in these lines balance in detail. Following Baker and Menzel (1938), cases (2) and (3) above are known as cases A and B, respectively.

Consider the evaluation of the ratio n_j/n_κ, where n_κ is the total ion population, in the optically thin case (A) above. From the conditions of the problem, the probability $q_{lj,\kappa}$ is zero for $l < j$ and therefore, by Equation (6.8), $q_{l\kappa,j} = 1$ for $l < j$. Also, since the only possible transition from the ground state is to the continuum, $q_{jl,\kappa} = q_{jl,1}$ which for $j > l$, is the probability that a path from j to the ground state passes through state l, and this may be readily computed from known values of the spontaneous emission rates. If we denote $q_{jl,\kappa}$ by $q_{j\ell}^*$, we then obtain from the solution (6.7) the result

$$\frac{n_j}{n_\kappa} = \frac{\sum_{m \geq j} P_{\kappa m} q_{mj}^*}{\sum_{n < j} P_{jn}}. \tag{6.84}$$

The absence of upward transitions has the immediate consequence that the matrices of the systems (6.9) are all triangular so that the factors q_{mj}^* may be very simply evaluated in terms of the basic probabilities p_{lm}.

Case B (the thick case) should be described by the same equation provided we substitute $P_{j1} = 0$ for values of j for which the resonance lines $(j \to 1)$ are supposed in detailed balance. This, however, introduces an immediate difficulty in principle, as has been pointed out by Thomas (1949), Pottasch (1960), and Burgess (1958), since there is then no way for an atom to return to the ground level from any of the levels j. The population of the $2p$ state would, therefore, grow proportionally with time. This is easily seen by setting $j = 2$ in Equation (6.84) to obtain

$$\frac{n_2}{n_\kappa} = \frac{\sum_{m \geq 2} P_{\kappa m} q_{m2}^*}{P_{21}}, \tag{6.85}$$

and for detailed balance we must put $P_{21} = 0$ so that the steady-state solution diverges. In fact, some Lyman α photons will escape from the nebula, and perhaps other processes (like 2 photon emission $2s \to 1s$) will occur which maintain the $n = 2$ state population in a steady state. In practice the case-B solutions are obtained parametrically in terms of n_2, which may in turn be determined from an estimate of the rate of the processes which transfer atoms from the 2 state to either the ground state or the continuum. A complete solution to the problem awaits a full study of the Lα transfer equation, though it is difficult to see that Osterbrock's (1962) conclusions on the loss of Lα from a gas are likely to be greatly modified by a more precise study.

Excellent summary articles dealing with recombination spectra have been given by Seaton (1960), and Osterbrock (1964).

REFERENCES

BAKER, J. G., and D. H. MENZEL, 1938, "Physical Processes in Gaseous Nebulae; III, The Balmer Decrement," *Astrophys. J. 88*, 52.

BURGESS, A., 1958, "The Hydrogen Recombination Spectrum," *Mon. Not. R. Astron. Soc. 118*, 477.

BURGESS, A., 1964a, *Atomic Collision Processes*, edited by M. R. C. McDowell. Amsterdam: North-Holland Publ. Co., p. 237.

BURGESS, A., 1964b, "Dielectric Recombination and the Temperature of the Solar Corona," *Astrophys. J. 139*, 776.

BURGESS, A., 1965a, "Dielectronic Recombination," *Proceedings, Second Harvard–Smithsonian Conference on Stellar Atmospheres*, p. 47.

BURGESS, A., 1965b, "A General Formula for the Estimation of Dielectronic Recombination Coefficients in Low-Density Plasmas," *Astrophys. J. 141*, 1588.

BURGESS, A., and M. J. SEATON, 1960, "The Hydrogen Recombination Spectrum," *Mon. Not. R. Astron. Soc. 120*, 121.

CHAMBERLAIN, G. E., D. W. O. HEDDLE, and S. J. SMITH, 1964, "Excitation of the $2p$ State of Hydrogen by Electrons of Near-Threshold Energy," *Phys. Rev. Letters 12*, 647.

FOWLER, R. H., 1955, *Statistical Mechanics*, Second ed. Cambridge: Cambridge University Press.

GAUNT, J., 1930, "Continuous Absorption," *Phil. Trans. Roy. Soc. A. 229*, 163.

GIOVANELLI, R. G., 1948, "Hydrogen Atmospheres in the Absence of Thermodynamic Equilibrium," *Aust. J. Sci. Res. 1*, 289.

GIOVANELLI, R. G., 1949, "The Hydrogen Spectrum of the Sun," *Mon. Not. R. Astron. Soc. 109*, 298.

GOLDBERG, L., 1964, "The Origin of the Emission Reversals in the Fraunhofer H- and K-Lines," *Astrophys. J. 140*, 384.

GRIEM, H. R., 1964, *Plasma Spectroscopy*. New York: McGraw-Hill.

GRYZINSKI, M., 1959, "Classical Theory of Electronic and Ionic Inelastic Collisions," *Phys. Rev. 115*, 374.

GRYZINSKI, M., 1965, "Classical Theory of Atomic Collisions; I, Theory of Inelastic Collisions," *Phys. Rev. 138*A, 336.

HUMMER, D. G., 1963, "The Ionization Structure of Planetary Nebulae; II, Collisional Cooling of Pure Hydrogen Nebulae," *Mon. Not. R. Astron. Soc. 125*, 461.

JEFFERIES, J. T., 1960, "Source Function in a Non-Equilibrium Atmosphere; VII, The Interlocking Problem," *Astrophys. J. 132*, 775.

JEFFERIES, J. T., and S. R. POTTASCH, 1959, "The Nova Outburst; III, The Ionization of Hydrogen Gas by an Exciting Star," *Ann. d'astrophys. 22*, 318

KIEFFER, L. J., 1964, "A Bibliography of Low Energy Electron Collision Cross Section Data," *JILA Report No. 4* (NBS Report 7993).

KLEIN, O., and S. ROSSELAND, 1921, "Collisions Between Atoms and Free Electrons," *Z. Physik 4*, 46.

NOYES, R. W., 1965, "Dielectronic Recombination and the Solar H and K Lines," *Proceedings, Second Harvard–Smithsonian Conference on Stellar Atmospheres*, p. 405.

OSTERBROCK, D. E., 1962, "The Escape of Resonance Line Radiation from an Optically Thick Nebula," *Astrophys. J. 135*, 195.

OSTERBROCK, D. E., 1964, "Planetary Nebulae," *Ann. Rev. Astron. and Astrophys. 2*, 95.

POTTASCH, S., 1960, "Balmer Decrements: The Diffuse Nebulae," *Astrophys. J. 131*, 202.

REGEMORTER, H. VAN, 1962, "Rate of Collisional Excitation in Stellar Atmospheres," *Astrophys. J. 136*, 906.

SARAPH, H. E., 1964, "Cross Sections for $n \rightarrow n + 1$ Transitions in Hydrogen Produced by Electron Impact," *Proc. Phys. Soc. 83*, 763.

SEATON, M. J., 1958, "The Quantum Defect Method," *Mon. Not. R. Astron. Soc. 118*, 504.

SEATON, M. J., 1960, "Planetary Nebulae," *Repts. Progr. Phys. 23*, 313.

SEATON, M. J., 1962a, *Atomic and Molecular Processes*, edited by D. R. Bates. London: Academic Press, p. 374.

SEATON, M. J., 1962b, "The Impact Parameter Method for Electron Excitation of Optically Allowed Atomic Transitions," *Proc. Phys. Soc. 79*, 1105.

SEATON, M. J., 1964a, "The Spectrum of the Solar Corona," *Planet. and Space Sci. 12*, 55.

SEATON, M. J., 1965, "Collision Cross Sections," *Proceedings, Second Harvard–Smithsonian Conference on Stellar Atmospheres*, p. 33.

TAIT, J. H., 1964, "Excitation in Li-like Ions," *Proceedings, Symposium on Atomic Collision Processes in Plasma*, Culham Lab., p. 55.

THOMAS, R. N., 1948, "Superthermic Phenomena in Stellar Atmospheres; II, Departure from Thermodynamic Equilibrium in an Idealized Chromosphere," *Astrophys. J. 108*, 142.

THOMAS, R. N., 1949, "Superthermic Phenomena in Stellar Atmospheres; V, On Emission Lines at High Kinetic Temperature," *Astrophys. J. 110*, 12.

THOMAS, R. N., 1960, "The Source Function in a Non-Equilibrium Atmosphere; IV, Evaluation and Application of the Net Radiative Bracket," *Astrophys. J. 131*, 429.

WHITE, O. R., 1961, "A General Solution of the Statistical Equilibrium Equations," *Astrophys. J. 134*, 85.

ZIRKER, J. B., 1959, "The High-Temperature Excitation of Ionized Helium," *Astrophys. J. 129*, 424.

ZIRKER, J. B., 1962, *Private Communication.*

7

Theory of the Line Source Function:
I. The Two-Level Atom

The equilibrium distributions of the atomic populations have been extensively discussed in the literature under the assumption that either the optically thick (i.e., detailed balance), or the optically thin, limit applies. More recently, attention has also been paid to the intermediate situation where the possibility of self-absorption without detailed balance is introduced parametrically through the net radiative bracket. While such calculations have their place, it must be emphasized that their self-consistency cannot always be assured without a more detailed investigation. Thus, if we assume the thin-atmosphere case we must ultimately check that this gives consistent results for the specific case treated, i.e., that the optical depth of the given atmosphere is indeed small in the transition of interest. If, on the other hand, the assumption of detailed balance is made for a particular line transition, the justification is less straightforward since this is fundamentally a situation where self-absorption is all-important and no simple general criterion exists for its applicability. If the general, net-radiative-bracket, description is used, we cannot meaningfully apply the results without a detailed study of the radiative transfer and the statistical equilibrium equations—since these alone can determine self-consistent values for the net radiative rates.

In any event, we must clearly develop a detailed theory of the line source function if we are to compute the radiation *emerging* from a gas of arbitrary physical structure. This general problem is exceedingly complex due to the multiplicity of energy levels encountered in any real problem and the correspondingly large number of spectral lines and continua emitted by even the simplest atom. The difficulty does not lie so much in the fact of the large number of distinct lines, but arises because they interact with one another so that the source function in one line depends—in general nonlinearly—on that in all others, and the radiation intensities must therefore be obtained either iteratively or simultaneously. In the special case of a two-level atom the complications of interlocking disappear and the theoretical description of the line-source function is relatively straightforward. Because of the physical insight which is gained through a discussion of the two-level atom, because the more general problem can be formulated in these terms, and because the main mathematical difficulties of the general case are equally present in this restricted problem, we shall study the two-level formulation in detail in this chapter, deferring to Chapter 8 the consideration of the multilevel interlocking problem.

7.1 Jefferies and Thomas' Discussion of the Two-Level Source Function

7.1.1 General Formulation

Let us consider a plane parallel homogeneous atmosphere made up of atoms having only two states designated as 1 and 2. The equation of statistical equilibrium

$$[A_{21} + 4\pi B_{21} \int J_\nu \phi_\nu \, d\nu + C_{21}]n_2 = [4\pi B_{12} \int J_\nu \phi_\nu \, d\nu + C_{12}]n_1 \quad (7.1)$$

is to be combined with the expression for the source function which, for complete redistribution, may be written

$$S_l = \frac{\varepsilon_\nu}{\kappa_\nu} = \left[\frac{A_{21}/4\pi}{B_{12} - B_{21}(n_2/n_1)} \right] \frac{n_2}{n_1} \quad (7.2)$$

to give the expression (see Section 3.3.2)

$$S_l = \frac{\int J_\nu \phi_\nu \, d\nu + \varepsilon B_\nu(T_e)}{1 + \varepsilon}. \quad (7.3)$$

The simultaneous solution of the equation of transfer and the equilibrium equation then follows through the solution of the equation

$$\mu \frac{dI_v}{d\tau_v} = I_v - \varpi_0 \int J_v \phi_v \, dv - \lambda B_v(T_e), \qquad (7.4)$$

where $\varpi_0 = 1/(1 + \varepsilon)$ and $\lambda = 1 - \varpi_0$. In the Eddington approximation this takes the simpler form

$$\frac{1}{3} \frac{d^2 J_v}{d\tau_v^2} = J_v - \varpi_0 \int J_v \phi_v \, dv - \lambda B_v(T_e). \qquad (7.5)$$

In the simple case when τ_v varies in proportion to τ_0—as, e.g., for a gaussian absorption coefficient when the Doppler width is independent of depth—the equation becomes

$$\frac{1}{y_v^2} \frac{d^2 J_v}{d\tau_0^2} = J_v - \varpi_0 \int J_v \phi_v \, dv - \lambda B_v(T_e), \qquad (7.6)$$

where $y_v = \sqrt{3} \, \kappa_v/\kappa_0$. The advantage, for simple calculations, of the Eddington approximation (7.6) lies in the requirement to solve only for a function of two variables (frequency and depth); Equation (7.4) involves the additional angle variable μ.

As they stand, these equations refer to the line radiation only, in the presence of continuum emission and absorption they must be modified. It is easily shown that if the continuum is formed in LTE, Equation (7.6) can be written more generally in the form,

$$\frac{1}{x_v^2} \frac{d^2 J_v}{d\tau_0^2} = J_v - \varpi_v \int J_v \phi_v \, dv - \lambda_v B_v(T_e), \qquad (7.7)$$

in which

$$x_v = (r_0 + \phi_v')\sqrt{3}, \qquad (7.8)$$

with ϕ_v' the ratio of the line absorption coefficients at frequencies v and v_0, and

$$\varpi_v = 1 - \lambda_v = \frac{\varpi_0}{1 + r_v} \qquad (7.9)$$

with r_v the ratio of continuum to line absorption coefficient; r_v is here presumed constant with depth.

Equation (7.7) has been extensively studied by Jefferies and Thomas in a series of papers, "The Source Function in a Non-Equilibrium

Atmosphere." Though their numerical results are now somewhat out-dated through the development of more exact mathematical procedures, their methods are simple to apply in practice and are capable of overall accuracy in the range of 5 to 10%, at worst. Because of this, and more significantly because their results brought to light, at least qualitatively, many important new physical effects in the theory of line formation, we shall discuss their work in some detail.

In their solution of Equation (7.7), Jefferies and Thomas used a discrete-ordinate technique based on a procedure introduced by Wick (1943) and developed by Chandrasekhar (1950) into a highly sophisticated form. To solve the exact equation of transfer for coherent isotropic scattering whose homogeneous part is

$$\mu \frac{dI}{d\tau} = I - \frac{\varpi_0}{2} \int_{-1}^{+1} I(\mu) \, d\mu, \tag{7.10}$$

Chandrasekhar replaced the integral over μ by a quadrature sum and solved the resulting system of linear differential equations. In deducing Equation (7.7) we have removed the angular dependence by applying Eddington's approximation, and have been left with an equation so similar to (7.10) that it is clearly indicated that we should attempt to represent the integral over frequency as a quadrature sum

$$\int_0^{+\infty} J_\nu \phi_\nu \, d\nu \simeq \sum_1^n a_i J(\nu_i), \tag{7.11}$$

where the weights a_i and division points ν_i are determined by the particular quadrature formula chosen. There is little evidence that one choice is greatly superior to another; Jefferies and Thomas followed Chandrasekhar in selecting a gaussian quadrature which has the property, unique among quadrature formulas, of determining the weights and division points so that an nth order quadrature gives an exact result for a polynomial integrand of order up to $2n - 1$. Chandrasekhar has shown that the gaussian division points are the zeros of those polynomials which are orthogonal over the range of integration with respect to the weighting function occurring in the integral. If we confine attention to the line core, our weighting function ϕ_ν is effectively gaussian and so we need to determine polynomials $F_n(\nu)$ (of order n) such that

$$\int_0^\infty F_n(\nu) F_m(\nu) \phi_\nu \, d\nu = \begin{cases} 1, & n = m, \\ 0, & n \neq m. \end{cases} \tag{7.12}$$

In practice we may transfer our zero of frequency to the line center and measure frequency shifts $\Delta\nu$ in units of the Doppler width so that our condition becomes

$$\int_{-\infty}^{+\infty} F_n(v)F_m(v)\frac{e^{-v^2}}{\sqrt{\pi}}\, dv = \begin{cases} 1, & n = m, \\ 0, & n \neq m, \end{cases} \qquad (7.13)$$

and it is well known that if $F_n(v)$ are chosen as the normalized Hermite polynomials they will satisfy this requirement. Since, in our problem, J_ν is symmetric about the line center, we may base our quadrature on the even-order polynomials; division points v_i and weights a_i are given, e.g., in the NBS Handbook of Mathematical Functions (NBS Applied Mathematics Series No. 55).

We may now replace Equation (7.7) by its approximate representation

$$\frac{1}{x_i^2}\frac{d^2 J_i}{d\tau_0^2} = J_i - \varpi_i \sum_{j=1}^{n} a_j J_j - \lambda_i B \qquad (i = 1,\ldots, n), \qquad (7.14)$$

where n is the order of the quadrature and we seek the solution of this coupled set subject to the relevant boundary conditions. The simplest procedure is to assume solutions to the homogeneous part of the form $J_i = g_i \exp(k\tau_0)$ when we find that, provided neither x_i nor ϖ_i are functions of depth, the k_i must satisfy the relation

$$1 = \sum_{i=1}^{n} \frac{a_i \varpi_i}{1 - k^2/x_i^2}, \qquad (7.15)$$

which constitutes an algebraic equation of order n in the unknowns k_α^2 ($\alpha = 1, \ldots, n$). It is also readily verified that the unknown coefficients g_i can then be written

$$g_i = \frac{\varpi_i L_\alpha'}{1 - k_\alpha^2/x_i^2}, \qquad (7.16)$$

where the L_α' are the set of integration constants.

7.1.2 The Isothermal Atmosphere

If the Planck function B is independent of depth—i.e., if the atmosphere is *isothermal* in the electron temperature—a particular integral of the system (7.14) follows immediately as $J_i = B$ (since $\sum a_i = 1$) and its full solution may then be written

$$J_i = B\left[1 + \varpi_i \sum_{\alpha=1}^{n} \frac{L_\alpha e^{-k_\alpha \tau_0}}{(1 - k_\alpha^2/x_i^2)} + \varpi_i \sum_{\alpha=1}^{n} \frac{M_\alpha e^{+k_\alpha \tau_0}}{(1 - k_\alpha^2/x_i^2)}\right]. \quad (7.17)$$

The $2n$ integration constants L_α, M_α are to be obtained from the boundary conditions.

In the particular case of a semi-infinite atmosphere we must require each M_α to be zero if the mean intensities are to remain finite at great optical depth. If, further, we specify that no radiation is incident over the surface, $\tau_0 = 0$, then Krook's boundary condition, namely,

$$J_i = \frac{1}{x_i} \frac{dJ_i}{d\tau_0} \quad (7.18)$$

applied to the solution (7.17) yields the following equations for the n integration constants L_α:

$$1 + \varpi_i \sum_{\alpha=1}^{n} \frac{L_\alpha}{1 - k_\alpha/x_i} = 0. \quad (7.19)$$

We are, however, not specifically interested in the quantities J_i, but rather in the line source function S_l, and this can be found immediately from the equation,

$$S_l = \varpi_0 \sum_{i=1}^{n} a_i J_i + \lambda B, \quad (7.20)$$

which can be reduced, using Equation (7.15), to the form

$$S_l = B\left[1 + \varpi_0 \sum_{\alpha=1}^{n} L_\alpha e^{-k_\alpha \tau_0}\right]. \quad (7.21)$$

The emergent intensity may then be computed from the expression (see Equation 2.57),

$$I_\nu(0, \mu) = \int_0^\infty \left(\frac{S_l + r_\nu S_c}{1 + r_\nu}\right) \exp\left[\frac{-(\phi_\nu' + r_0)\tau_0}{\mu}\right](\phi_\nu' + r_0)\frac{d\tau_0}{\mu}. \quad (7.22)$$

It is worth noting, parenthetically, that the expressions (7.21), (7.19), and (7.17) are formally very similar to those derived by Chandrasekhar in his study of coherent scattering. Indeed, in the special case when $r_0 = 0$, and so $\varpi_i = \varpi_0$, the transfer equations (7.14) in the Eddington approximation for complete redistribution are similar in form to those of Chandrasekhar and his elegant methods for elimination of the constants L_α may be applied to allow a determination of the emergent intensity $J_\nu(0)$ in terms of the well-known H-functions of the quantity ϕ_ν; we shall find little use for this development, however. A general conclusion which follows in the case B constant, and which is valid in all orders n of approximation, is

$$S_l(0) = \sqrt{\lambda}\, B. \tag{7.23}$$

In fact, as shown by Avrett and Hummer (1965), the same result not only applies in the Eddington approximation but in all orders of

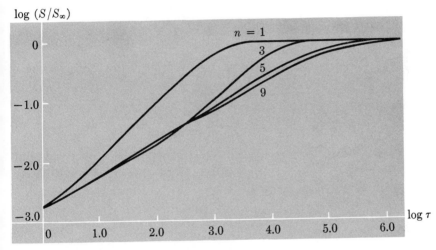

Figure 7.1. Depth dependence of the line source function in an isothermal semi-infinite atmosphere as computed in the various orders of approximation indicated against the curves. Calculations are based on the Eddington approximation and are for $\lambda = 10^{-6}$.

approximation to the *exact* transfer equation (7.4)—it holds, therefore, quite generally for an isothermal atmosphere satisfying the other restrictions of our present problem and so constitutes a valuable check on the accuracy of numerical procedures used in solving the transfer equation.

As a basis of discussion for some significant results of Jefferies and Thomas' theory, we show in Figure 7.1 the depth dependence of S_l computed from Equation (7.21) in various orders of approximation—specifically $n = 1$, 3, 5, and 9—for the case $\lambda = 10^{-6}$, $r_0 = 0$. In Figure 7.2 we illustrate the influence of the value of λ in determining the depth dependence of S_l, while Figure 7.3 shows a corresponding line profile for $\mu = 1$, $r_0 = 0$.*

A number of interesting points arise from these results. First, Figure 7.1 shows that accurate results can only be obtained if the order of approximation is sufficiently high. Indeed, as a general rule, the order of approximation must be such that the value of the integration constant L_α corresponding to the smallest value of k_α is itself small. The calculations of Jefferies and Thomas were restricted to a third-order quadrature and this condition was generally violated. Their results are, therefore, quantitatively inaccurate, even accepting the

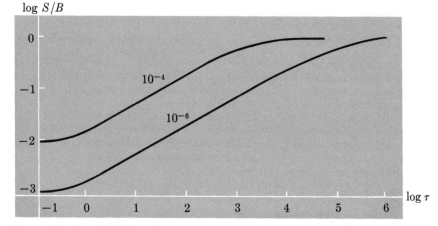

Figure 7.2. Depth variation of the line source function for an isothermal, semi-infinite atmosphere for $\lambda = 10^{-4}, 10^{-6}$; computations are in the ninth-order quadrature for the Eddington approximation.

Eddington approximation—although the qualitatively correct behavior of their computed source functions is borne out by more exact computations.

In fact it turns out, from an asymptotic study of the differential equation, that the representation of S_l by a sum of exponentials is a relatively poor one at large depths; the corresponding solutions (7.21) are therefore unreliable, even in quite high orders of approximation, for determining the approach of S_l toward B, that is, for computing the departure from detailed balance at large optical depths.

* Figure 7.3 is actually taken from the more accurate calculations by Avrett and Hummer (1965). As these authors have shown, their results are generally only marginally different from those given in the earlier calculations of Jefferies and Thomas.

A second important point arising in this simple theory of the line source function is illustrated in Figure 7.2. In accordance with Equation (7.23) the two source functions for $\lambda = 10^{-4}$ and 10^{-6} assume the very different values of $10^{-2}B$ and $10^{-3}B$ at the surface, while their scales of variation are even more divergent. In fact, as the figure illustrates, the line source functions do not saturate to the value B until reaching line center optical depths of about 10^4 and 10^6, respectively. This again reflects a general conclusion, for a Doppler-broadened line, that the saturation, or thermalization, length is of order λ^{-1} as measured in units of the optical depth at the line center. The reason for this behavior is to be traced to the influence of scattering on the propagation of the photons through the gas. At each absorption a photon has a probability of order λ of being destroyed through a collisional de-excitation. In all other cases it is re-emitted and so is free to be re-absorbed and again re-emitted until it ultimately is destroyed or escapes from the atmosphere. In other words, it executes a random walk through the gas. *If the scattering were coherent*, a photon would travel in steps of, statistically, constant length and would therefore travel an average distance $1/\sqrt{\lambda}$ as measured in units of optical depth in its own (unchanging) frequency. The influence of the surface would therefore be felt for a frequency ν down to $\tau_\nu = 1/\sqrt{\lambda}$, and not until this depth were reached would the monochromatic line source function $S_l(\nu)$ be saturated. In our case, however, the scattering is *not* coherent but is completely redistributed and so the random walk, though still numbering λ^{-1} steps on the average, takes place in steps of varying length to accompany the varying frequency as the photon is absorbed and re-emitted. The net result is that a photon will travel a distance governed by λ and by the frequency profile of the absorption coefficient; if this is gaussian it turns out (see Section 7.2.2) that the photon diffuses a mean optical length of λ^{-1} measured at the line center. Correspondingly, the photon intensity, and so the source function, will reach saturation only at this large optical distance from the surface.

A third important result is contained in the line profile shown in Figure 7.3. In keeping with the Eddington-Barbier relation $I_\nu(\mu) \simeq S_l(\tau_\nu = \mu)$, the profiles are roughly a mapping of the variation of S_l with depth. The line-source function decreases toward the boundary only because of the presence of the boundary, and for small λ it varies over a large optical depth. Consequently an *absorption* line is produced, although the atmosphere itself is *isothermal* throughout. The presence

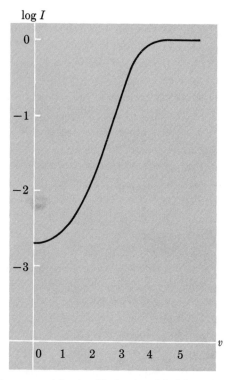

Figure 7.3. Normally emergent line profile for $\lambda = 10^{-6}$ for a semi-infinite isothermal atmosphere.   (After Avrett and Hummer, 1965.)

of an absorption line in a spectrum is, therefore, no guarantee at all of a corresponding *temperature* decrease toward the surface; it is simply a guarantee of the presence of a decrease in the *source function*.   These simple consequences to our theoretical description of the line source function should be contrasted with the results obtained if we supposed LTE to apply to the same *isothermal* atmosphere.   Since there is then no gradient of the Planck function, we would predict the emergent intensity as

$$I_v(0, \mu) = \int_0^\infty B_v(T)e^{-\tau_v/\mu} \, d\tau_v/\mu$$
$$= B_v(T) = \text{const}, \tag{7.24}$$

that is, we would predict no line at any value of μ.   This, indeed, is what we might anticipate for an isothermal gas; our more detailed theory, however, shows that this is only a limiting case reached when $\varpi_0 = 0$ (that is, $\lambda = 1$), as follows immediately from Equation 7.21. In general, however, we have shown that an *isothermal* gas will produce an absorption line simply because of the presence of a boundary to the gas.

The consequences of this simple illustration are far-reaching. Of course it neither proves nor disproves the existence of LTE in any given case; it merely serves as a disquieting indication of the extreme errors possible in an uncritical approach to the analysis of a line spectrum.

7.1.3 Variable Temperature Atmosphere; The *H* and *K* Lines

The temperature in the solar chromosphere is known to increase outward, and the same result may be presumed to hold for those stars —of spectral type later than about G0—which exhibit chromospheric behavior as inferred by the presence of the H and K emission cores. It is, therefore, of considerable interest to apply this simple source-function theory to a variable-temperature atmosphere to determine the characteristics of the emitted line.

A full discussion of the problem for a multilevel atom has not been given so far, but we may gain some insight into the physical nature of spectral line formation through the formulation introduced above. Since we are interested only in general results, we may choose any convenient representation for the temperature distribution and here we shall adopt the simple expression used by Jefferies and Thomas, namely,

$$B(T_e) = B_1[1 + \beta\tau_0 + Ae^{-c\tau_0}], \qquad (7.25)$$

in which $B(T_e)$ is the Planck function of the electron temperature at the relevant wavelength, τ_0 is the line center optical depth, and B_1, β, A, and c are constants which we may choose at will to vary the temperature structure of the atmosphere. The character of the temperature distribution following from the representation (7.25) is illustrated schematically in Figure 7.4. The four parameters B_1, A, c, and β may be determined from a specification of the four quantities—the surface temperature, the minimum temperature, the line center optical depth at which the minimum occurs, and the slope of the Planck function at large optical depths.

If we assume, as above, that the scattering parameter λ, the absorption coefficient ratio r_0, and the absorption coefficient profile, are

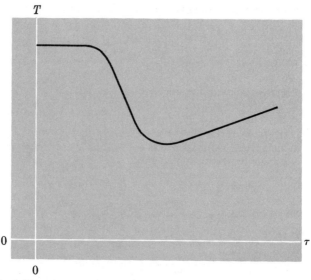

Figure 7.4. Schematic representation of a chromospheric temperature distribution implied by the expression (7.25) of the text.

constant with depth, the solution to the transfer equations (7.14) with the Planck function (7.25) can be readily obtained by standard methods, and the line source function may then be expressed, following Jefferies and Thomas (1959), in the form

$$S_l = B_1 \left[1 + \beta\tau_0 + A(\lambda + \varpi_0 q)e^{-c\tau_0} + \varpi_0 \sum_{\alpha=1}^{n} L_\alpha e^{-k_\alpha \tau_0} \right] \quad (7.26)$$

with the integration constants L_α given by the solution of the linear system of equations

$$1 - \frac{\beta}{x_i} + A\left[\frac{\lambda_i + \varpi_i q}{1 - c/x_i} \right] + \varpi_i \sum_{\alpha=1}^{n} \frac{L_\alpha}{1 - k_\alpha/x_i} = 0, \quad (7.27)$$

while the factor q is determined from the expression

$$q = \sum_i \left(\frac{\alpha_i \lambda_i}{1 - c^2/x_i^2} \right) \left(1 - \sum_i \frac{\alpha_i \varpi_i}{1 - c^2/x_i^2} \right)^{-1}. \quad (7.28)$$

Figure 7.5 illustrates a calculation of the line-source function computed in the ninth-order quadrature for an atmosphere with the specific values $A = 200$, $r_0 = 0$, $\lambda = 10^{-4}$, $\beta = 0$, and $c = 10^{-5}$. The normally emergent line profile corresponding to this source function may be computed, as usual, from Equation (7.22); as illustrated in Figure 7.6.

Before discussing these results we should point out that our model chromosphere–photosphere is, in effect, no more than a superposition, slightly smoothed out, of a hot atmosphere on a cold one.   The line center optical thickness of the hot gas is roughly equal to the reciprocal of the index c—as can be seen at once from Equation (7.25).   We could as well have discussed such a two-component model, but it is mathematically more convenient to avoid a temperature discontinuity through the use of the smoothed distribution (7.25).

Figure 7.5 clearly illustrates the influence of scattering of radiation on the depth distribution of the line-source function, and the influence of departures from local thermodynamic equilibrium.   The characteristic diffusion length of a photon is 10^4 optical depth units as measured in the line center, for this case when $\lambda = 10^{-4}$, so that the photons are influenced by the presence of a surface for all depths $\tau_0 \lesssim 10^4$.   However, their rate of creation, which depends on $B(T)$, is greater by a factor of A in the chromosphere than in the photosphere. Depending on the optical thickness of the chromosphere, this influence may overbalance the leak through the surface with a consequent local

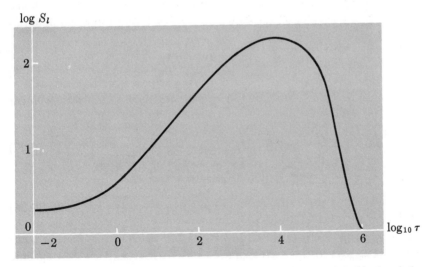

Figure 7.5. Depth dependence of the line source function S_l as computed in the ninth-order approximation for a semi-infinite atmosphere in which the temperature increases toward the surface according to the law (7.25) of the text with $A = 200$, $r_0 = 0$, $c = 10^{-5}$.   The curve represents the values of S_l for $\lambda = 10^{-6}$.

log I

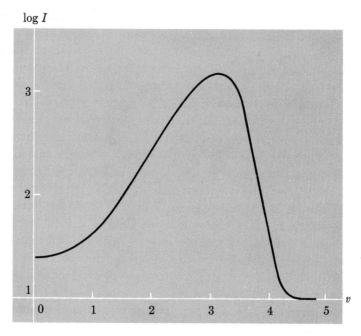

Figure 7.6. The normally emergent line profile for the semi-infinite atmosphere of Figure 7.5 : $\lambda = 10^{-4}$. Only half the profile is illustrated ; it is symmetric about $v = 0$.

rise in the radiation intensity, and so in the line source function S_l, since the two are related through the equation

$$S_l = \varpi_0 \int J_\nu \phi_\nu \, d\nu + \lambda B. \tag{7.29}$$

Closer to the surface, however, the rate of production has leveled off, since $B(T)$ has essentially assumed its surface value, while the photon leak has naturally become stronger. As a result the source function will decrease toward $\tau_0 = 0$ and this will produce the characteristic variation illustrated in Figure 7.5. Note also that the long photon diffusion distance causes the influence of the chromosphere to be felt back into the photosphere where, indeed, the line source function may sometimes exceed the corresponding Planck function.

In terms of a two-layer model the picture is the same. If the outside—chromospheric—layer is optically thick to the radiation then, just as in Section 7.1.2, we shall find an absorption line produced by the chromosphere—i.e., the line intensity will start to increase away from the line center. Beyond a certain value of $\Delta\lambda$, however, the monochromatic optical thickness $\tau(\Delta\lambda)$ of the hot chromospheric layer becomes small and the emergent photons at this wavelength will start to reflect conditions in the photosphere. The intensity at these values of $\Delta\lambda$ will correspondingly begin to decrease until finally the line merges with the basic absorption line formed in the much colder photosphere. Thus, we expect to find, as indeed we do in Figure 7.6, that a self-reversed emission core is formed in the center of a basic absorption line.

In the case $\beta = 0$ the temperature always *increases* outward; our simple theory predicts, nevertheless, that the line center is in absorption and that the overall line is in absorption with an emission feature in the core. There is no cold absorbing gas necessary to explain the central core; it is simply and inevitably predicted and is due solely to the fact that the chromosphere is hotter than the photosphere and that the gas has a surface from which the photons can escape.

The attitude of mind which predisposes us to the idea that an absorption line arises from a cold absorber is deeply rooted. It cannot be too strongly urged, however, that the radiation we see emerging from a glowing object is a reflection *not* of the temperature but of the source function; if the object is in LTE the source function uniquely reflects the temperature; if it is not in LTE it is related also to the radiation intensity inside the gas, and since this must decrease toward the surface from which it can escape, so in general must the source function. An absorption line is, therefore, the natural shape to be emitted by a gas, and a self-reversed emission core is to be *expected* from a star with a chromosphere.

The correspondence between the H and K profiles observed in later type stars and the line shapes predicted, on this theory, to be formed in a photosphere–chromosphere model atmosphere makes it tempting to pursue a quantitative analysis of the observations. This, however, would be premature at this stage. A suitably detailed theory would have to take proper account of the variation in the physical structure of the gas, which we implicitly ignored in setting various parameters constant and, more importantly, would have to consider the interlocking of H with K, and of these with the infrared triplet lines and perhaps with other levels of the singly ionized Ca atom. In other words, we must use both a more sophisticated method for the solution of the transfer equation and a more complete description of the atomic energy level structure before a comparison can be fully meaningful.

Nevertheless, some qualitative remarks can be made even from these simple studies. First, it is clear that the strength of the emission peaks (the so-called H and K features) are controlled by the value of the chromospheric temperature, by the thickness ($1/c$) of the chromosphere, and by the gas density which enters in the parameters λ and r_0. The wavelength separation of the peaks is controlled by the value of c and, of course, by the Doppler width, which is just a scaling factor in our calculations.

Because of the intense interest in the H and K lines which has followed the remarkable discoveries of Wilson, and his co-workers—cf. Wilson and Bappu (1957), Wilson (1963), Wilson and Skumanich (1964) —a great deal of effort is currently directed toward an interpretation of the line profiles in terms of the atmospheric models, and we may look forward to rapid developments in this field.

There exists a variety of alternative explanations for the appearance of the H and K profiles—we may refer, e.g., to the work of Suemoto (1963) in this respect. While our suggested mechanism is not the only possible way to form the lines, it seems certainly to be the simplest since it predicts them to be inevitable with a stellar atmosphere having a chromospheric temperature distribution.

7.1.4 Finite Atmospheres

Early studies of the source function for complete redistribution in a finite atmosphere were carried out by Miyamoto (1954), and Jefferies (1953, 1956); more recent work, using the formulation of this section, was undertaken by Thomas and Zirker (1961a, b). The results of all these calculations are completely consistent with those given for a semi-infinite atmosphere in the preceding subsections—indeed, on that basis we may *predict* the form of the profile for a finite atmosphere as follows. Consider, for simplicity, an isothermal un-irradiated layer in which only line opacity is present. In terms of our results in Section 7.1.2, the source function will increase inward if scattering is significant (i.e., if $\lambda \ll 1$) until at the middle of the layer it reaches a maximum before dropping off symmetrically toward the back surface. According to the Eddington-Barbier relation, the emergent intensity will then *increase* away from the line center—as the effective depth of formation increases—until we reach a value of $\Delta\lambda$ such that the corresponding total optical thickness $\tau_1(\Delta\lambda)$ of the finite layer becomes of order unity;

for larger values of $\Delta\lambda$ the atmosphere will become optically thin and the radiation intensity will decrease in accordance with the relation

$$I_\lambda(0, 1) \simeq \int_0^Z S_l(z)\kappa_\lambda \, dz = \int_0^Z \varepsilon_l(\Delta\lambda) \, dz. \qquad (7.30)$$

In the far-line wings, therefore, where the emission coefficient $\varepsilon_l(\Delta\lambda)$ tends to zero, so does the emergent intensity. Hence the line profile must have the self-reversed character shown schematically in Figure 7.7; clearly this is a special case of the problem treated in Section 7.1.3

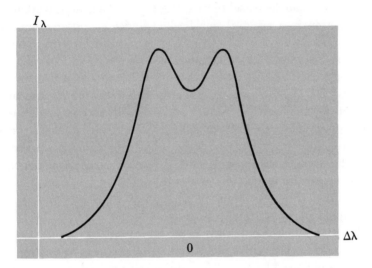

Figure 7.7. A schematic representation of the predicted line profile for a plane parallel isothermal layer of material with negligible continuous opacity.

—namely that in which the lower atmosphere has an effectively zero temperature. It is also clear, after a little consideration, that the positions of the line maxima correspond to those wavelengths $\Delta\lambda_M$ for which $\tau_1(\Delta\lambda_M) \simeq 1$; to the extent that the absorption coefficient is gaussian, therefore, we see that the peak separation is given by the equation

$$2\Delta\lambda_M = 2\Delta\lambda_D\sqrt{\ln \tau_0}; \qquad (7.31)$$

a relation which should also be approximately valid for the separation of the K emission peaks provided that we interpret τ_0 as the optical thickness of the chromosphere. Of course if the atmosphere is optically thick enough that the peaks lie in the damping wings, the separation

$\Delta\lambda_M$ will vary much more rapidly with the optical thickness—and will depend only slightly on the Doppler width.

The appearance of the central reversal in the profile of a line emitted by a finite layer is a natural consequence to our simple theory. The qualitative agreement between this predicted line profile and that observed to be emitted by optically thick lines in (say) a solar prominence is no less striking than the correspondence noted above for the chromospheric H and K lines. The predicted line shapes in the three cases treated in Sections 7.1.2, 7.1.3, 7.1.4 have the common origin that they arise from the decrease, toward the top of the atmosphere, of the source function in a spectral line formed under conditions departing from LTE. As we pointed out in Chapter 3, a stellar atmosphere is normally so tenuous that radiative emissions are more frequent than their collisional counterparts; i.e., the excitation cannot be expected to be as in LTE. On the basis of this more general rate-process theory, we predict line shapes which in fact are observed, and we predict them without appeal to any special atmospheric properties or undemonstrable hypotheses; their origin is natural and, physically, completely clear.

Nevertheless, the theory is distinctly limited in application—especially as regards its restriction to a two-level atom. We shall discuss the removal of the restriction in Chapter 8, but a partial discussion of this important question may be given following Thomas (1957). As we will see, this discussion leads to an important qualification on the above remarks, in particular in answering the question as to why some chromospheric lines, like H and K, exhibit self-reversals whereas others (like Hα), which are equally strong, do not.

7.1.5 The Influence of a Third (Continuum) Level—Thomas' Photoelectrically and Collisionally Controlled Source Functions

In general the optical thicknesses in the free–bound continua of an atom are substantially less than in the stronger lines. In a first approximation, therefore, it would seem reasonable to suppose that in that atmospheric region where the lines are formed, the continuum radiation can be treated as if it were simply incident from outside—i.e., that we can adopt a "thin atmosphere" approximation for the free–bound continua.* On this basis, Thomas (1957) has discussed the form

* If we were interested in the formation of the free–bound continua, on the other hand, we might choose, with Strom and Kalkofen (1966), to adopt the optically *thick* (detailed balance) approximation for the *lines*.

of the line source function for an atom with two bound levels, between which the line is formed, together with a continuum. In these circumstances the source function assumes a much more cumbersome form and for simplicity in exposition we may agree to simplify it by ignoring the influence of stimulated emissions. The ratio of the two-bound state populations is given in our standard notation by the equation

$$\frac{n_2}{n_1} = \frac{P_{12} + P_{1\kappa}p_{\kappa 2}}{P_{21} + P_{2\kappa}p_{\kappa 1}}. \tag{7.32}$$

Since, neglecting stimulated emissions, the line source function is given by the equation

$$S_l = \frac{2h\nu^3}{c^2} \frac{g_1}{g_2} \frac{n_2}{n_1},$$

we find

$$S_l = \frac{\int J_\nu \phi_\nu \, d\nu + \varepsilon(1 + \delta)B_\nu(T_e) + \eta B_\nu^*}{1 + \varepsilon(1 + \delta') + \eta}, \tag{7.33}$$

in which

$$\varepsilon = \frac{C_{21}}{A_{21}}, \qquad\qquad \eta = \frac{R_{2\kappa}P_{\kappa 1}}{T_\kappa A_{21}};$$

$$\delta = \frac{C_{1\kappa}P_{\kappa 2}}{T_\kappa C_{12}}, \qquad\qquad \delta' = \frac{C_{2\kappa}P_{\kappa 1}}{T_\kappa C_{21}}; \tag{7.34}$$

$$B_\nu(T_e) = \frac{2h\nu^3}{c^2} e^{-h\nu/kT_e}, \qquad B_\nu^* = \frac{2h\nu^3}{c^2} \frac{g_1}{g_2} \frac{R_{1\kappa}P_{\kappa 2}}{R_{2\kappa}P_{\kappa 1}}.$$

Note that the numbers δ, δ' are normally much less than unity.

The physical meaning of the different terms in the numerator and denominator of the expression (7.33) is to be traced as follows: The denominator represents the ways in which the atom may return from the upper state to the lower, the first term (normalized to unity) represents the direct spontaneous radiative processes; the other terms specify the relative rates for processes which do *not* result in emission of a line photon. Thus, ε is the relative rate of a direct collisional de-excitation, $\varepsilon\delta'$ and η are the relative rates respectively for collisional and photoelectric ionization followed by recombination, the fraction

$$\varpi_0 = \frac{1}{1 + \varepsilon(1 + \delta') + \eta} \tag{7.35}$$

represents, therefore, the probability that an atom in the *upper state* will make a spontaneous transition to the ground state with emission of a photon.

The term

$$\varpi_0 \int J_\nu \phi_\nu \, d\nu$$

specifies, as usual, the contribution to S_l which arises from scattering of the radiation absorbed in the line; the second term

$$\varpi_0 \varepsilon B_\nu(T_e)$$

gives the contribution to S_l from direct collisional excitations, and the associated term

$$\varpi_0 \varepsilon \delta B_\nu(T_e)$$

arises in collisional ionization from the lower state followed by recombination to the upper.   The final contribution to S_l, namely

$$\varpi_0 \eta B_\nu^*,$$

is due to the photoelectric ionization from the lower state followed by recombination to the upper.

Evidently the form chosen for the expression (7.33) is not unique; however, it allows us to bring out an important physical distinction in the line-formation process depending on the relative importance of the second to the third term in the numerator, as a source of new line photons in the radiation field.

In accordance with the "thin-atmosphere" approximation which we have agreed to assume for the *continua* ($1-\kappa$ and $2-\kappa$), we may specify in advance the corresponding intensities at the depth of formation of the spectral *line* ($1-2$).

For convenience in exposition we may agree to adopt the forms

$$J_\nu = B_\nu(T_r) \tag{7.36}$$

for the intensities in these two continua.   In general the values of T_r for the two free–bound continua will not only be different, because a stellar atmosphere does not radiate like a blackbody, but will also vary with wavelength in the continua; for our purposes we may neglect the latter variation.

A general discussion of the relative sizes of ε and η; B_ν and B_ν^*, valid for all electron and radiation temperatures and for all atoms, is not feasible; we shall instead confine ourselves to the hydrogenic case and to conditions relevant to the solar atmosphere. A parallel study for any other specific situation is straightforward.

If the electron density is small enough—less than about 10^{14} cm^{-3}—we may neglect three-body recombination and we find, for a hydrogenic atom, that the recombination rate to level n is (see Equation 6.63)

$$P_{\kappa n} \simeq R_{\kappa n} = 3.26 \times 10^{-6} n^{-3} T_e^{-3/2} \exp{(\alpha)} E_1(\alpha) n_e, \quad (7.37)$$

where $\alpha = \chi_n/kT_e$ and χ_n is the ionization potential of state n. Since we shall assume $\alpha \gtrsim 1$, this reduces to the simpler form

$$P_{\kappa n} \simeq 3.26 \times 10^{-6} n^{-3} T_e^{-3/2} \alpha^{-1} n_e. \quad (7.38)$$

The corresponding rate of photoelectric ionization follows from Equations (6.59) and (6.64) as

$$R_{n\kappa} = \frac{7.90 \times 10^9}{n^5} \frac{\exp{(-\beta_n)}}{\beta_n}, \quad (7.39)$$

with $\beta_n = \chi_n/kT_r$. The rate of collisional excitation follows from Equations (6.24) and (4.42) as

$$C_{12} \simeq 2.7 \times 10^{-10} \alpha_0^{-1.68} \exp{(-\alpha_0)} T_e^{-3/2} A_{21} \left(\frac{g_2}{g_1}\right)\left(\frac{I_H}{\chi_0}\right)^2 n_e, \quad (7.40)$$

and the de-excitation rate is, therefore,

$$C_{21} = 2.7 \times 10^{-10} \alpha_0^{-1.68} T_e^{-3/2} A_{21} \left(\frac{I_H}{\chi_0}\right)^2 n_e, \quad (7.41)$$

where χ_0 is the excitation energy E_{12}, and $\alpha_0 = \chi_0/kT_e$.

The ratio ε/η is approximately representable as the ratio $C_{21}/R_{2\kappa}$. For example if we consider, as typical values, a case for which $A_{21} = 10^8$ sec^{-1}, $\chi_0 \simeq 2$ ev, $n_e = 10^{11}$ cm^{-3}, $T_e \simeq 10^4$ °K, and the quantum number of the upper state is 2, we obtain, to a sufficient accuracy,

$$\varepsilon/\eta \sim 10^{-6} \exp{(\beta_2)}. \quad (7.42)$$

Similarly, we find

$$\frac{\varepsilon B}{\eta B^*} \sim 10^{-6} \exp{[\beta_1 - \alpha_0]}. \quad (7.43)$$

It is physically clear that the character of the source function, and so of the line profile, may be critically dependent on which of the terms, εB or ηB^*, dominates as the source of fresh photons in the line. If ηB^* dominates, the photons will be produced through the "fluorescence" mechanism which is represented by this term, namely photoelectric ionization from the lower state followed by recombination to the upper state. If, in addition, η is greater than ε, then direct collisions play no part in destroying the line photons either. Thus, the production and destruction of line photons is then dominated by the continuum radiation and the strength of this radiation is *quite unassociated* with *local* values of the electron temperature and density in the region where the *line* is formed; rather it reflects these parameters at the levels where the *continuum* arises.

If, on the other hand, the collision term εB dominates in the creation of photons, the position is reversed. Then the electron temperature in the line-forming region enters directly into the expression for S_l so that the line profile may directly reflect some characteristic of the temperature structure in the atmospheric region where the line is formed.

This distinction is an important one; Thomas (1957) has designated a spectral line as having a "collisionally controlled" or a "photoelectrically controlled" source function according to whether the term εB or ηB^* dominates in the numerator of expression (7.33). On the basis of Equations (7.42) and (7.43) we see that whether a given line falls into one or other of these classes depends on the excitation and ionization energies, along with the electron and radiation temperatures. In a general way we may consider with Thomas the example of the resonance lines, for which we may distinguish three general classes of atoms, (1) those, like H, He, and the other nonmetals, for which χ_{12} is large (~ 10 ev) and so $\chi_{1\kappa}$ is large, (2) those, like the ionized metals, for which χ_{12} is small (~ 3 ev) while $\chi_{1\kappa}$ is large, and (3) those, like the neutral metals, for which both χ_{12} and $\chi_{1\kappa}$ are small. The corresponding ratios ($\varepsilon B/\eta B^*$), as computed from Equation (7.43) for the solar case $T_r \simeq 5000$ °K, are illustrated in Table 7.1—along with the ratios ε/η.

TABLE 7.1. Classification of Resonance Lines

Ratio	(1)	(2)	(3)
$\log_{10}(\varepsilon B/\eta B^*)$	$7 - (50000/T_e)$	$7 - (15000/T_e)$	$-1 - (10000/T_e)$
$\log_{10}(\varepsilon/\eta)$	-3	$+4$	-3

From the table we conclude that, while resonance lines of classes (1) and (2) are essentially collisionally controlled, those of type (3) are photoelectrically controlled. Thus, e.g., the resonance, H and K, lines of Ca^+, or their Mg^+ analogues, will show in their line profiles the influence of collisions in producing new photons and so they will reflect, in some degree, the temperature structure of the gas in the region where the lines are formed. For neutral metal resonance lines, such as the Mg b lines, this is not to be expected; note in this context that $H\alpha$ may be regarded as a resonance line to the extent that detailed balance holds in the Lyman series in the region where $H\alpha$ is formed; the excitation and ionization energies for $H\alpha$ (~ 2 and ~ 3 ev) clearly place it in the "photoelectrically controlled"—type (3)—class.

The relative values of ε and η are also important in predicting the atmospheric influence on S_l. In particular the denominator controls the scale of variation of S_l through its control of the thermalization length τ_0^T of the photons

$$\tau_0^T \simeq \left\{ 1 + \frac{1}{\varepsilon + \eta} \right\} \simeq (\varepsilon + \eta)^{-1}. \qquad (7.44)$$

Now, since ε is proportional to the electron density, while η is not, the numbers in Table 7.1 indicate that the scale of variation of S_l for the class (2) lines should increase as n_e decreases, while no such effect should be found for the resonance lines of classes (1) and (3), for which the photon destruction is controlled by transitions of the type $2 \to \kappa \to 1$ whose rate is set by the incident continuum intensity and so does not reflect the local gas density.

Now let us consider the relevance of our discussion above to the prediction of the shapes of spectral lines falling within our categories (1), (2), and (3). An interesting case is that of a model atmosphere consisting of a lower-temperature photosphere above which is found a higher-temperature chromosphere, i.e., a model of the character described in Section 7.1.3.

Let us consider first lines of class (3), of which $H\alpha$ is an example. The line source function S_l will reflect neither the temperature nor the density of the *chromosphere** since, from Table 7.1, $\eta B^* > \varepsilon B(T_e)$ and $\eta > \varepsilon$. Thus, the line source function is given as

$$S_l \simeq \frac{\int J_\nu \phi_\nu \, d\nu + \eta B^*}{1 + \eta}, \qquad (7.45)$$

---

* We suppose, of course, that the relevant continua are formed in the underlying photosphere; for $H\alpha$ these are the Balmer and Paschen continua.

and, as B^* and η are determined by the continuum intensities (which are constant throughout the line-forming region) the line shape will be equivalent to that predicted in Section 7.1.2, i.e., it will be a simple absorption line.

For lines of class (2), e.g., H and K of the Ca II spectrum, the situation is opposite since here we find from Table 7.1, that

$$S_l \simeq \frac{\int J_\nu \phi_\nu \, d\nu + \varepsilon B(T)}{1 + \varepsilon}, \tag{7.46}$$

and for the chromospheric case the line shape is that found in Section 7.1.3 above, i.e., a self-reversed emission core is predicted. Furthermore, the scale of depth variation of S_l will depend on that of the electron density—since ε is proportional to n_e—so that the line profile contains information both on the temperature and density* distributions in the chromosphere.

Finally, the class (1) lines, like Lα of hydrogen, will reflect the temperature structure of the chromosphere in their profiles and, to some extent that of the density.

The detailed correspondence between the shapes predicted on this simple theory, and those observed to be emitted from stellar chromospheres in such lines as H and K of Ca II and Mg II, Hα and the other Balmer lines, Lα and Lβ of hydrogen, is so remarkable that it makes a strong case for the validity of our theory. Certainly the predictions are inescapable—they may be criticized on the basis that the adopted atomic or atmospheric model is still too simple to permit a meaningful calculation; however, it is very difficult to see how the inclusion of a multiplicity of levels in the discussion could alter the *nature* of the predictions.

7.2 More Detailed Studies

While the excellent qualitative agreement between observed stellar spectral line shapes and those predicted on the simple theory of Section 7.1 is encouraging, the theory is too restrictive for valid quantitative comparison. Not only is this because of the neglect of interlocking between lines of comparable strength but also because of the restriction to constant values of the parameters λ, r_0, and the Doppler width, and

---

* We did not consider a depth-dependent λ in the solutions given in Section 7.1.3 since no simple general solution of the transfer equation can be obtained in that case.

in the limitation to complete redistribution and to a gaussian absorption coefficient. A great deal of attention has recently been given to the solution of the basic equation of radiative transfer

$$\mu \frac{dI_\nu}{d\tau_\nu} = I_\nu - S_\nu \tag{7.47}$$

for situations where one or more of the above restrictions is relaxed. It is beyond the scope of this book to discuss adequately the detailed numerical solutions obtained by the various authors; for this, reference must be made to the original articles and the recent detailed review by Hummer and Rybicki (1967). We shall therefore merely *outline* the basic procedures adopted so far in this rapidly developing field.

It is convenient to distinguish two general classes of procedures which have been used to solve Equation (7.47)—or its corresponding Eddington approximation—according to whether they make use directly of this differential equation, or proceed from the equivalent integral equation for S_ν which may be derived from the formal solution to the transfer equation once we have specified S_ν in terms of the intensity I_ν, or, as is more commonly the case, in terms of J_ν. We shall first consider solutions of the differential equation, after which the integral equation will be formulated and discussed.

7.2.1 Solutions of the Differential Equation

AVRETT'S AND HUMMER'S DISCUSSIONS

In the case of complete redistribution, the line-source function for a two-level atom is given by Equation (7.3) and the exact transfer equation with continuous absorption then follows, in correspondence with (7.7), in the form

$$\frac{\mu}{\xi_\nu} \frac{dI_\nu}{d\tau_0} = I_\nu - \frac{\varpi_\nu}{4\pi} \iint I_\nu \phi_\nu \, d\nu \, d\omega - \lambda_\nu B_\nu(T_e), \tag{7.48}$$

with $\xi_\nu = (r_0 + \phi_\nu')$. To the extent that the appropriate parameters are constant with depth, we may replace the frequency and angle integrals on the right of this equation by quadrature sums and obtain the solution in the same general manner as that described in Section 7.1.

This procedure has been applied by Avrett and Hummer (1965) to the case of line transfer ($r_0 = 0$), with a Doppler absorption coefficient, in a semi-infinite atmosphere, and by Hummer (1965*a*) to the

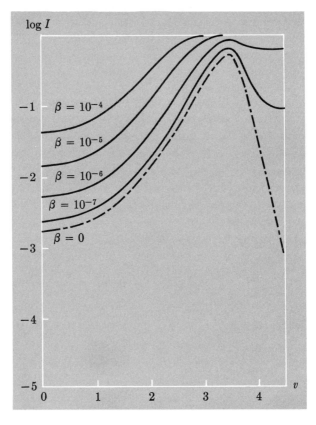

Figure 7.8. The influence of continuous opacity on the profile of the radiation emerging from a finite atmosphere of line-center optical thickness $10^6 \times \sqrt{\pi}$ and for which the line scattering parameter $\lambda = 10^{-6}$; $\beta = r_0/\sqrt{\pi}$. (After Hummer, 1965 b.)

corresponding case of a finite and semi-infinite atmosphere with nonzero continuous opacity. The algebraic development is complicated, and is not reproduced here; Avrett and Hummer (1965) concluded that the discrete ordinate procedure based on the differential equation was unnecessarily complicated, and therefore chose to study in detail the corresponding integral equation. An important conclusion in Hummer's (1965a) work, as also in that of Avrett (1965), lay in re-emphasizing the importance of continuous opacity on the form of the solution of the transfer problem. Thus, as pointed out earlier by Jefferies and Thomas (1958), the scattering parameter λ_v is given by the equation

$$\lambda_v = \frac{r_v + \lambda}{1 + r_v} \qquad (7.49)$$

with

$$\lambda = \frac{\varepsilon}{1 + \varepsilon}$$

and for the very small values ($\sim 10^{-6}$) which λ may assume for a strong line, even small contributions from the continuum may make a great change in the value of λ_v, and so of the form of the emergent line profile. For illustration we reproduce in Figure 7.8 the emergent intensity computed by Hummer (1965a) for various values of r_0 for a finite atmosphere of total line center optical thickness $\sqrt{\pi} \times 10^6$, and in which $\lambda = 10^{-6}$.

HUMMER'S DISCUSSION OF GENERAL NONCOHERENT SCATTERING

Recently Hummer (1965b) has formulated a discrete-ordinate method for the solution of the transfer equation when the scattering function $R(v, v')$ of Chapter 5 is arbitrary. Again, the algebraic development is lengthy and will not be restated here.

The method has been applied by Hummer to the case of redistribution according to the law (see Equation 5.22),

$$R_{\mathrm{I}}(v, v') = \frac{1}{\sqrt{\pi}} \int_{|\bar{v}|}^{\infty} e^{-x^2} \, dx ; \qquad (7.50)$$

results for some specific cases are shown in Figures 7.9 and 7.10.

The most striking feature of Hummer's results lies in the relatively small difference between the frequency-dependent and the frequency-independent source functions, especially at large depths.

Indeed, as Hummer points out, the two source functions approach equality at a *monochromatic* optical depth of unity. A comparison of the normally emergent intensity, for atmospheres of various total optical thickness, T, in the frequency-independent, and the present frequency-dependent, cases is shown in Figure 7.11—the ratio is close to unity in all frequencies which contribute sensibly to the line. For example, in the case $T = 10^3$, the ratio of emergent intensities shown in the figure increases linearly with v beyond about $v = 2.5$; at that frequency, however, the intensity is down to about 10^{-2} of the maximum intensity in the line, and from then on decreases roughly as e^{-v^2}/v.

Hummer's results are important in giving us confidence in the use of the approximation of complete redistribution which leads, of course, to a greatly simplified formulation of the transfer problem.   The more

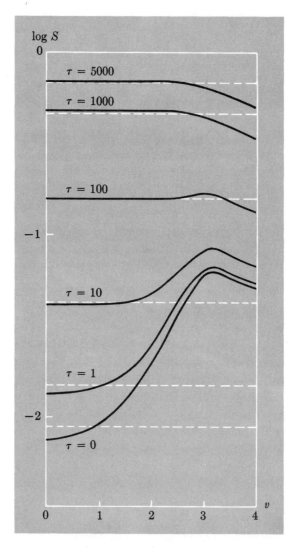

Figure 7.9. The *frequency* variation of the line source function, for Hummer's Type I redistribution, at different optical depths.   Source functions for complete redistribution are shown as broken lines; total optical thickness at line center is $10^4 \times \sqrt{\pi}$, $\lambda = 10^{-4}$. The optical depths shown against the curves are $1/\sqrt{\pi}$ times those at the line center. (After Hummer, 1965 *b*.)

complicated type II redistribution (see Section 5.3.1) will be expected
to produce some modification to the picture given above; however as
yet no calculations have been made, though they can be handled in
Hummer's formulation and are understood to be in progress.

It was suggested by Avrett and Hummer (1965) that a good approximation to the frequency-dependent source function could be obtained

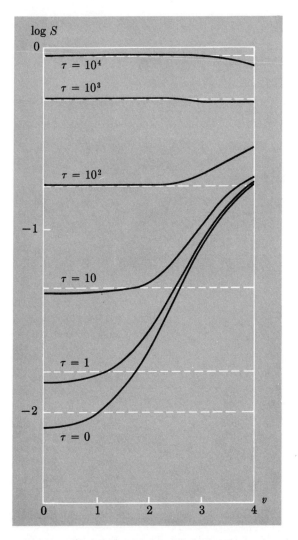

Figure 7.10. The depth and frequency variations of the line source function in a semi-
infinite atmosphere; other conditions as for Figure 7.9. (After Hummer, 1965 *b*.)

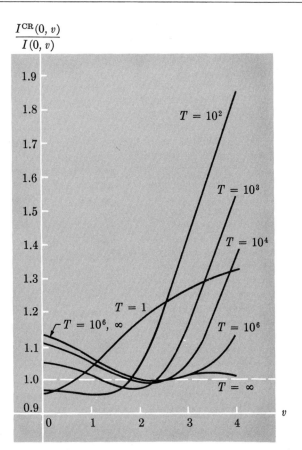

Figure 7.11. The ratio of the normally emergent intensity for complete redistribution to that computed for Hummer's Type I redistribution for atmospheres of the different total optical thicknesses shown against the curves.   (After Hummer, 1965 *b*.)

through a calculation of the mean intensity for complete redistribution, J^{CR}, and the subsequent calculation of the monochromatic source function, $S_{\ell}^{*}(v', \tau)$, through the equation

$$S_{\ell}^{*}(v', \tau) \simeq \varpi_0 \int_{-\infty}^{+\infty} J^{CR}(v, \tau)\, \frac{R_{\mathrm{I}}(v, v')}{\phi(v')}\, dv + \lambda B. \qquad (7.51)$$

Comparisons of $S_{l}(v, \tau)$ and $S_{l}^{*}(v, \tau)$ indicate, as we would expect, that the agreement is extremely good.   As Hummer points out, this constitutes an important computational simplification.

METHODS OF FEAUTRIER AND OF RYBICKI AND USHER

An entirely different numerical procedure has been developed by Feautrier (1964), who introduced a change of intensity variables through the definitions

$$J(\nu, \mu, x) = \frac{I(\nu, \mu, x) + I(\nu, -\mu, x)}{2},$$

$$F(\nu, \mu, x) = \frac{I(\nu, \mu, x) - I(\nu, -\mu, x)}{2},$$

(7.52)

where x is the depth variable, to obtain the modified transfer equation

$$\frac{\mu^2}{\kappa} \frac{d}{dx} \left(\frac{1}{\kappa} \frac{dJ}{dx} \right) = J - S,$$

(7.53)

with its auxiliary equation

$$F = \mu \frac{dJ}{\kappa \, dx}.$$

(7.54)

Note that the quantities J and F, being functions of the angle variable μ, are different from the mean intensity and net flux which were represented in Chapter 2 by the same symbols. The boundary conditions can be expressed in a straightforward way as linear combinations of J and (dJ/dx). By replacing the second-order differential system by their finite-difference equivalents, and making use of the boundary conditions at each end of the optical depth range, Feautrier was able to develop an elimination scheme which allowed him to solve for the quantity J at each depth, frequency, and direction in his quadrature scheme and hence, through Equation (7.54), to determine the intensity, and ultimately the source function S. The procedure, which is a valuable one for solving two-point boundary-value problems of this kind, appears similar to those introduced for the same purpose in stellar-interior calculations.

A different method has been used by Rybicki and Usher (1966), though it is said by its authors to be equivalent to Feautrier's procedure in the limit of infinitesimally small steps in the depth variable x. Rybicki and Usher transform the (coupled) transfer equations for the inward ($\mu < 0$) and outward ($\mu > 0$) intensities by a Riccati transformation to obtain a system of three differential equations which may be integrated serially.

These methods appear to be stable and are capable of great flexibility; it is too soon to say how they will compare in convenience with the methods using the integral equation, although they give indications of being superior—especially for cases where the absorption coefficient varies with depth.

7.2.2 The Integral Equation of Transfer

The two-level source function of Equation (7.3) may be combined with the formal solution to the transfer equation (7.47) to obtain an integral equation. The case most frequently studied is that in which no radiation is incident on either face of a plane parallel layer, in which case we find, as in Equation (2.30),

$$J_\nu(\tau) = \frac{1}{2} \int_0^T S_\nu(t) E_1(|t_\nu - \tau_\nu|) \, dt_\nu \qquad (7.55)$$

where

$$S_\nu(t) = \left[\frac{S_l \phi'_\nu + S_c r_0}{\phi'_\nu + r_0} \right]_t, \qquad (7.56)$$

$$t_\nu = \int_0^t (\phi'_\nu + r_0) \, dt, \qquad (7.57)$$

$$\tau_\nu = \int_0^\tau (\phi'_\nu + r_0) \, dt, \qquad (7.58)$$

and the unsubscripted t and τ variables are optical depths in the line at the line *center* while, as usual, ϕ'_ν is the ratio of the absorption coefficient at frequency ν to that at the line center. In the case of complete redistribution, the line-source function is given by Equation (7.3) so that, from Equation (7.55), we obtain at once the following integral equation for S_l;

$$S_l(\tau) = \lambda B + \frac{\varpi_0}{2} \int_0^\infty \int_0^T S_\nu(t) \phi_\nu(\tau) E_1(|t_\nu - \tau_\nu|) \, dt_\nu \, d\nu. \qquad (7.59)$$

Many of the essential difficulties in the solution of this equation are met in the rather simpler case in which $r_0 = 0$ and ϕ'_ν is independent of depth; in that case Equation (7.59) takes the form

$$S_l(\tau) = \lambda B + \frac{\varpi_0}{2} \int_0^T S_l(t) \int_0^\infty \phi_\nu \phi'_\nu E_1(\phi'_\nu |t - \tau|) \, d\nu \, dt. \qquad (7.60)$$

In the Eddington approximation this becomes

$$S_l(\tau) = \lambda B + \frac{\varpi_0 \sqrt{3}}{2} \int_0^T S_l(t) \int_0^\infty \phi_\nu \phi_\nu' \exp\left(-\sqrt{3}\,\phi_\nu'|t - \tau|\right) d\nu\, dt,$$

$$(7.61)$$

though in fact there is little simplification between the forms (7.61) and (7.60). It should be noted that the frequency integration is over frequency and not over the frequency separation ($\nu - \nu_0$) from the line center.

As noted above, the parameter ϖ_0 often differs only slightly from unity, and this introduces severe numerical difficulties in the solution of the integral equation. As early as 1958, Jefferies and Waddell (unpublished) attempted to solve Equation (7.61) for the case of the hydrogen Lα line; however, their iteration technique—which simply consisted in resubstituting successive estimates for $S_l(t)$—failed to converge and the attempt was abandoned. More recently Avrett and Hummer (1965) have studied the two-level integral equation (7.61) for the case of a depth-independent λ, and for three separate forms of the function ϕ_ν, namely

$$\phi_\nu = e^{-v^2}/\sqrt{\pi}, \qquad (7.62)$$

$$\phi_\nu = \frac{a}{\pi^{3/2}} \int_{-\infty}^{+\infty} \frac{e^{-y^2}\,dy}{a^2 + (v - y)^2}, \qquad (7.63)$$

$$\phi_\nu = \frac{1}{\pi} \frac{1}{(1 + v^2)}, \qquad (7.64)$$

where v is a dimensionless frequency; the forms correspond respectively to the cases of Doppler, Voigt, and Lorentz broadening. Equations (7.62) and (7.64) are, of course, special cases of Equation (7.63) in the limits as $a \to 0$ and $a \to \infty$.

Avrett and Hummer's procedure lay in representing the kernel function

$$K\left(|\tau - t|\right) \equiv \int_0^\infty \phi_\nu \phi_\nu' E_1\{\phi_\nu'|\tau - t|\}\, d\nu \qquad (7.65)$$

by a sum of exponentials, in which case the solution of Equation (7.61) can be written down at once provided that λ is independent of optical depth. The procedure is mathematically equivalent to the discrete-ordinate solution of the corresponding differential equation and is capable of high precision. It is, of course, too limited in application to be useful as a general method. In the context of Avrett and Hummer's didactic approach, however, it made the very useful contribution of exhibiting the influence on S_l of variations in such parameters as T and λ, and on the consequences to S_l, and so to the line profile of the emergent radiation, of changes in the form of the absorption coefficient ϕ_ν.

As a particularly interesting case we illustrate in Figure 7.12 Avrett and Hummer's computed values of $S_l(\tau)$ for a semi-infinite atmosphere

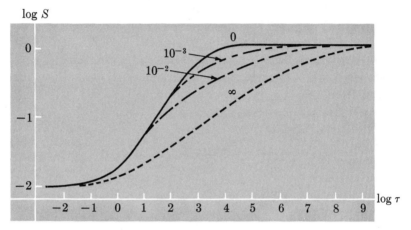

Figure 7.12. Depth variation of the line source function in a semi-infinite isothermal gas for the series of values of the damping constant a (shown against the curves) ranging from pure Doppler ($a = 0$) to pure Lorentzian ($a = \infty$); $\lambda = 10^{-4}$. (After Avrett and Hummer, 1965.)

with $\lambda = 10^{-4}$, in which they have adopted a variety of values of the damping constant a ranging from zero to infinity. The influence of a finite a is to cause a decrease of S_l at a given depth from the corresponding Doppler case $a = 0$. Thus the variation of S_l is extended over greater and greater depths, corresponding to the fact that the opacities in the line wings increase, as a takes larger and larger values.

Avrett and Hummer have discussed these results in terms of the saturation, or thermalization, length τ^T introduced above. Their analysis gives the limiting results

$$\tau^T \sim \lambda^{-1}(a = 0), \qquad \tau^T \sim \lambda^{-2}(a \to \infty). \tag{7.66}$$

It should be noted that the actual profile of the absorption coefficient is often representable, to a good approximation, as the Doppler form

(7.62) in the line core and the Lorentz form (7.64) in the wings. Hence, we should expect that the scale of variation of S_l would be $\sim \lambda^{-1}$ at depths where the line core photons control the transfer (i.e., for $\tau_0 \lesssim 10^4$ in a case where $\underline{a} \sim 10^{-2}$) while it should be much more slowly varying at high depths. Thus for an isothermal, semi-infinite atmosphere we should predict an emergent absorption line with a relatively steep core and wide extended wings. Note especially that this line shape is predicted in the explicit absence of (a) continuous opacity or (b) any temperature gradients. In a practical case some continuous opacity will be present, and the atmosphere will not be isothermal. The extended wings and the approach to the continuum of (say) the H and K lines in a stellar atmosphere, however, is by itself an *a priori* reflection neither of the gradual dominance of continuum opacity in the wings, nor of the presence of a temperature gradient since the same shape is predicted without continuous absorption and with an isothermal layer.

We shall not discuss in detail the other results of Avrett and Hummer's paper; they are generally consistent with, though numerically more precise than, the corresponding results obtained in the Eddington approximation by Jefferies and Thomas' formalism and their physical interpretation has been studied above.

A number of attempts have been made to solve the integral equation (7.60) directly through an expansion of $S(t)$ in terms of a set of basis functions whose coefficients are determined so that $S(t)$ satisfies the integral equation. This procedure has the greater flexibility in that it can readily handle situations in which λ and r_0 vary with depth and, at the cost of some complexity, when $\phi(v)$ is depth-dependent. The scheme most extensively applied is due to Avrett (1965), who chose a set of expansion functions $f(t)$ such that

$$S(t) = \sum_{j=1}^{N} f_j(t)c_j, \qquad (7.67)$$

with

$$f_j(t) = \begin{cases} 1, & j = 1, \\ t, & j = N, \end{cases} \qquad (7.68)$$

$$f_j(t) = \begin{cases} (1 - t/t_j)^2, & 0 \le t < t_j, \\ 0, & t \ge t_j, \end{cases} \quad j \ne 1, N. \qquad (7.69)$$

Avrett further expanded the kernel function in terms of a sum of exponentials in the argument $|t - \tau|$ and finally obtained the equations for the unknowns c_j in the form, suitable for discussion of the semi-infinite atmosphere,

$$\sum_{j=1}^{N} c_j \left\{ f_j(\tau_i) + \frac{1 - \lambda(\tau_i)}{\lambda(\tau_i)} \sum_{k=1}^{M} \frac{2a_k}{b_k} \left[f_j(\tau_i) - \int_0^\infty \frac{b_k}{2} e^{-b_k |t - \tau_i|} f_j(t)\, dt \right] \right\}$$
$$= B(\tau_i), \qquad i = (1, 2, \ldots, N), \quad (7.70)$$

where the numbers a_k and b_k are the expansion coefficients in the approximation

$$\sum_{k=1}^{M} a_k e^{-b_k |t - \tau|} \simeq \frac{1}{2} \int_0^\infty \phi_v \phi_v' E_1(\phi_v' |t - \tau|)\, dv. \qquad (7.71)$$

Tables of the coefficients a_k, b_k for different broadening functions ϕ_v are in preparation by Avrett and Loeser. Proper normalization of the kernel requires that

$$\sum_{k=1}^{M} \frac{a_k}{b_k} = \frac{1}{2}, \qquad (7.72)$$

and this relation must be strictly preserved—it is incorporated in the form (7.70).

In fact, Avrett worked in terms of an optical depth τ' scaled so that $d\tau' = [\phi'(v)/\phi(v)]\, d\tau$, with $d\tau$ measured at the line center; thus, for Doppler broadening $d\tau' = \sqrt{\pi}\, d\tau$. The notation removes the distinction between ϕ and ϕ' in equations such as (7.60) and is a convenient one—in the interest of consistency in this book we continue to refer to the unsubscripted line optical depth as that in the line center.

Avrett (1965) has applied his technique extensively to the solution of the transfer problem for cases where $B(T)$ and λ are separately either constant or variable, and for the standard absorption coefficient profiles given in Equations (7.62) to (7.64). To illustrate the influence of a variable λ we reproduce in Figure 7.13 the line-source functions computed by Avrett for a gaussian absorption coefficient and a semi-infinite isothermal atmosphere for which $\lambda = 10^{-5}$ (case b in the Figure) and, in case a, for which

$$\lambda = 10^{-5}[100 - 99 \exp{(-\tau)}]. \qquad (7.73)$$

The influence of the depth variation of λ is, as expected, to reduce the scale of variation of S_l.

Similar methods have been used by Bainbridge and Jefferies (1965)

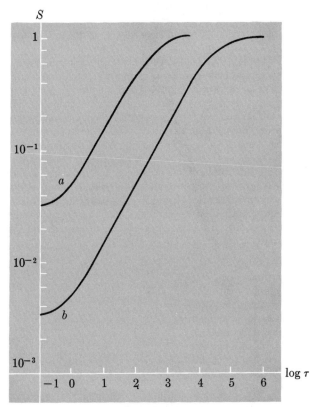

Figure 7.13. The influence of a depth-dependent scattering parameter on the depth variation of the line source function; see text for further details. (After Avrett, 1965.)

and by Finn (1966). In the first of these an expansion of $S(t)$ was made in terms of a sum of exponentials, that is,

$$S(t) = \sum_{i=1}^{N} a_i e^{-k_i t}, \tag{7.74}$$

where the exponents k_i were chosen to range from very large values ($\sim 10^2$) to values $\sim 10^{-1}\lambda$. A least-square procedure was used in determining the coefficients a_i, while the relevant integrals over the kernel K,

$$I_i = \int_0^{\infty} K(|t - \tau|)e^{-k_i t}\, dt, \tag{7.75}$$

were evaluated numerically. The method was applied in the Eddington approximation in order to permit comparison with corresponding solutions to the differential equation which, at the time, only existed in this approximation. Agreement was generally obtained to better than 1%.

A third procedure, recently developed by Jefferies and Finn, consists in replacing the line-source function in the integral term with the step-like basis functions

$$f_i(t) = \begin{cases} a_i, & t_i \le t < t_{i+1}, \\ 0, & \text{otherwise}, \end{cases} \qquad i = 1, \ldots, N-1, \qquad (7.76)$$

while for $t > t_N$, the source function was taken to have the same depth variation as $B(T)$. The practical application of this method consists in partitioning the optical depth scale into more or less equal intervals in $\log t$—which specifies the partition $\{t_i\}$ in Equation (7.76)—so that one obtains an equation for the unknowns a_i of the form

$$a_i = (\lambda B)_{\tau_i} + \varpi_0 \sum_j a_j F_j(\tau_i), \qquad t_i < \tau_i < t_{i+1}, \qquad (7.77)$$

with $F_j(\tau)$ a simple integral of the kernel over the range t_j to t_{j+1}. A problem arises in this procedure as to the specification of the value of τ_i to be chosen within the interval (t_i, t_{i+1}). In the cases tested excellent results were obtained when τ_i was chosen as the geometric mean, i.e., when we set

$$\log \tau_i = \tfrac{1}{2}(\log t_i + \log t_{i+1}). \qquad (7.78)$$

7.3 Summary

The two-level source function has been exhaustively studied here, not because it is regarded as an adequate representation for an actual transition in an actual atom but because of the light it throws on the basic physical problem which we are seeking to understand. There is the additional point, however, that we shall find that the multilevel atom may be expressed in a formalism identical to that treated in the two-level case, so that the numerical techniques devised for this limited problem can be directly taken over in more general problems.

Little apology is needed, in any case, for a theoretical development that so naturally predicts the self-reversed emission cores observed in H and K, that can account for the self-reversed Lyman α and β profiles, along with the self-reversed profiles of strong solar prominence lines, that concludes naturally that certain chromospheric lines must be self-reversed whereas others equally strong will be observed simply in absorption. Certainly this does not constitute the whole story—at least it is a good beginning.

REFERENCES

AVRETT, E. H., 1965, "Solutions of the Two-Level Line Transfer Problem with Complete Distribution," *Second Harvard–Smithsonian Conference on Stellar Atmospheres*, p. 101.

AVRETT, E. H., and D. G. HUMMER, 1965, "Non-Coherent Scattering; II, Line Formation with a Frequency Independent Source Function," *Mon. Not. Roy. Astron. Soc. 130*, 295.

BAINBRIDGE, JANET, and J. T. JEFFERIES, 1965, "A Direct Inversion of the Integral Equation of Transfer," *Final Report, AFSWC Contract No. AF 29 (601)-6013*, Section IId.

CHANDRASEKHAR, S., 1950, *Radiative Transfer*. Oxford: Clarendon Press.

FEAUTRIER, P., 1964, "Sur la résolution numérique de l'équation de transfert," *Comptes Rendus 258*, 3189.

FINN, G. D., 1966, "Comments on Multilevel Atom Radiation Problems," *Proceedings, Second Symposium on Interdisciplinary Aspects of Radiative Transfer* (in press).

HUMMER, D. G., 1965a, "Discrete Ordinate Analysis of Complete Redistribution with Continuous Absorption," *Final Report, AFSWC Contract No. AF 29 (601)-6013*, Section IIb.

HUMMER, D. G., 1965b, "General Noncoherence by Discrete Ordinate Method-Computational Approach," *Final Report, AFSWC Contract No. AF 29 (601)-6013*, Section IIc.

HUMMER, D. G., and G. B. RYBICKI, 1967, "Computational Methods for Line Transfer Problems," *Methods in Computational Physics*, Vol. 7, *Astrophysics*. New York: Academic Press, p. 53.

JEFFERIES, J. T., 1953, "Emission of Radiation from Model Hydrogen Chromospheres," *Aust. J. Phys. 6*, 22.

JEFFERIES, J. T., 1956, "The Hα Emission of Prominences," *Mon. Not. R. Astron. Soc. 115*, 617.

JEFFERIES, J. T., 1960, "Source Function in a Non-Equilibrium Atmosphere; VII, The Interlocking Problem," *Astrophys. J. 132*, 775.

JEFFERIES, J. T., and R. N. THOMAS, 1958, "Source Function in a Non-Equilibrium Atmosphere; II, Depth Dependence of Source Function for Resonance and Strong Subordinate Lines," *Astrophys. J. 127*, 667.

JEFFERIES, J. T., and R. N. THOMAS, 1959, "Source Function in a Non-Equilibrium Atmosphere; III, The Influence of a Chromosphere," *Astrophys. J. 129*, 401.

JEFFERIES, J. T., and R. N. THOMAS, "Source Function in a Non-Equilibrium Atmosphere; V, Character of the Self-Reversed Emission Cores of Ca+ H and K," *Astrophys. J. 131*, 695.

JEFFERIES, J. T., and O. R. WHITE, 1960, "Source Function in a Non-Equilibrium Atmosphere; VI, The Frequency Dependence of the Source Function for Resonance Lines, *Astrophys. J.* *132*, 767.

MIYAMOTO, S., 1954, "Residual Intensity and Contour of the Solar K-line II." *Publ. Astron. Soc. Japan 6*, 196.

RYBICKI, G. B., and P. D. USHER, 1966, "The Generalized Riccati Transformation as a Simple Alternative to Invariant Imbedding," *Astrophys. J. 146*, 871.

STROM, S. E., and W. KALKOFEN, 1966, "The Effect of Departures from LTE on the Stellar Continuum Fluxes in the Spectral-Type Range B5-AO," *Astrophys. J. 144*, 76.

SUEMOTO, Z., 1963, "Turbulence in the Chromosphere," *Publ. Astron. Soc. Japan 15*, 531.

THOMAS, R. N., 1957, Source Function in a Non-Equilibrium Atmosphere; I, "The Resonance Lines," *Astrophys. J. 125*, 260.

THOMAS, R. N., 1960, Source Function in a Non-Equilibrium Atmosphere; IV, "Evaluation and Application of the Net Radiative Bracket," *Astrophys. J. 131*, 429.

THOMAS, R. N. and J. B. ZIRKER, 1961*a*, "The Source Function in a Non-Equilibrium Atmosphere; VIII, Solution for a Two-Level Atom in a Finite Atmosphere," *Astrophys. J. 134*, 733.

THOMAS, R. N., and J. B. ZIRKER, 1961*b*, "Departures from the Saha Equation for Ionized Helium; II, Atmospheric Thicknesses too Small to Satisfy Detailed Balance in the Resonance Lines," *Astrophys. J. 134*, 740.

WICK, G. C., 1943, "Über ebene Diffusionsprobleme," *Z. Physik 121*, 702.

WILSON, O. C., 1963, "A Probable Correlation Between Chromospheric Activity and Age in Main-Sequence Stars," *Astrophys. J. 138*, 832.

WILSON, O. C., and M. K. VAINU BAPPU, 1957, "H and K Emission in Late-Type Stars: Dependence of Line Width on Luminosity and Related Topics," *Astrophys. J. 125*, 661.

WILSON, O. C., and ANDREW SKUMANICH, 1964, "Dependence of Chromospheric Activity Upon Age in Main-Sequence Stars: Additional Evidence," *Astrophys. J. 140*, 1401.

8

Theory of the Line Source Function: II. The Multilevel Atom

Although the two-level atom (and its simple generalization to include a continuum) allowed us to reach some important physical conclusions on the theoretical distribution of the line source function with depth, we could not be satisfied that important effects were not being overlooked or obscured by adopting this simplified model. The generalization to a multilevel system, however desirable, leads to some fundamental problems—as a moment's thought will reveal. Particularly, we notice that no longer may we think in terms of the transfer of radiation in a single line. The generalization from coherent to non-coherent scattering made necessary the consideration of the simultaneous transfer of photons of all frequencies in the line, along with the parallel recognition that the photons belonged to the whole line and no longer just to a particular frequency. Correspondingly, when we generalize our discussion to a multilevel atom, we should be prepared to extend our formalism to take account of the fact that the photons no longer pertain to a particular line but in a real sense belong to the radiation fields in the totality of transitions emitted by the atom. Such "interlocking" through which photons in a given spectral region (line or continuum) are converted back and forth into photons in another region is fundamental to the multilevel problem, though it has not properly been incorporated into the formalism as yet.

Nor does the extension cease there; in an atmosphere consisting of a variety of atomic species, the radiation frequencies peculiar to each will also interlock with one another, producing a coupling of the excitation of hydrogen, say, with that of sodium. The full generalization, based on the recognition that photons are simply a form of energy which may excite an atom other than that in which it had its origin, lies beyond the scope of our discussion—except in the trivial case of thermodynamic equilibrium. We shall put aside the general problem for the present and concentrate here on a situation in which we are concerned with the interaction of photons formed in a single species of atom; this, in any event, is complicated enough.

Some indication of an approximate treatment, applicable equally to the more general case, may be found in the possibility of distinguishing levels of formation for different spectral regions, depending on the opacity in each region. Thus, as we have seen in Chapter 7, we may extend the two-level situation to a simple multilevel one to the extent that the transfer in the spectral line of interest is essentially uncoupled from that in the other interlocking regions. This approximation will only be justified if the corresponding absorption coefficients are widely different. For example, if we were content to discuss the Lα transfer in terms of a model atom of two bound states and a continuum, we may perhaps be justified in a first approximation in uncoupling the radiation transfer problems in the Lyman and Balmer continua on the one hand, from that in the Lyman α line on the other. We may be able to justify this from a demonstration that the opacities in these two continua are very small compared to that in the line, but we must be prepared to demonstrate essentially that over the whole thermalization length of Lα the continuum opacities are small. Certainly we shall not then have *proved* that this uncoupling will be legitimate, although at a first glance it would seem to be so. Correspondingly, we may, perhaps, uncouple the continuum transfer problems from those in Lα by assuming the line to be in detailed balance in regions where the continuum is formed. The fact remains that we shall have to develop a formalism to test such an hypothesis before we can be quite sure it is legitimate.

No such procedure is possible, even as a first approximation, when we wish to discuss the simultaneous transfer of lines, or free–bound continua, which are formed in a common region of the gas. Thus we could not divorce the transfer of Lyman α from that of Lyman β, nor that of the Ca II H and K lines from one another or from that of the infrared triplet with which they combine. In these cases we face a problem quite outside the formalism introduced in Chapter 7—and one whose solution is far from our present understanding. In this chapter we shall consider some aspects of the multilevel problem and the degree, however limited, to which it is understood. Accordingly, in the following section we shall discuss the formulation of the general problem, and of some special cases after which, in Section 8.2, we shall consider some of the solutions obtained for simplified models. As will become clear, a central question of profound importance in the analysis of line spectra lies in the degree to which the line source functions in two lines of a common multiplet share a common depth variation. In Section 8.3 this subject will be discussed and some validity criteria established for the conditions under which this will be so.

8.1 Formulation of the Multilevel Transfer Problem

To the extent that we may suppose redistribution to be complete, the source function in a line formed between an upper level (u) and a lower level (ℓ) can be written, see Equation (3.33),

$$S_l = \frac{2h\nu^3}{c^2} \left[\frac{g_u}{g_\ell} \frac{n_\ell}{n_u} - 1 \right]^{-1} \tag{8.1}$$

If we substitute for the population ratio the formal expression derived for the solution of the equations of statistical equilibrium, the form (8.1) reduces to the equation (see Equation 6.7),

$$S_l = \frac{2h\nu^3}{c^2} \frac{(R_{\ell u} + C_{\ell u} + \Sigma_\ell)}{\left[(R_{u\ell} + C_{u\ell} + \Sigma_u) \dfrac{g_u}{g_\ell} - (R_{\ell u} + C_{\ell u} + \Sigma_\ell) \right]}, \tag{8.2}$$

where

$$\Sigma_\ell = \sum_{j \neq u} P_{\ell j} q_{ju,\ell} \tag{8.3}$$

and

$$\Sigma_u = \sum_{j \neq \ell} P_{uj} q_{j\ell,u}. \tag{8.4}$$

Equation (8.2) may, in turn, readily be reduced to the more compact and familiar form

$$S_l = \frac{\int J_\nu \phi_\nu \, d\nu + \varepsilon B_\nu(T_e) + \eta B_\nu(T^*)}{1 + \varepsilon + \eta} \tag{8.5}$$

when we define

$$\varepsilon = \frac{C_{a\ell}[1 - \exp{(-E_{a\ell}/kT_e)}]}{A_{a\ell}}, \tag{8.6}$$

$$\eta = \frac{\Sigma_a \left[1 - \dfrac{g_\ell}{g_a} \dfrac{\Sigma_\ell}{\Sigma_a}\right]}{A_{a\ell}}, \tag{8.7}$$

and

$$B_\nu(T^*) = \frac{2h\nu^3}{c^2} \left[\frac{g_a}{g_\ell} \frac{\Sigma_a}{\Sigma_\ell} - 1\right]^{-1} \tag{8.8}$$

or, equivalently,

$$\frac{g_a}{g_\ell} \frac{\Sigma_a}{\Sigma_\ell} = \exp\left[\frac{-E_{a\ell}}{kT^*}\right].$$

It is easy to see from the definitions of the quantities Σ that the radiation intensity *in the line formed between the levels ℓ and a* does not enter into the terms η or $B_\nu(T^*)$; nor, of course, does it appear in the term $\varepsilon B_\nu(T_e)$. Hence, the mean intensity J_ν enters linearly in the expression (8.5) for S_l so that we may write, formally,

$$S_l = \varpi_0 \int J_\nu \phi_\nu \, d\nu + \lambda b, \tag{8.9}$$

where $\lambda = 1 - \varpi_0$. The equation of transfer then takes the form

$$\mu \frac{dI_\nu}{d\tau_\nu} = I_\nu - \varpi_0 \int J_\nu \phi_\nu \, d\nu - \lambda b. \tag{8.10}$$

This is precisely the same form as treated in the two-level case and its solution may be obtained by the methods discussed in the preceding chapter once we know the depth variation of the quantities λ and b.

While λ and b in Equation (8.9) are explicitly independent of the mean intensity in the line, they do depend on the intensity of each other line formed by the atom, and on each collision rate. Hence, there is an implicit dependence of λ and b on the intensity of the line of interest, or, to state it in another way, we must solve simultaneously the entire set of Equations (8.10) obtained by permuting the indices ℓ and a through all states of the atom between which lines can form. It can be seen at once that the resulting system is highly nonlinear and a solution is probably only to be found iteratively.

Some quite general remarks on the solution of the system (8.10) are perhaps not out of place. We may first recall that a basic difficulty arose in the solution of the two-level transfer problem in the physically interesting case when the scattering parameter λ was small. This was itself only a reflection of the fact that a photon on absorption preferentially returns to the radiation field so that, although the term λB controlled the rate of production of new photons, it was itself small compared to the diffusion term. Hence, in a numerical solution a small error in the estimate of this term can introduce a fictitious source for photons, with disastrous results to the solution. As an extreme case, let us compare, for example, the attempt by Athay and Thomas (1956), to solve the differential equation by adopting the approximation

$$\bar{J} \equiv \int_0^\infty J_\nu \phi_\nu \, d\nu = W J_0 \tag{8.11}$$

with $W \neq 1$. This, as is easily shown, is equivalent to replacing the parameter λ by $1 - W + W\lambda$, and unless W is taken strictly as unity, this approximation can produce results in error by many orders of magnitude if λ is small.

In the multilevel problem this difficulty will be enhanced through the possibility that photons can be interchanged among different spectral lines without necessarily being destroyed. Thus the term λb, which in the two-level problem represents the production and destruction of photons in the (single) line, now represents additionally their transfer into other lines, while corresponding terms in the other transfer equations contain components representing the contribution of photons back into the original line. It is clear that this interchange of a photon's identity will produce significant cancellations between the transfer equations, and it is desirable—perhaps essential—to remove this analytically before attempting to solve the system.

These remarks again point to the desirability of a reformulation of the transfer problem to give recognition to the physical fact that the photons travel as a "pool" rather than in individual lines. In this manner we may hope at least to remove the "physical cancellation" discussed in the preceding paragraph. If numerical cancellations then cause problems they should be no more severe than in the two-level case. We shall return to this question later in this section; meanwhile we consider a further aspect of the standard formulation (8.10).

To the extent that we may neglect stimulated emissions, the quantities ε, η, $B(T_e)$, $B(T^*)$ take the forms

$$\varepsilon = \frac{C_{u\ell}}{A_{u\ell}}$$

$$\eta = \frac{\Sigma_u}{A_{u\ell}}$$

$$B_\nu(T) = \frac{2h\nu^3}{c^2}\, e^{-h\nu/kT} \qquad (8.12)$$

$$B_\nu(T^*) = \frac{2h\nu^3}{c^2}\, \frac{g_\ell \Sigma_\ell}{g_u \Sigma_u}.$$

For a series of lines having a common lower level, ℓ, Σ_u is independent of the associated intensities which enter linearly through the terms $R_{\ell j}$ in the quantity Σ_ℓ. Furthermore, the probabilities $q_{j\ell,u}$, $q_{ju,\ell}$ are readily seen to be independent of the $R_{\ell j}$ terms, so that the corresponding line source functions will be linear in these intensity integrals.

Thus it follows at once from Equation (8.5) that the source function $S_l(\ell, u)$ for the line originating between the levels ℓ and u can be expressed formally as

$$S_l(\ell, u) = \sum_{j > \ell} [\varpi_0(u, \ell, j)\bar{J}(\ell, j)] + \beta(u, \ell), \qquad (8.13)$$

where

$$\varpi_0(u, \ell, j) = \left(\frac{\nu_{u\ell}}{\nu_{j\ell}}\right)^3 \frac{g_j}{g_u} \frac{A_{j\ell}}{A_{u\ell}} \frac{q_{ju,\ell}}{1 + \varepsilon + \eta} \qquad (8.14)$$

and

$$\beta(u, \ell) = \frac{2h\nu_{u\ell}^3}{c^2} \frac{g_\ell}{g_u} \frac{1}{A_{u\ell}} \frac{1}{(1 + \varepsilon + \eta)} \left\{ \sum_{\text{all } j} C_{\ell j} q_{ju,\ell} + \sum_{j < \ell} A_{\ell j} q_{ju,\ell} \right\}. \qquad (8.15)$$

This linear system applies only to the lines sharing the lower level ℓ; all other radiation intensities are still explicitly present in the quantity β. However, the representation is frequently useful in allowing a simultaneous solution for all of the transfer equations in a series of spectral lines.

The remaining radiation intensities present in the term β, or more generally in the term λb, can be retained as intensities to be computed step by step in an iterative procedure, or may be introduced implicitly through the net radiative rates discussed in Chapter 6. These in turn may be expressed in terms of the associated source functions through Equation (8.9) as follows:

$$Z_{ij} = \left\{ 1 - \frac{\int J_\nu \phi_\nu \, d\nu}{S_{ij}} \right\}$$

$$= \left[\frac{\lambda(b - S)}{\varpi_0 S} \right]_{ij}, \tag{8.16}$$

or

$$Y_{ij} = \frac{g_i}{g_j} \left[\frac{(S - \int J_\nu \phi_\nu \, d\nu)}{(S + 2h\nu^3/c^2)} \right]_{ij}$$

$$= \frac{g_i}{g_j} \left[\frac{\lambda(b - S)}{\varpi_0(S + 2h\nu^3/c^2)} \right]_{ij}, \tag{8.17}$$

where, for definiteness, we suppose $i > j$. The departures from detailed balance are then to be introduced through either of the replacements

$$R_{ij} = A_{ij} Z_{ij},$$
$$R_{ji} = 0, \tag{8.18a}$$

or

$$R_{ij} = 0,$$
$$R_{ji} = -A_{ij} Y_{ij}. \tag{8.18b}$$

Equation (8.13) suggests a possible reformulation when written in the matrix form obtained when we allow α to range over its possible values,

$$\mathbf{S} = \varpi_0 \bar{\mathbf{J}} + (\mathbf{1} - \varpi_0)\mathbf{b}. \tag{8.19}$$

The vector $\mathbf{b}$ is, of course, only formally defined by this equation; its components may be obtained through the defining equations (8.14), (8.15), but this is tedious in practice.   A simpler procedure follows from the recognition that at large optical depths the net radiative brackets in the line series will tend to zero—at least for an isothermal atmosphere. In accordance with Equations (8.18a and b), the source functions at large depths will formally be given by Equations (8.2) with $R_{\alpha\ell}$ and $R_{\ell\alpha}$ each set to zero.   Hence, at large depths,

$$S_l(\alpha, \ell) \to \frac{2h\nu^3}{c^2} \frac{g_\ell}{g_\alpha} \left(\frac{\sum_j C_{\ell j} q_{j\alpha,\ell}^* + \sum_{j < \ell} A_{\ell j} q_{j\alpha,\ell}^*}{C_{\alpha\ell} + \sum_{j \neq \ell} P_{\alpha j} q_{j\ell,\alpha}^*} \right), \tag{8.20}$$

where the asterisks denote that the probabilities are to be evaluated for the formal detailed balance conditions $R_{j\ell} = 0$.   If we may neglect radiative transfer in the αj lines—so that the terms $P_{\alpha j}$ are depth-independent—the component $b(\alpha, \ell)$ is therefore given by the right-hand side of the expression (8.20).

If collisions constitute the only significant transition mechanism other than radiative processes in the (j, ℓ) series of lines, then deep enough in an isothermal atmosphere $\bar{\mathbf{J}}$ and $\mathbf{S}$ of Equation (8.19) must approach the vector $\mathbf{W}$ defined by the relevant Wien functions. Hence, it is clear that the vector $\mathbf{b}$ must, in that case, be everywhere equal to $\mathbf{W}$ in an isothermal gas.

Each of the terms in the vector $\boldsymbol{\varpi}_0\bar{\mathbf{J}}$ represents a way in which photons can be transferred among the different lines of the series. For example, the term $\boldsymbol{\varpi}_0(3, 1, j)$ represents the probability that a photon absorbed in the $(j, 1)$ line is re-emitted in the $(3, 1)$ line. Following the lines of an argument by Kalkofen (1965) and Rybicki (unpublished) we may transform the equation to obtain

$$(\boldsymbol{\varpi}_0)^{-1}\mathbf{S} = \bar{\mathbf{J}} + (\boldsymbol{\varpi}_0^{-1} - \mathbf{1})\mathbf{b} \tag{8.21}$$

and now the contribution to the photon field by scattering in each line has been isolated. It would appear that the components of the vector $\mathbf{S}' \equiv \boldsymbol{\varpi}_0^{-1}\mathbf{S}$ are the photon "pools" which we have suggested as being the physically more meaningful quantities than the individual source functions. In Equation (8.21) we may identify the first term on the right-hand side as representing the contribution of scattering in a particular line to the associated net source function $\mathbf{S}'$, while the second term represents the contribution of processes other than those occurring in lines of the ℓ–j series.

Making use of the representation (2.30) of J in terms of S, Equation (8.21) may be written in the form of an integral equation for S'. For example, in the three-level case in which only collisions connect the 2 and 3 states directly, we find

$$S_1'(\tau_1) = \int_0^{T_1} (\varpi_{11}S_2' + \varpi_{12}S_2')K(|t_1 - \tau_1|)\,dt_1 + (\varpi_{22}' - 1)B_1 - \varpi_{12}'B_2,$$

$$\tag{8.22}$$

$$S_2'(\tau_2) = \int_0^{T_2} (\varpi_{22}S_2' + \varpi_{21}S_1')K(|t_2 - \tau_2|)\,dt_2 + (\varpi_{11}' - 1)B_2 - \varpi_{21}'B_1,$$

$$\tag{8.23}$$

where the subscripts 1 and 2 refer to the parameters for the (2, 1) and

(3, 1) lines respectively, the B are the Wien functions.   The remaining
parameters are defined through the equations:

$$\varpi'_{ij} = \varpi_{ij}/D \qquad (8.24)$$

and

$$D = (\varpi_{11}\varpi_{22} - \varpi_{12}\varpi_{21}). \qquad (8.25)$$

No attempt has so far been made to apply this formulation to the
coupled transfer equations, beyond the very simple preliminary argument due to Kalkofen (1965); however, the formulation may lead to
substantial simplification in the numerical work.

8.2 Solutions of the Multilevel Problem

An early solution for a simple three-level case of coupled transfer was
given in a paper by Jefferies (1960).   The procedure adopted, which was
relatively crude, was to represent the source functions in the (2, 1) and
(3, 1) lines by the linear form (8.13) and to solve the two simultaneous
differential equations of the Eddington approximation using a one-
point quadrature for the frequency integration.

The most significant, and highly important, result obtained was that
the line source functions in the two lines showed a common depth
variation over a large part of the atmosphere.   The computations were
done for parameters representative of the hydrogen Lα and Lβ lines,
but an obvious application of the theory to close lying multiplet lines,
like Na D, would predict their source functions to be *equal* at a given
physical depth over a large part of the atmosphere.   As we shall see in
Section 8.3, this result (which was later confirmed observationally by
Waddell) represents a synthesis of very great power and indeed opens
up the possibility of an analysis of solar-line profile observations from
a standpoint more general than LTE.

More powerful mathematical techniques of the type discussed briefly
in Chapter 7 have recently been applied to an archetype problem in the
excitation of hydrogen.   This work was done mainly with the objective
of testing different procedures for the solution of the multilevel problem; since they represent the first efforts in what will certainly be a
rapidly developing field, it is worth reviewing them in some detail.

Johnson and Klinglesmith (1965) studied the excitation of atoms
having three bound states corresponding to the lowest hydrogen levels,
plus a continuum at 13.6 ev, in a plane parallel atmosphere isothermal

at 10^4 °K in which the total number density of particles was 10^{12} cm^{-3} throughout. Collisional and radiative transition rates appropriate to hydrogen were adopted and other parameters were fixed as necessary —see Johnson and Klinglesmith's paper for details. The authors adopted an integral equation formulation for computing the relevant source functions; in solving for a given line the unknown radiative transition rates in the other lines were represented in terms of their net radiative brackets Z_{ij}. The procedure used, therefore, was to assume an initial set of values of Z_{ij} as a function of depth, use equations similar to (8.5) to (8.8) to compute, for a given line, the quantities ϖ_0 and b of Equation (8.9) as functions of depth, and finally to solve the integral equation using Avrett's method to determine S_l and so, via Equation (8.16), new values for the net radiative bracket at each depth for the given line. This procedure was then repeated for the next transition and, after application to all transitions, the process was recycled until convergence was reached; in fact, the solutions appeared to converge satisfactorily.

A second computation by Kalkofen and Avrett (1965) attempted a solution to the same problem in a similar fashion except that the intensities in the interlocking lines were carried specifically, instead of being represented as net radiative brackets as in Johnson and Klinglesmith's study. The convergence properties of Kalkofen and Avrett's method do not seem satisfactory, especially near the surface of the gas —these authors have discussed the physical origin of the difficulty and seem to have correctly isolated it as originating in the fact that the coupling probability for the Lα, Lβ photon interchange is strong. As a consequence, one is simply iterating back and forth between the two almost identical equations for the Lα and Lβ source functions

$$\frac{S_\alpha}{B_\alpha} \simeq \frac{S_\beta}{B_\beta} + \delta_1, \qquad \frac{S_\beta}{B_\beta} \simeq \frac{S_\alpha}{B_\alpha} + \delta_2, \qquad (8.26)$$

with δ_1 and δ_2 representing the small contributions of the collisions in giving fresh photons in the two lines. The convergence is correspondingly slow. In the net radiative bracket formulation the "condition" of the simultaneous system which determines S_α and S_β seems to be improved.

The third study along these lines was by Cuny (1964, 1965) who again used a net radiative bracket formulation and solved the differential equations of transfer using Feautrier's procedure. She again had no convergence difficulties, reaching a satisfactory result within 10 iterations.

The principal outcome of these initial studies was to bear out the earlier conclusion that the Lα and Lβ source functions share an essentially common depth variation over much of the atmosphere—or equivalently that the ratio b_2/b_3 of the "departure coefficients" is constant with depth to a first approximation. The position is still not

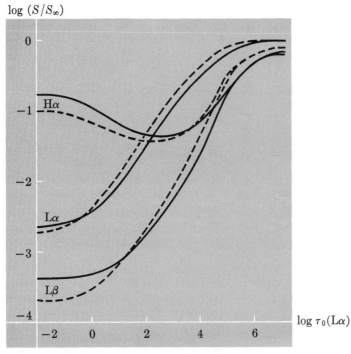

Figure 8.1. Comparison of the normalized source functions for Lα, Lβ, and Hα computed by Johnson and Klinglesmith (full lines) and those of Cuny (broken lines) for the archetype problem in which the radiation-transfer problem is solved in all lines and continua of the model atom.

completely satisfactory, however, as substantial differences in detail exist between the solutions, as is illustrated in the comparison shown in Figure 8.1 between the results of Cuny, shown as a broken line, and those of Johnson and Klinglesmith for the case in which the transfer equations were solved for all the lines and continua emitted by the model atom. In a parallel study, Cuny computed the simultaneous transfer in Lα, Lβ, and Hα for the artificial case in which the continuum source functions were taken equal to those in a blackbody at the electron temperature (10^4 °K).   Her results are reproduced in Figure 8.2, and show the interesting phenomenon that $S(L\alpha)$ rises above the continuum at great depths.   The same effect was found by Kalkofen and Avrett in their solutions of the complete set of transfer equations (line *plus* continuum); it does not show up in the corresponding results

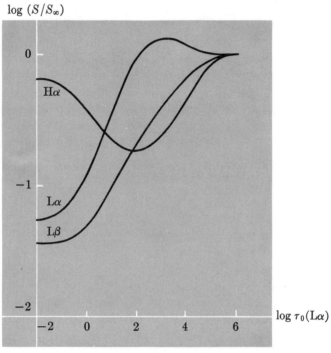

Figure 8.2.   The normalized source functions for Lα, Lβ, and Hα computed by Cuny for the artificial case when the continua are in LTE.

shown in Figure 8.1, however, so that perhaps Kalkofen and Avrett's results are suspect—and their convergence difficulties make this probable—and the "emission peak" in $S(L\alpha)$ arises from the artificial nature of the problem represented in Figure 8.2.

This is a rapidly developing field and the initial results will certainly soon be superseded; it is perhaps too early to comment in detail on the results.   However, the rough equality of the depth dependence of the source functions in the Lα, Lβ multiplet is very significant.

8.3 Source-Function Equality in Multiplets

It is clear that a fundamental question in the multilevel transfer problem lies in clarifying the relationship between the individual line source functions at each depth in the atmosphere. To the extent that some general relationship may be established, its value in the practical problem of line profile analysis is inestimable since it immediately provides a physical relationship which must be reflected in the observed profiles. This in turn severely restricts the range of physical parameters consistent with the production of the observed radiation. Indeed, we shall see in Chapter 9 that without such a relationship the analysis of a line spectrum cannot in general be carried out to yield a unique physical structure for the radiating atmosphere.

If we were to assume LTE, we would automatically assume such a relationship between the source functions of the lines formed in the atmosphere since they would then be taken to be Planckian at the local temperature. An alternative, applicable to the more general case when only *statistical* equilibrium is assumed, is indicated in the conclusion that the source functions in lines which share a common lower level seem to share also a common depth-dependence. If the upper states of such lines are close together and are strongly coupled, we can often conclude that the corresponding source functions will be *equal at a given depth* over much of the gas*—such would seem to be the case for the Na *D* lines, for example.

Some physical insight into this question of source-function equality may be obtained from a consideration of a simple three-level atom in which the upper two states, denoted 2 and 3, lie close together and are coupled via collisions alone. First, it is clear that if C_{23} and C_{32} are small enough the photons in the two lines (2, 1) and (3, 1) must propagate independently through the gas, and a two-level formulation may be used for each line to compute the source functions. It follows from our earlier discussion that these will saturate in the thermalization lengths

$$\tau_\alpha^* \simeq \frac{A_{21}}{C_{21}}, \qquad \tau_\beta^* \simeq \frac{A_{31}}{C_{31}} \tag{8.27}$$

* We shall not *always* expect this simple relationship, however. For example the *H* and *K* lines couple radiatively, and with different strengths, to the infrared triplet lines, and this should produce a departure from equality of the *H* and *K* source functions—though the degree to which they will differ depends on the collisional coupling between the fine structure levels and on the strength of the infrared transitions.

provided that the absorption coefficients are effectively gaussian and that each optical depth is measured at the corresponding line center. From first principles it is clear that this case will apply if and only if the inequalities

$$C_{21} \gg C_{23}, \qquad C_{31} \gg C_{32} \qquad (8.28)$$

are separately satisfied, since then a photon in either line will normally be destroyed through a collision to the ground state before having its energy converted into a photon in the other line. The corresponding depth variation of the source functions in this *uncoupled* case is represented schematically in Figure 8.3.

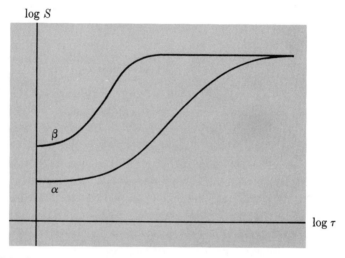

Figure 8.3. *Schematic* representation of the depth dependence of the normalized line source functions S_α and S_β in the *uncoupled* case; the abscissa is a common depth scale.

If *either* of the inequalities (8.28) is violated, photons may transfer back or forth between the two lines before being destroyed by collisions. The distinction between the two lines now loses some force and to an extent they will be propagated in common; their source functions, therefore, will share a common depth variation below a certain optical depth—in our simple example they would be essentially *equal* at a given depth. This situation is shown schematically in Figure 8.4.

We may simply estimate the depth at which the two source functions begin to separate. From the discussion of the two-level problem we see that an α photon created at an optical depth τ_α will escape the atmosphere as an α photon—i.e., it will neither be destroyed nor converted to a β photon—provided that τ_α is less than a critical depth $\tau_\alpha^\dagger$ such that

$$\tau_\alpha < \tau_\alpha^\dagger = \left[\frac{C_{21} + C_{23}}{A_{21} + C_{21} + C_{23}}\right]^{-1}. \tag{8.29}$$

Correspondingly, for a β photon created at τ_β to escape before conversion or destruction, we require

$$\tau_\beta < \tau_\beta^\dagger = \left[\frac{C_{31} + C_{32}}{A_{31} + C_{31} + C_{32}}\right]^{-1}. \tag{8.30}$$

These optical lengths may be referred to as the "conversion lengths."

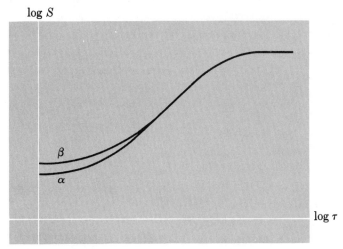

Figure 8.4. *Schematic* representation of the depth dependence of the normalized line source functions S_α and S_β in a *coupled* case ; the abscissa is a common depth scale.

The photons will propagate independently above the depth corresponding to the smaller of $\tau_\alpha^\dagger$, $\tau_\beta^\dagger$.

In more general circumstances than those envisaged in our simple model, it may happen that the conversion distance for a β photon is much less than for an α photon;* correspondingly we may discuss the transfer in the α line as if the emission and absorption of β photons balanced in detail. This can be a useful approximation, as shown by Jefferies (1960); its validity in the hydrogen transfer problem has been further established by the detailed calculations referenced above.

* This can happen, for example, in hydrogen in a dilute radiation field, see Jefferies (1960).

In an extreme case of strong coupling when $C_{32} > A_{31}$ or C_{31}, $C_{23} > A_{21}$ or C_{21}, the *relative* populations of the upper states is as in LTE, that is

$$\frac{n_3}{n_2} \simeq \frac{C_{23}}{C_{32}} = \frac{g_3}{g_2} \exp\left(-E_{32}/kT_e\right); \qquad (8.31)$$

this is the case of "complete interlocking" between spectral lines and in many ways is closely akin to "complete redistribution" in a single spectral line.

With these points in mind we may briefly review the question of the source function equality in multiplets raised separately by Waddell, Athay, and Avrett. From his observations of the solar D lines, Waddell (1962) was able to demonstrate—in a manner discussed in Chapter 9—that they could be interpreted in terms of the hypothesis that, at a given depth in the gas, $S_l(D_1) = S_l(D_2)$. Waddell was convinced that his observations established this equality out to an optical depth of at least 0.3 in the center of the stronger (D_2) line. It is obvious that this result is obtained *if* the inequalities $C_{32} > A_{31}$ and $C_{23} > A_{21}$ apply*—Waddell (1963) noted this but also, on the basis of a simplified transfer equation, established that the result applies *only if* these inequalities hold. Since for the D lines $A_{21} = A_{31} = 6 \times 10^7$ sec^{-1}, it follows at once that this condition requires an electron collision cross section Q_{23} of the order 10^4 to $10^5 \pi a_0^2$. Waddell recognized this difficulty, but he found the result inescapable if one required source-function equality out to essentially *zero* optical depth. Waddell's conclusion is unquestionably correct; indeed, it is obvious from first principles since it merely states that the photons must travel together right out to the surface, and this is only possible if the coupling between them is "complete" in the sense introduced above.

Athay (1964) has questioned Waddell's conclusions. He discussed the requirement for source-function equality in terms of a three-level atom with a continuum. However, nothing is lost to the physics, and much is gained in clarity, if we restrict discussion to the algebraically simpler problem of three bound levels with equal statistical weights for which the ratio of the source functions in the (1, 2) and (1, 3) lines is

$$\frac{S(1, 2)}{S(1, 3)} = \frac{n_2}{n_3} = \frac{P_{12}(C_{32} + P_{31}) + P_{13}C_{32}}{P_{13}(C_{23} + P_{21}) + P_{12}C_{23}}, \qquad (8.32)$$

---

* The states $3S$, $3P_{1/2}$, $3P_{3/2}$ are, for convenience, denoted 1, 2, 3 respectively; D_2 is then the (1, 3) and D_1 the (1, 2) line.

and with Athay we suppose $C_{21} \ll C_{23}$; $C_{31} \ll C_{32}$. In discussing this equation, Athay introduced the net radiative brackets—see Section 6.3.5—in the two lines to obtain

$$\frac{S(1,\, 2)}{S(1,\, 3)} = \frac{C_{12}(C_{32} + C_{31} + A_{31}Z_{31}) + C_{13}C_{32}}{C_{13}(C_{23} + C_{21} + A_{21}Z_{21}) + C_{12}C_{23}}, \tag{8.33}$$

and he then stated that the *sufficient* condition for equality of the source functions is that $A_{31}Z_{31} \ll C_{32}$ and $A_{21}Z_{21} \ll C_{23}$. In fact, he combined these into the single requirement

$$(A_{21}Z_{21} + A_{31}Z_{31}) \ll (C_{32} + C_{23}), \tag{8.34}$$

which is to be compared with Waddell's corresponding requirement

$$(A_{31} + A_{21}) \ll (C_{32} + C_{23}). \tag{8.35}$$

Athay then stated that in many cases the quantities Z are small near the surface of the gas so that his requirement (8.34) is less restrictive than Waddell's.

Athay's reformulation *by itself* cannot lead to different results than Waddell's since it is only an algebraic rearrangement, and since Waddell's is clearly the correct result in terms of the requirement for equality *out to the surface*, the source of Athay's conclusion must lie in his assertion that the parameters Z remain small when C_{23} and C_{32} become large. Waddell solved the transfer equation in a first approximation, and so—since in this way he derived his requirement (8.35)—by implication, he showed that the Z are *not* in fact small near the surface. Athay has criticized Waddell's solution of the transfer equation, but as Avrett (1966) has shown in a detailed study of this question, this criticism is unjustified. Avrett's accurate solutions exhibit the same form as Waddell's near the surface. Indeed, if we recognize the important fact—cf. Avrett (1966)—that Z_{21} and Z_{31} may have opposite signs, then the fact that Athay's equation (8.33) arises simply from an algebraic rearrangement of terms in the equilibrium equation shows that the simultaneous satisfaction of the pair of inequalities

$$|A_{31}Z_{31}| \ll C_{32}, \qquad |A_{21}Z_{21}| \ll C_{23} \tag{8.36}$$

must imply the simultaneous fulfillment of

$$A_{31} \ll C_{32}, \qquad A_{21} \ll C_{23}, \tag{8.37}$$

provided that $C_{31} \ll C_{32}, C_{21} \ll C_{23}$.

The above discussion has concerned a purely theoretical problem and it is questionable to what extent Waddell was justified, on the basis of his observations, in demanding the strict equality in $S(D_1)$ and $S(D_2)$ right out to the surface.   If this requirement is relaxed, even to the extent that they be equal only for $\tau_0 \gtrsim 1$, the conditions are much less stringent (as shown by Avrett, 1966).   Indeed, his discussion brings out an important point for the analysis of multiplet lines of comparable strengths.   Avrett has considered the situation when $A_{31} = A_{21}$, $C_{31} = C_{21}$, and $C_{32} = C_{23}/2$; for two lines for which the absorption coefficient ratio $\alpha(1, 3)/\alpha(1, 2)$ is equal to 2.   In this case the line source functions in the uncoupled case do not differ greatly, though enough to make it observationally easy to distinguish the difference.   The introduction of relatively small coupling perturbs the source-function distributions in such a way as to give the line profile congruence observed by Waddell for quite small values of the ratio $\eta_{31} = C_{32}/A_{31}$.   Results from Avrett's calculations are illustrated in Figure 8.5 for the line source functions, while in Figure 8.6 the corresponding line profiles are shown.   In each case a Doppler absorption coefficient was used, the atmosphere was taken as isothermal, and the parameter $\varepsilon_{31} = C_{31}/A_{31}$ was assumed constant and equal to 10^{-4}.   According to Avrett, the maximum difference between $I_{31}(\mu)$ and $I_{21}(\mu/2)$ in Figure 8.6 is 5% in

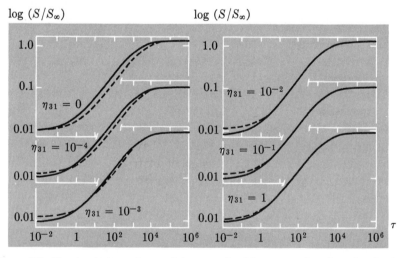

Figure 8.5. The depth dependence of the normalized line source functions S_{12} (broken line) and S_{13} (full line) for a range of values of η_{31} and for $\varepsilon_{31} = 10^{-4}$ in each case. (From Avrett, 1966, Figure 4.)

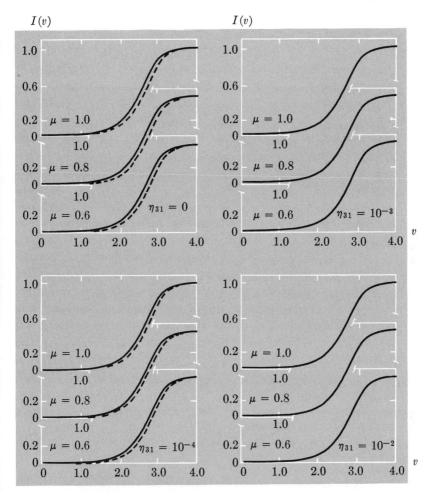

Figure 8.6. Line profiles computed from the source functions shown in Figure 8.5. The graphs show the values of $I_{31}(\mu)$ (full line) and $I_{21}(\mu/2)$ (broken lines) for $\mu = 1$, 0.8, 0.6 and for a range of values of the parameter η_{31}. (From Avrett, 1966, Figure 5.)

the case $\eta_{31} = 10^{-3}$. This effect is undoubtedly associated with the crossing of the source-function curves, which is clearly illustrated in Figure 8.5.

8.4 Summary

The study of multilevel problems is being actively pursued at a number of institutions around the world and much will certainly be added to the literature before this book is published. The value of such studies lies in the fact that they allow us theoretically to relate the behavior of multiplet lines under various atmospheric conditions. Hence, from the observed relationships between such lines we should ultimately be able to set restrictions on the physical structure of the atmosphere producing the radiation.

So far the progress in this direction has been limited. Even so, however, important syntheses are available whose power will be demonstrated in the following chapter.

R E F E R E N C E S

ATHAY, R. G., 1964, "Source Function Equality in Multiplets," *Astrophys. J.* *140*, 1579.

ATHAY, R. G., and R. N. THOMAS, 1956, "Lyman-α and the Structure of the Solar Chromosphere," *Astrophys. J. 124*, 586.

AVRETT, E. H., 1966, "Source Function Equality in Multiplets," *Astrophys. J.* *144*, 59.

CUNY, Y., 1964, "Détermination de la fonction source d'une raie spectrale formée par un atome hors de l'équilibre thermodynamique," *Comptes Rendus 258*, 3192.

CUNY, Y., 1965, "Solution of the Transfer Problem," *Proceedings, Second Harvard–Smithsonian Conference on Stellar Atmospheres*, p. 275.

JEFFERIES, J. T., 1960, "Source Function in a Non-Equilibrium Atmosphere; VII, The Interlocking Problem," *Astrophys. J. 132*, 775.

JOHNSON, H. R., and D. A. KLINGLESMITH, 1965, "On the Coupled Line-Transfer Problem for Hydrogen," *Proceedings, Second Harvard–Smithsonian Conference on Stellar Atmospheres*, p. 221.

KALKOFEN, W., 1965, "Radiative Transfer in Lines for Media in Statistical Equilibrium," *Proceedings, Second Harvard–Smithsonian Conference on Stellar Atmospheres*, p. 187.

KALKOFEN, W., and E. H. AVRETT, 1965, "Solution of the Line and Continuum Transfer Problem for a Three Level Atom," *Proceedings, Second Harvard–Smithsonian Conference on Stellar Atmospheres*, p. 249.

WADDELL, J. H., 1962, "Analysis of the Center to Limb Observations of the Sodium D Lines," *Astrophys. J. 136*, 231.

WADDELL, J. H., 1963, "Causes of Source Function Equality in Multiplet Lines," *Astrophys. J. 138*, 1147.

9

The Analysis of Spectral Line Profiles: I. General Theory and Applications to Strong Lines

The emphasis in the preceding chapters of this book has been on the problems involved in the computation of the radiation emerging from a plane parallel homogeneous gas in a statistically steady state which is not necessarily that of local thermodynamic equilibrium. While the full development of that theory remains incomplete, it nevertheless seems that recent progress has advanced us to the stage where conceptual and mathematical difficulties have been largely overcome. The theory is, of course, essential to a physical understanding of the important processes determining the line shape; however, it is not always precisely what is needed for an analysis of an observed spectrum. It is true that for this purpose we could postulate a set of models, compute the emergent intensity in each case and, to the extent that the computed spectrum did not agree with that observed, we could vary the model parameters until we found a set which did yield agreement. Within the basic restrictions imposed on the model, we could then assert that this gave a possible—though not necessarily unique— description of the physical system whose radiation was observed. Such a procedure, however, lacks a certain elegance, quite apart from its laborious nature, and in this and the subsequent chapter, we shall study the inverse analytical problem of attempting to derive the atmospheric properties directly from the observed radiation.

While some information on the constitution and structure of a stellar atmosphere is certainly contained in its spectral line and continuum emission, as with any physical system there are restrictions to the recovery of this information. These are of two kinds, a fundamental limitation dictated by the specific kind of observation made, and an observational one determined by the measurement accuracy. Before we consider the details of possible procedures for the analysis of spectroscopic data, therefore, we shall look in the following two sections at the limitations to the information which we can hope to recover first in principle and second in practice. With these understood we can more meaningfully lay down a procedure for the analysis of line spectra formed in an optically thick atmosphere.

9.1 Some Fundamental Limitations

For a plane parallel, homogeneous, semi-infinite atmosphere the emergent intensity is given by the formal solution of the transfer equation, that is,

$$I_\nu(0, \mu) = \int_0^\infty S_\nu(t_0) \exp\left[-\int_0^{t_0} \frac{dt_\nu}{\mu} \right] \frac{dt_\nu}{\mu} \qquad (9.1)$$

in which (see Equation 2.55)

$$S_\nu = \left[\frac{S_l + rS_c}{1 + r} \right]_\nu, \qquad (9.2)$$

$$\tau_\nu = \int_0^z \kappa_\nu \, dz, \qquad (9.3)$$

with κ_ν representing the sum of continuous and line absorption coefficients, κ_c and κ_l, at the corresponding frequency and where

$$r_\nu \equiv \frac{\kappa_c}{\kappa_l} \equiv \frac{r_0}{\phi'_\nu}. \qquad (9.4)$$

It is immediately evident that we can discover nothing from the emergent intensity which determines at once the usual macroscopic parameters of temperature, pressure, and composition—other than the simple fact that a certain element is present. As emphasized in Chapter 1, the spectroscopic state of the gas at a point is described by the local values of the source function S_v, and of the absorption coefficient κ_v. The task of relating these to the physical parameters involves a separate study. In the first instance we shall be concerned only with the question of the inference of the *spectroscopic* state, i.e., of the determination either of S_v and κ_v as functions of frequency and some standard optical depth, or equivalently of the corresponding determination of S_l, S_c, r_0, and ϕ_v'.

Suppose then that we were to measure the intensity $I_v(0, \mu)$, at each of n frequencies v_i and m angles μ_j, of the radiation emerging from an atmosphere which we knew to have properties consistent with those implicit in Equation (9.1). Since we wish to discuss *fundamental* limitations, let us suppose that these measurements are made with indefinitely high precision. If we measure depths in terms of the optical depth at some definite frequency (say the line center) then, from the limb-darkening observations at a given frequency v', we can, by inverting Equation (9.1), determine $S_{v'}$ at just m depths $\tau_{v'}$. Equivalently, we may determine m pieces of information on the depth variation of a combination of S_l, S_c, r_0, ϕ_v'. From the totality of observations we acquire mn data values; for a consistent description of the observations, however, we need to determine S_l, S_c, r_0, and ϕ_v' at each of m depths and (in general) to determine S_l, ϕ_v' at n frequencies, subject to the condition that $\phi_v' = 1$ at the line center. Thus we need to determine $m(2n + 1)$ unknowns and, with only mn data points, this clearly leads to no unique solution. Nor does it help in principle to go to the limiting case as m and n approach infinity.

Thus, while it is possible in principle to infer S_v at each of m monochromatic optical depths τ_v by an inversion of Equation (9.1), unless we have some auxiliary relationships between the S_v or the τ_v at different frequencies, we can proceed no further in the analysis of the line.* The implication is simply that we must seek out such relationships; indeed, as we shall see, our previous studies have given us sufficient insight to permit the necessary relationships to be obtained.

It is instructive however to see first how this difficulty has been treated in the past. Consider first the classical problem of the analysis of solar continuum limb-darkening curves for which one takes r_0 infinite so that, from Equation (9.2), $S_v \equiv S_c$ or, with the LTE assumption, $S_v = B_v(T)$. Since in normal situations T is a unique function of

---

* The situation is worse for the analysis of *stellar* spectra where limb darkening data is not obtainable.

position, we may relate values of τ_ν at different frequencies through the requirement that the same value of T must refer to the same depth. Hence, we may derive τ_ν in terms of the optical depth τ_0 at some standard frequency.   Since

$$\tau_\nu = \int_0^{\tau_0} \frac{\kappa_\nu}{\kappa_0} \, dt_0, \qquad (9.5)$$

we may, by differentiation of the inferred $\tau_\nu(\tau_0)$ relation, obtain the frequency variation of the absorption coefficient (which corresponds to ϕ'_ν in this case) as a function of depth.   Our spectroscopic analysis can take us no further; to relate τ_0 to a physical height scale we need to know not only the absorption coefficient, but the chemical composition and the atmospheric structure; however, we cannot digress to study that problem here.   We note merely that the consistent continuum analysis requires the determination of m values of S_ν—the frequency dependence is given from the LTE assumption—and $(n - 1)$ values of the ratio (κ_ν/κ_0) at each depth.   Since we have mn data values, the analysis is, in principle, possible.   The fact that in practice we can make neither m nor n arbitrarily large is associated with observational limitations discussed in the following section.

A second special case arises when we assume LTE to describe the excitation state of the gas for both the line and continuous spectrum, so that $S_l = S_c = S_\nu = B_\nu(T)$.   Now, however, a consistent analysis would require the specification of $m(n + 1)$ unknowns namely m values of T, m values of r_0, and $m(n - 1)$ values of ϕ'_ν; the *a priori* analysis of the center to limb observations of a single spectral line is therefore impossible, even with the LTE assumption, without imposing further conditions such, e.g., as the form of the absorption coefficient.

The fact that an analysis can be carried out for a given set of assumptions can mean either that the analysis was made determinate through the introduction of sufficient auxiliary conditions or that the number of parameters determined was equal to the number of observations available.   If there is redundancy to the analysis (i.e., more data available than parameters sought) we may find evidence in support of the assumptions if an analysis of all the data leads to consistent results; if this consistency is not found, however, we shall have reason to question the assumptions.   In fact, it was in precisely such circumstances that Pecker and his associates were led to question the assumption of

LTE for the analysis of certain solar photospheric spectral lines. This matter is examined in detail in Chapter 10.

If we wish to analyze an observed spectrum on a basis more general than LTE, we must overcome the fundamental limitations given above; e.g., we must find a way to specify the variation of the line source function with frequency, the way it relates to the source function in some other line, or the way ϕ'_ν varies with frequency. A fundamental step in the solution of the analytical problem was taken in the demonstration by a variety of authors, cf. Chapter 5, that S_l is essentially frequency independent—i.e., the line is formed in complete redistribution—at least over the line core, and, for most lines in stellar atmospheres, over the wings as well. A second crucial point is contained in the theoretical demonstration in Chapter 8, and in Waddell's observational confirmations discussed below, that the line source functions for certain multiplet lines are closely related over much of the atmosphere. As we shall see when we come to study the analysis of the solar D lines, these far-reaching results, while only approximate, allow us to develop a general method for the detailed analysis of multiplet lines without having to make recourse to the assumption of LTE.

9.2 Observational Limitations

9.2.1 Limb-Darkening Data

Even when it is possible in principle to effect an analysis, inevitably there will be observational limitations which, by limiting the quality of the data, will necessarily further limit the recoverable information. Thus, in measuring the limb darkening of the solar emission one finds it impossible in general to observe very close to the limb because of seeing excursions; in addition, we can measure the intensity only to a certain accuracy: How do these inadequacies reflect themselves in the parameters derived via Equation (9.1)?

Böhm (1961), recognizing the nature of this problem, attempted to obtain a solution on the basis of information theory. His discussion invokes Shannon's sampling theorem—see, e.g., Brillouin (1956)—namely that, if a function of time $G(t)$ contains no frequencies above W, then it is completely described by its ordinates spaced $1/2W$ apart in time and extending along the time axis to infinity on either side. An equivalent statement of the theorem is that a signal of maximum frequency W can have no *independent* values of signal strength separated by less than $1/2W$ in time. Consider, then, a signal $G(t)$ which contains no frequency greater than W and is T units in length. According to the sampling theorem, the signal is completely described (except maybe near its end points) by the specification of its values at $2TW + 1$ points. Now in limb-darkening analyses limitations arise in that (1) the values of $I(\mu)$ are specified only within certain observational accuracy, and (2) the function $I(\mu)$ is observed only over a certain range of μ. Böhm points out a correspondence to Shannon's problem in the sense that the errors under (1) are such as to limit the frequency of the signal to values below a certain frequency W, while those under (2) limit its length T.

The integral equation for limb darkening,

$$I(\mu) = \int_0^\infty S(t)e^{-t/\mu}\,\frac{dt}{\mu},\tag{9.6}$$

may be conveniently expressed, following Sykes (1953), in the form

$$I(\xi) = \int_{-\infty}^{+\infty} S(\eta)\exp\left[\xi - \eta - e^{\xi-\eta}\right]d\eta,\tag{9.7}$$

where $t = \exp(-\eta)$, $\mu = \exp(-\xi)$. If we assumed that ξ could be extended along the negative axis, the Fourier transform of the integral Equation (9.7) could be written, after some simple algebra, as

$$I^*(k) = S^*(k)\Gamma(1 - ik),\tag{9.8}$$

with $S^*(k)$ representing the Fourier transform of the source function; its multiplier, the gamma function, is the Fourier transform of the kernel. Strictly speaking, we may not accept Equation (9.8) as physically meaningful since the variable ξ is undefined along the negative axis, while $I(\xi)$ is unspecified beyond a certain ξ_{max}.[*] For example, we know very well that observations at a *single* value of μ (or ξ) can yield us no data on the spectral composition of $S^*(k)$ for k other than zero; however, this fact cannot be reflected in the equation, which implicitly assumes $I(\xi)$ to have been measured over an infinite range in

---

[*] It might be thought that an arbitrary definition of $I(\xi)$ outside its observational limits could overcome this problem, but any such procedure introduces Fourier harmonics at the break points in ξ and these are troublesome to handle. Problems also arise in the redefinition of ξ through the equation $\xi = \ln\left[(\mu - \mu_{min})/(\mu_{max} - \mu)\right]$, which has the limits $\pm\infty$. An essential difficulty is that one simply does not know $I(\mu)$ outside the observational limits; in particular, one does not know that it is zero.

ξ. The gamma function in the above expression acts as a filter which damps the higher harmonics of the source function, thus making their recovery more and more uncertain.   Now $I^*(k)$ is only meaningful so long as it exceeds the corresponding quantity $I_N^*(k)$ of the "noise" associated with the observation, and this allows us to determine the maximum wave number k_m for which we can hope to recover data on $S^*(k)$.   For a relative error of observation ε, this is found from the requirement $|\Gamma(1 - ik)| < \varepsilon$, for the favorable case when $S^*(k)$ is independent of k.   Values of this modulus taken from Böhm's paper are reproduced in Table 9.1.   For a 1% error of observation, this

TABLE   9.1.   The   modulus $|\Gamma(1 - ik)| \equiv |K^*(k)|$.
[After Böhm (1961), Table 1]

k	$|K^*(k)|$	k	$|K^*(k)|$
0	1.0000	3.2	0.0294
0.8	0.6402	3.6	0.0166
1.2	0.4170	4.0	0.00936
1.6	0.2568	4.4	0.00524
2.0	0.1531	4.8	0.00292
2.4	0.0895	5.2	0.00162
2.8	0.0516	5.6	0.000897

indicates that k_m is about 4, while for 0.1% accuracy, k_m is only increased to about 5.5.   In Shannon's theorem as applied to this problem, we may therefore interpret W as $k_m/2\pi$ and T as the interval $\Delta\xi = \xi_{max} - \xi_{min}$, so that, for 1 and 0.1% accuracy, respectively, we find that observations from $\mu = 1$ to $\mu = 0.2$ ($\Delta\xi = 1.6$) lead to a maximum of 3 and 4 parameters of S which may be independently determined. This argument must be incomplete, however, since it implies that as $\Delta\xi$ is increased indefinitely by observing closer and closer to the limb, e.g., at a solar eclipse,* the recoverable data would increase indefinitely irrespective of the error of observation.   This conclusion is simply not tenable on a variety of grounds.   The resolution of this difficulty lies in the recognition that the relevant $\Delta\xi$ to be used in Shannon's theorem may be fixed not by the observed range of μ but by the error of observation, as we shall see in the following section.

* The spherical figure of the sun ultimately invalidates the description (9.6) for the emergent intensity, but this is irrelevant to the present argument.

9.2.2 Line Profile for a Finite Atmosphere

A similar problem arises in the analysis of the normally emergent emission line profiles from an optically thick (but not semi-infinite) slab of gas, for which case we encounter the integral equation, Jefferies and Orrall (1960),

$$I(\alpha) = \int_0^1 S(t)e^{-\alpha t}\alpha \, dt, \tag{9.9}$$

where $\alpha = t_1\phi'_\lambda$; t_1 being the total optical thickness at the line center λ_0, and ϕ'_λ the ratio of the absorption coefficients at λ and λ_0, which we shall assume to be independent of position in the slab. The problem is simply that of determining the source function $S(t)$ given $I(\alpha)$. In practice, one measures the line profile $I(\Delta\lambda)$ and, knowing t_1 and the Doppler width from other considerations, expresses $I(\Delta\lambda)$ as $I(\alpha)$; the correspondence between Equations (9.9) and (9.6) is obvious. If we again transform variables by writing $\alpha = \exp(\xi)$, $t = \exp(-\eta)$, Equation (9.9) takes the form

$$I(\xi) = \int_0^\infty S(\eta) \exp[\xi - \eta - e^{\xi-\eta}] \, d\eta. \tag{9.10}$$

Again, $I(\xi)$ is only meaningfully observed over a limited range in ξ; certainly ξ has an upper bound $\xi_{\max} = \ln t_1$. In contrast to the limb darkening case where the lower bound may be set by the closeness we can observe to the limb, the corresponding bound in this case is fixed by the accuracy of measurement, since necessarily $I(\alpha) \to 0$ as $\alpha \to 0$. In other words, we can meaningfully measure the emission line profile only out to such a wavelength that the intensity is about equal to the noise level. If this distance is $\Delta\lambda_m$ the range $\Delta\xi$ is simply equal to $(\Delta\lambda_m/\Delta\lambda_D)^2$ if we are still within the Doppler core. We certainly cannot, therefore, treat this problem in the same way as the limb darkening case above, i.e., we cannot let $\xi_{\max} \to \infty$. Consider, for example, the case where t_1 is very small, yet the observed intensity can be followed above the noise out to a finite $\Delta\lambda$—such cases are common enough in practice. The line profile would then reflect the emission coefficient profile as averaged through the gas, and it is intuitively evident that the *only* information recoverable on $S(t)$ is its mean value, i.e., we can determine *one* piece of information. If we uncritically applied the analysis of Section 9.2.1 above, we would conclude that both $\Delta\xi$ and k_m were finite and accordingly that more than one parameter of S could be obtained.

An (incomplete) extension of the above analysis can be obtained as follows.

Let us define quantities

$$\mathscr{I}(\xi) = \begin{cases} I(\xi), & \xi_{min} \leq \xi \leq \xi_{max}, \\ 0, & \text{otherwise;} \end{cases}$$
$$\mathscr{S}(\eta) = \begin{cases} S(\eta), & \eta \geq 0, \\ 0, & \eta < 0. \end{cases} \tag{9.11}$$

Equation (9.10) can then be written

$$\mathscr{I}(\xi) = \int_{-\infty}^{+\infty} \mathscr{S}(\eta)\psi(\xi) \exp\left[\xi - \eta - e^{\xi-\eta}\right] d\eta, \tag{9.12}$$

with $\psi(\xi) = 1$ or 0 depending on whether $\mathscr{I}(\xi)$ is equal to $I(\xi)$ or 0. The Fourier transform of this equation is found by making the transformation $y = \xi - \eta$, as

$$\mathscr{I}^*(k) = \int_{-\infty}^{\xi_{max}} dy \int_{L}^{y+\xi_{max}} e^y \exp\left[-e^y\right] e^{-iky} S(\eta) e^{-ik\eta} \, d\eta, \tag{9.13}$$

where $L = \max(0, \xi_{min} - y)$. Frequently the information is not limited by the wavelength distance into the wings to which one can measure the line intensity, and in such cases it seems adequate to put $\xi_{min} = -\infty$ in these integrals. In this case we find, for the particular case $S(\eta) = \bar{S}\delta(\eta)$, that

$$\mathscr{I}^*(k) = \bar{S} \int_{-\infty}^{\xi_{max}} e^y \exp(-e^y) e^{-iky} \, dy = \bar{S}\Gamma_{inc}(1 - ik, e^{\xi_{max}}), \tag{9.14}$$

where the incomplete gamma function is defined by

$$\Gamma_{inc}(1 + \alpha, z) = \int_{0}^{z} e^{-x} x^{\alpha} \, dx. \tag{9.15}$$

As t_1 tends to zero (and so $\xi_{max} \to -\infty$), the gamma function also tends to zero. A more careful study shows that $I^*(k)$ remains of order $(\xi_{max} - \xi_{min})$ as $k \to 0$, and that the only information we can obtain in the limit of small t_1 is on the mean value of $S(t)$, a conclusion which is physically acceptable.

9.2.3 The Inversion of the Limb-Darkening Equation

As the above analysis shows, there are severe limitations on the amount of recoverable data which a particular set of observations will allow. This result is familiar to those who have tried, for example, to determine a polynomial expansion for the source function from solar limb-darkening data—if one attempts to fit the data with too many parameters, instabilities appear in the solution. This seems simply a reflection of the fact that we are going beyond the natural limitations imposed ultimately by Shannon's theorem.

The problem of the solution of Fredholm integral equations of the first kind—of which Equations (9.6) and (9.9) are examples—is an outstanding one in numerical analysis and one of singular importance to astrophysics, as has been emphasized by Pecker (1965). The discussion above is quite inadequate in this context, but it seems possible that a more satisfactory treatment along these lines could lead, for example, to a general procedure for eliminating physically meaningless Fourier components from the data and so could yield a modified integral equation having better "condition." The problem is earnestly recommended to students of numerical analysis.

In the meantime we face the practical question of the inversion of such integral equations, and for this purpose a variety of procedures has been developed of which we may recognize four main categories:

PROCEDURES USING THE APPROXIMATION $S(t) = I(\mu = t)$

These first-order inversions can be most readily justified in terms of Equation (9.7). The exponential kernel function is peaked at $\xi = \eta$ so that the contribution to $I(\xi)$ arises primarily from the region $S(\eta = \xi)$. Hence, provided the source function does not vary too rapidly, we shall obtain the approximate result

$$S(t) = I(\mu = t), \tag{9.16}$$

which embodies the so-called Eddington-Barbier relation: It is exact if S is linear in t.

PROCEDURES ADOPTING EXPANSIONS OF $S(t)$

This second category has been widely used in a variety of forms; basically it consists in assuming a simple expansion for $S(t)$, e.g., as a power series in t, and then determining the coefficients in the expansion from the observed values of $I(\mu)$—an example of this procedure is given in Section 9.6. Normally one is forced to limit the expansion to about three terms and to seek the coefficients through a least-squares fit to $I(\mu)$; higher-order expansions seem to lead to instability. As mentioned above, this is presumably associated with the presence of observational error in the data and also with the fact that $S(t)$ is generally not representable in the assumed terms and that, in any case, the representation (9.6) is perhaps not sufficiently accurate for an obviously inhomogeneous source such as the solar atmosphere.

PROCEDURES WHICH REPLACE THE INTEGRAL BY A QUADRATURE SUM

It would seem, perhaps, that better results may be obtained were we to allow $S(t)$ more flexibility than can be achieved through a three-term series expansion in terms of some arbitrarily chosen basis functions. Accordingly some efforts have been made—Hummer and Jefferies (1965)—in the direction of replacing the integral by a simple quadrature sum of the form

$$I(\xi_i) = \int_{-\infty}^{+\infty} S(\eta) \exp\left[\xi_i - \eta - e^{\xi_i - \eta}\right] d\eta$$

$$\simeq \sum_{j=1}^{N} C_{ij} S_j \qquad (i = 1, \ldots, M \geq N), \qquad (9.17)$$

and then solving the resulting linear system as a least-square set. One quickly finds that the equations have very poor condition so that the derived values S_j fluctuate wildly. In order to impress some stability on the system one may introduce an auxiliary condition. Suppose, therefore, that we choose to solve the system (9.17) subject to the additional "smoothness" condition that the integral

$$A = \int_{-\infty}^{+\infty} S^2(\eta) g(\eta) \, d\eta \simeq \sum_{j=1}^{N} a_j S_j^2 \qquad (9.18)$$

be minimized, where the weighting factor $g(\eta)$ is chosen to vanish at each end of the range of η so that the effect on A of the source function in these extreme ranges is minimized. To solve the sets (9.17) and (9.18) simultaneously, we combine them through an undetermined multiplier λ whose value is chosen from a second auxiliary condition. The solution for S_j is then derived from the condition that the sum

$$\sum^2 = \sum_{i=1}^{M} \left[I(\xi_i) - \sum_{j=1}^{N} C_{ij} S_j \right]^2 + \lambda \sum_{j=1}^{N} a_j S_j^2 \qquad (9.19)$$

be stationary for variation of each S_j. As a best choice for λ we may

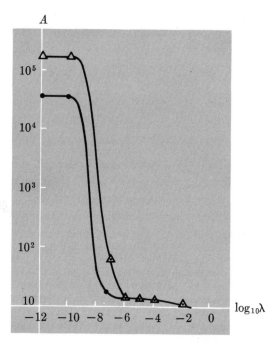

Figure 9.1. Variation of the quantity A with weighting parameter λ for the case of three-significant-figure (triangles) and seven-significant-figure data (dots). (From Hummer and Jefferies, 1966, Figure 25.)

require, for example, that the rate of change of A with λ shall be a minimum, i.e., that

$$\frac{d^2A}{d\lambda^2} = 0. \tag{9.20}$$

The choices (9.18) and (9.20) are perhaps a little arbitrary, though not unreasonable; in practice they turn out to give good results.

As an illustration of the procedure we have selected an extreme case of the segmented source function

$$S(t) = \begin{cases} 30t, & 0 \leq t \leq 0.2, \\ 11.80 - 29t, & 0.2 \leq t \leq 0.4, \\ t - 0.20, & t \geq 0.4, \end{cases} \tag{9.21}$$

and have evaluated the corresponding specific intensities $I(\xi_i)$ within the range $\mu = 1$ to 0.1 with the object of attempting to recover the form (9.21) from these values of the intensity. For the weighting function $g(\eta)$ we chose the form

$$g(\eta) = \exp\left[\xi_1 - \eta - e^{\xi_1 - \eta}\right] + \exp\left[\xi_2 - \eta - e^{\xi_2 - \eta}\right] \tag{9.22}$$

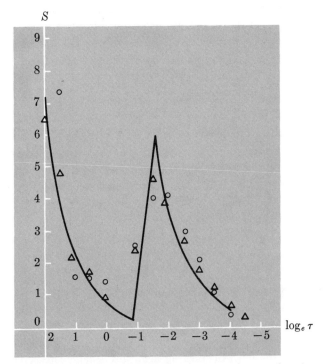

Figure 9.2. Comparison of the input (full line) and recovered source functions for three-significant-figure data on $I(\mu)$. The recovered values indicated by dots (triangles) refer to the case $\lambda = 10^{-6}$ (10^{-4}). (From Hummer and Jefferies, 1966, Figure 26.)

with ξ_1, ξ_2 the smallest and largest values in the list of the angle variables ξ.* To represent the sums (9.17) and (9.18) it has been supposed that the range of variation of η may be restricted to -2.0 to $+4.5$.

Figure 9.1 shows the variation of A with λ for a case when the basic data $I(\xi_i)$ was truncated to three significant figures; it is clear that the "best" value of λ lies between 10^{-4} and 10^{-6}. Figure 9.2 shows a plot of the original source function (solid line) and the source function recovered for $\lambda = 10^{-4}$ and $\lambda = 10^{-6}$; the quality of the inversion over a wide range of t is surprisingly good.

King (1964, 1965) has recently given a quadrature method for the

---

* This would not always be adequate; one must be sure that $g(\eta)$ sufficiently weights $S^2(\eta)$ over the η range for all ξ values within the range ξ_1 to ξ_2; however (9.22) is adequate for our illustration.

inversion of the limb-darkening equation which possesses some remarkable features.   If, following King, we approximate the atmosphere by one consisting of m slabs within each of which the source function is constant, the limb darkening equation reduces to the form

$$I(0, \mu) = S_1 + \sum_{j=1}^{m} \Delta S_j \exp\left(- \tau_j/\mu\right),$$

in which S_1 is the value of the source function in the first slab, ΔS_j is the source-function increment between slabs $j + 1$ and j, while τ_j is the optical depth of the boundary between the slabs $j + 1$ and j.   King applies the Prony algorithm (see, e.g., Whittaker and Robinson, 1932) to solve for the m values of ΔS_j and m values of τ_j for an assumed value of S_1 and a given set of $2m$ values of the observed quantity $I(0, \mu)$, which must be chosen so that $1/\mu$ has the integral values $0, 1, 2, 3, \ldots,$ $2m - 1$.   Thus, King's procedure determines not only the source function but the division points τ_j between the slabs and so allows maximum flexibility in fitting the given data.   Even as such, it is an interesting method.   However, of far greater importance is the remarkable, empirical property that the number of physically meaningful slabs (i.e., those for which the computed τ_j are positive) found in the solution decreases with decreasing accuracy in the observational data. This self-limiting property is unique among existing inversion methods; its origin is quite unknown and evidently very profound.

As Twomey (1965) has pointed out, King's method suffers from the need to specify the intensity at the physically inaccessible location $1/\mu = 0$.   This limitation is not essential, however.   As White (1967) points out, it can be overcome by writing the limb-darkening equation in the form

$$I(0, \mu) = S_1 + \sum_{j=1}^{m} [\Delta S_j \exp\left(- \tau_j\right)] \exp\left(- \tau_j/A\right)^p,$$

with

$$p = A(\mu^{-1} - 1).$$

The Prony algorithm then requires that p take the sequential values $0, 1, 2, \ldots, 2m - 1$ and, with $A > 0$, these all lie in the physically available range $1 \geq \mu > 0$.   However, we now face the problem of determining a "best" value for the parameter A, and so far as is known, no criterion exists for this purpose.

9.3 Waddell's Analyses

An important contribution to our understanding of the formation of spectral lines is found in two papers by Waddell (1962b, 1963). In the first of these he concluded, on the basis of observations of the limb darkening of the solar D line profiles, that the line source functions of these two lines were equal at a given geometrical depth, while in the second he showed that an equivalent result held for the three b-group lines of the neutral magnesium spectrum of the sun. The basis of Waddell's procedure is as simple as it is elegant, and is reproduced below.

The emergent intensity in the core of a strong line—where continuous opacity may be neglected—can be written (see Equation 7.22),

$$I_\lambda(0, \mu) = \int_0^\infty S_l(t_0) \exp\left[-\int_0^{t_0} \phi'_\lambda \frac{dt_0}{\mu}\right] \phi'_\lambda \frac{dt_0}{\mu}, \qquad (9.23)$$

with ϕ'_λ the usual absorption coefficient ratio. Consider two multiplet lines, like Na D_1 and D_2, whose wavelength separation is small, and suppose that the ratio of the line absorption coefficients at equal values $\Delta\lambda$ from their respective line centers is written

$$\frac{\kappa_1(\Delta\lambda)}{\kappa_2(\Delta\lambda)} = \frac{\sigma_1}{\sigma_2}, \qquad (9.24)$$

then we may write Equation (9.23) in the form

$$I_{\lambda j}(0, \mu) = \int_0^\infty S_{lj}(t) \exp\left[-\int_0^t \phi'_\lambda \sigma_j \frac{dt}{\mu}\right] \phi'_\lambda \sigma_j \frac{dt}{\mu} \qquad (9.25)$$

in which the subscript j references the individual multiplet line, while t is a *common* optical depth variable independent of the value of $\Delta\lambda$. It is readily seen that the necessary and sufficient condition that $S_{lj}(t)$ be the same for each line at all depths t is that, for all directions μ,

$$I_{\lambda 1}(0, \mu) = I_{\lambda 2}\left(0, \frac{\mu\sigma_1}{\sigma_2}\right). \qquad (9.26)$$

In terms of our implicit assumptions that ϕ'_λ is the same for each line and that S_l is frequency independent, we should expect also that if the invariance (9.26) holds at one wavelength $\Delta\lambda$ it should hold at all— within the limitation that continuous opacity is negligible.

To determine whether the condition (9.26) applied to the solar D lines, Waddell obtained limb-darkening curves for a series of values of $\Delta\lambda$ in each of the lines, using the Sacramento Peak high-dispersion spectrograph. A comparison of the appropriate line profiles, corrected to the same continuum intensity at three positions on the disk ($\mu = 1.0$,

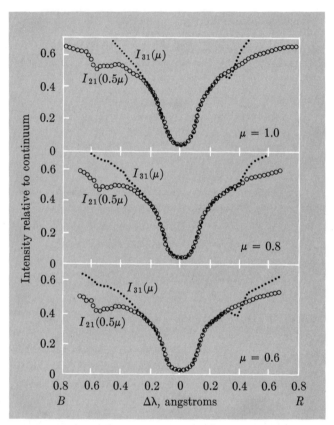

Figure 9.3. Comparison of the solar D-line profiles. (From Waddell, 1962b.)

0.8, 0.6 in D_2 and $\mu = 0.5$, 0.4, 0.3 in D_1), is reproduced from his publication in Figure 9.3. The agreement over the cores is remarkable, and leaves no doubt as to the general correctness of the conclusion that the D-line source functions do, in fact, share a common value at a given physical depth in the solar atmosphere. The breakdown of the profile congruences beyond about 0.2 Å from the line centers may reasonably be attributed to the onset of significant continuous opacity.

The interest of Waddell's b-group comparison is twofold; first, the b-group consists of *three* lines of Mg, and second, the lines share a common *upper* level, in contrast to the D lines. The observational comparison is rather more difficult in this case because the line strengths are in the ratio $1:0.6:0.2$. Since seeing excursions made it difficult to measure closer to the limb than $\mu = 0.2$, Waddell was able to make the comparison at only one set of positions $\mu(b_1) = 1$, $\mu(b_2) = 0.6$, and $\mu(b_4) = 0.2$. The degree of congruence of the corresponding line profiles is shown in Figure 9.4. Again the agreement breaks down in the wings, but rather earlier than for the D lines.

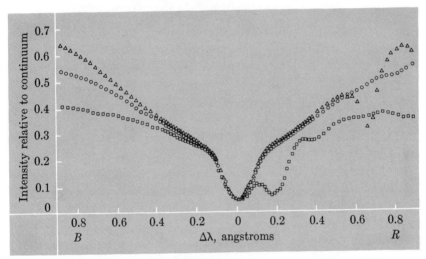

Figure 9.4. Comparison of the solar Mg b-line profiles. (From Waddell, 1963.)

It is as well to remark that Waddell's results in no sense imply the existence of LTE for the line source functions, nor was this claim made. Equally, of course, they do not deny this hypothesis. The demonstrated equality of the line source functions of a multiplet at a given depth is a necessary condition for LTE; however, it is not sufficient to ensure it. Indeed, as discussed in Chapter 8, the interlocking between the lines will ensure such essential equality for close-lying upper levels in a situation which is far from LTE, and in any case it is well recognized, cf. Finn and Mugglestone (1966), that the observed central intensities of the D lines are too low to be accounted for on an LTE model consistent with current ideas on the temperature structure of the outer solar atmosphere. Nor, of course, do Waddell's results imply anything other than a common depth dependence of the excitation temperature for the *D* lines, and separately a common dependence for the Mg *b*-group; no suggestion is made, or implied, that a single distribution of excitation temperature is shared by both the *D* lines *and* the three Mg lines.

The remaining question arising from Waddell's analysis concerns the frequency dependence of S_l and to this he has given a partial answer for

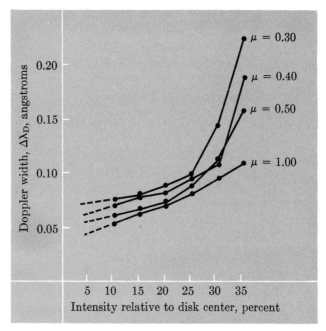

Figure 9.5. Doppler widths inferred by Waddell (1962*b*) for the solar *D*-lines—depth inof the atmosphere will increase to the right, corresponding to the increase in depth to formation for increasing $\Delta\lambda$.

the *D* lines from his determination of the Doppler width by the intercomparison procedure described by Goldberg (1958)—see Section 9.7. In Figure 9.5 we reproduce the Doppler widths derived by Waddell for different points on the line profiles and for different values of the parameter μ. For Goldberg's method to be valid, S_l must be independent of frequency and the Doppler width independent of depth. The values shown in the figure are sufficiently slowly varying with position in the profile for us to conclude that they do, in fact, seem to indicate at worst only a very slight frequency dependence of the line source function. The sudden increase in $\Delta\lambda_D$ found at a relative intensity of about 35% can be reasonably attributed to the onset of significant continuous opacity, when Goldberg's method breaks down.

The variation of $\Delta\lambda_D$ with μ shown in Figure 9.5 suggests that the Doppler width decreases with increasing depth; the variation with position on the profile, however, suggests an opposite trend. Waddell has suggested that this is to be interpreted as a manifestation of anisotropic turbulence in which the vertical motions outweigh those in the horizontal plane. This is in qualitative agreement with his earlier results—Waddell (1958)—which were obtained in a quite different fashion. The increase in $\Delta\lambda_D$ with depth agrees with the trend found by Unno (1959) and Suemoto (1957), but as we shall see in Section 9.5, a more refined analysis fails to confirm the details of Waddell's Doppler width determinations.

9.4 White's Analysis of the Solar Balmer Lines

A basically different analytical method was adopted by White (1963) for interpretation of his observations—White (1962)—of the solar center-limb variation of the cores of the early Balmer lines Hα, Hβ, and Hγ. His approach, like that of Waddell, was a general one proceeding from no *a priori* assumption of LTE. Though they have a common lower level in the $n = 2$ state, the large wavelength separation of the Balmer lines would introduce ambiguities into a congruence test of the type used by Waddell, even were this not precluded by the large ratio in their relative strengths. Necessarily, therefore, their analysis is more troublesome than was that of the D or the Mg b lines.

The first step in White's analysis lay in establishing that the line source function is frequency independent, which he did theoretically by considering, and rejecting as negligible, the physical processes which could lead to a frequency dependence. He next supposed that the lines were strong enough that continuous opacity was negligible over the cores which must, therefore, reflect the *line* source function; this assumption he was subsequently able to justify. In the context of Section 9.1 it remains to determine, for each line, values of S_l at m depths, and values of $\phi'_\lambda(\tau)$ at m depths and $n - 1$ frequencies; since there are an equal number mn of observations in each line the analysis is, in principle, determinate. Furthermore, since the relative line center opacities vary in proportion to the relative values of the quantities $gf\lambda$ (see Equation 4.97) one may in principle test the consistency of the assumptions by inquiring to what extent one finds a continuity in depth of the appropriate parameters. In fact, White makes the reasonable assumption that the lines are Doppler broadened in the core; his analysis then has the two main aims of determining the run of Doppler width with depth, and the depth dependence of the line source functions of the three lines.

If the observed center-limb variation at a particular wavelength in one of the lines is represented as a power series in μ, that is,

$$I_\lambda(\mu) = a_\lambda + b_\lambda\mu + c_\lambda\mu^2, \tag{9.27}$$

the line source function must be represented as

$$S(t_\lambda) = a_\lambda + b_\lambda t_\lambda + \tfrac{1}{2}c_\lambda t_\lambda^2, \tag{9.28}$$

so that if a least-square fit of the form (9.27) can be made to the observations at each wavelength, it will yield Equation (9.28) as a possible variation of the line source function with the corresponding monochromatic optical depth. If we accept that S_l is independent of frequency then it is simply a function of depth in the atmosphere. Thus, two monochromatic *optical* depths $t_{\lambda 1}$ and $t_{\lambda 2}$ which are such that

$$S_l(t_{\lambda 1}) = S_l(t_{\lambda 2}) \tag{9.29}$$

must refer to the same *physical* depth in the atmosphere (provided that S_l is monotonic). From graphical plots of $S_l(t_\lambda)$, or from the expansions (9.28) we may then determine the relationship $t_{\lambda 2}(t_{\lambda 1})$. In fact, this relation is readily shown to be given in the terms of the expansion coefficients in Equation (9.27) by the equation [White (1963)]

$$c_2 t_2 = -b_2 + \left\{ b_2^2 + 2c_2 \left[\frac{I_1(\mu = 1)}{I_2(\mu = 1)} \left(a_1 + b_1 t_1 + \frac{c_1}{2} t_1^2 \right) - a_2 \right] \right\}^{1/2}, \tag{9.30}$$

where, for convenience, we have omitted the symbol λ in the subscripts. The Doppler width then follows immediately from the defining relation,

$$\left. \frac{dt_1}{dt_2} \right]_{t_2} = \left. \frac{\kappa_1}{\kappa_2} \right]_{t_2} = \exp \left[\frac{\Delta\lambda_2^2 - \Delta\lambda_1^2}{\Delta\lambda_D^2(t_2)} \right]. \tag{9.31}$$

Of course, we may only use these expressions where the source functions in Equation (9.29) are meaningfully determined; i.e., within the depth interval common to $0.2 < \tau_1 < 1$ and $0.2 < \tau_2 < 1$. Doppler widths determined by White in this way for Hα, Hβ, and Hγ are represented in Figure 9.6 for the values of $\Delta\lambda_1$ shown against the curves; $\Delta\lambda_2$ was taken as zero in each case.   The agreement between the curves is, on the whole, not particularly good—although the curve for -0.19 Å for Hα is apparently based on an observational inaccuracy.   The results indicate a marked increase in Doppler width toward the outer regions where the Hα core is formed, a more or less constant value near $\tau_0(\text{H}\beta)$ $= 1$, followed by a slight inward decrease in the region where Hγ is formed.

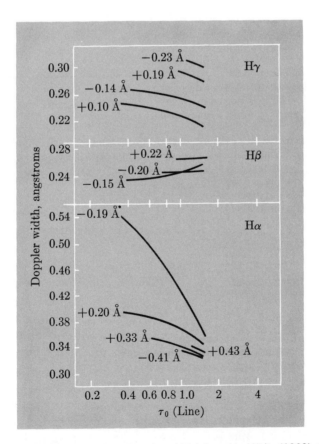

Figure 9.6. Depth distribution of the Doppler width inferred by White (1963); these were subsequently modified ; see text.   The numbers shown against the curves are the values of $\Delta\lambda_1$ (in Å) used, with $\Delta\lambda_2 = 0$, to obtain the Doppler width.

White obtained similar values of the Doppler width from other wavelength combinations. To illustrate an interesting trend in his results we have reproduced, in Table 9.2, some values of $\Delta\lambda_D$ for the

TABLE 9.2. Effective Doppler widths at $\tau(\Delta\lambda_2) = 1$.* [After White (1963), Table 1]

Hα			Hβ			Hγ		
$\Delta\lambda_2$	$\Delta\lambda_1$	$\Delta\lambda_D$	$\Delta\lambda_2$	$\Delta\lambda_1$	$\Delta\lambda_D$	$\Delta\lambda_2$	$\Delta\lambda_1$	$\Delta\lambda_D$
0.43	0.47	0.34	0.29	0.32	0.61	0.19	0.23	0.32
0.43	0.58	0.54	0.29	0.38	0.56	0.19	0.30	0.44
0.43	0.60	0.52	0.29	0.40	0.71	0.19	0.40	0.61
			0.29	0.54	0.83	0.19	0.43	0.65
			0.29	0.66	1.05			

* All wavelengths are in angstroms.

same optical depth $[\tau(\Delta\lambda_2) = 1]$ using different values of $\Delta\lambda_1$. For each spectral line Table 9.2 shows that the inferred value of $\Delta\lambda_D$ increases with increasing $\Delta\lambda_1$; one could, perhaps, associate this with an increase of $\Delta\lambda_D$ with depth—however, this seems unlikely. In an attempt to clarify this point, White constructed some artificial profiles using a constant Doppler width and a source function of the form

$$S(t) = 1 - Ae^{-kt} \qquad (9.32)$$

with A and k chosen to fit his mean Hα source function. Precisely as above, he then analyzed the computed center-limb profiles and determined Doppler widths which should, of course, be constant and equal to the value adopted in the profile calculations. In fact, he found that the inferred values agreed with the assumed value when the wavelength pairs $\Delta\lambda_1$, $\Delta\lambda_2$ were chosen near the line center, but farther out in the line the inferred Doppler width was found to increase rapidly. This can only arise from inadequacies in the inversion of the limb darkening equation. As White points out, the method fails for values of $\Delta\lambda$ such that at $\tau(\Delta\lambda) = 1$ the source function is changing rapidly with depth; this suggests that a different expansion for the original limb darkening data may have given more satisfactory results. So far as is known, this has not been tested.

To determine the run of line source function with depth we must first recall that the individual segments are probably only determined adequately, if at all, by the limb darkening inversion procedure in the range $0.2 \lesssim t_\lambda < 1.0$.* To the extent that S_l is independent of $\Delta\lambda$ within a line, we may generate a single curve $S_l(t_0)$ spanning a wide range of depth only if we can map the segments $S_l(t_\lambda)$ onto $S_l(t_0)$. This in turn requires a knowledge of the transformation $t_\lambda(t_0)$ which we can obtain, in the Doppler core, through the evaluation of the integral;

$$t_\lambda = \int_0^{t_0} \exp\left\{ -\left[\frac{\Delta\lambda}{\Delta\lambda_D\,(t)} \right]^2 \right\} dt. \tag{9.33}$$

However, as mentioned above, the inference of the Doppler width is uncertain, especially in the deeper layers of the gas, because of uncertainty in the quality of the limb darkening inversion.

As a first approximation, White therefore restricted attention to the line cores—where the inferred Doppler widths seem fairly reliable—and in this way obtained the depth variation of $\Delta\lambda_D$ down to $t_0(\text{H}\alpha) \simeq 20$. The corresponding first approximation to $S_l(t_0)$ indicated that substantial differences existed at a given depth between the excitation temperatures of the three lines Hα, Hβ, and Hγ.

This conclusion was challenged by Pierce and Waddell (1964). Using the Eddington-Barbier relation

$$I_\lambda(\mu) = S_\lambda(t_\lambda = \mu)$$

and the definition of the excitation temperature

$$T_{\text{ex}}^{-1} = \frac{k\lambda}{hc} \ln\left[1 + \frac{2hc^2}{\lambda^5 S_\lambda} \right], \tag{9.34}$$

these authors obtained values of T_{ex} corresponding to the line-center intensities observed by White (1962) for Hα, Hβ, and Hγ, and by David (1961) for Hα, Hβ, Hγ, and Hδ. In order to represent the results on a single depth scale they constructed a "common μ scale" via the relation, cf. Waddell (1963),

$$\mu_{\text{common}} = \frac{\mu_i}{s_i},$$

in which the line strength s_i is proportional to the corresponding

---

* This, at least, is the usual feeling and is based on the Eddington-Barbier relation (9.16). It is this author's experience that this is often unnecessarily restrictive at the larger depths.

absorption coefficient, i.e., to the quantity $gf\lambda$. In a scale in which $s(H\delta)$ is unity—so that $s(H\alpha) = 0.0215$, $s(H\beta) = 0.157$, $s(H\gamma) = 0.467$ —the excitation temperatures derived from David's observations by Pierce and Waddell are plotted against $\mu_{common} \equiv \mu(H\delta)$ in Figure 9.7. There is clearly a strong indication that the early Balmer line excitation temperatures are almost equal at a given depth. Pierce and Waddell's analysis of White's data yielded essentially the same result.

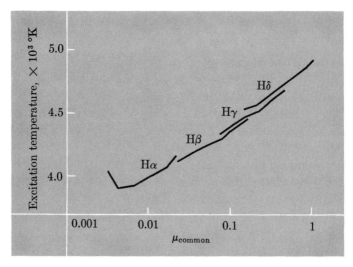

Figure 9.7. Variation of T_{ex} for the first four Balmer lines, as a function of the common μ-variable. The abscissa may be read directly in terms of optical depth at the center of the Hδ line. The results are derived from David's (1961) observations. (From Pierce and Waddell, 1964.)

Subsequent work by White has sought to clarify the question by seeking a better determination of the depth variation of the Doppler width. Accepting his representations (9.28) as valid, and starting with his previously derived depth distribution of $\Delta\lambda_D$ as a first approximation, White varied this distribution until the Hα source-function segments $S(t_\lambda)$ gave the best coalescence into a single curve. The process was extended to Hβ and Hγ until a final distribution of Doppler width was obtained which yielded the best coalescence for each line individually. No demand was made that the source functions in all three lines coalesce into a single curve; because of the large wavelength differences it is not obvious theoretically that they must do so. Final distributions of the excitation temperatures and the kinetic temperature derived from the inferred Doppler widths are shown in Figure 9.8. The differences in T_{ex} from line to line are of order 100 °K, and they are greater than White's estimates of the probable errors.   Still, whether the observations indicate significant differences between the excitation temperature for the first three Balmer lines is hard to say; a major unknown factor remains the reliability of the basic inversion of the limb darkening equation, and until more is known about that problem it seems that estimates of probable errors in T_{ex} must be treated with reserve.

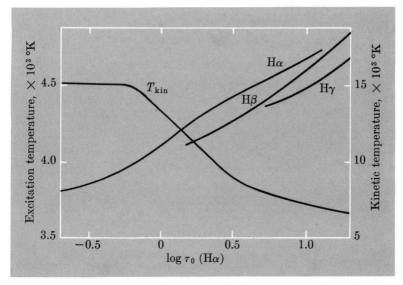

Figure 9.8. Kinetic and excitation temperature distributions deduced by White (1965) from his observations of the first three Balmer lines in the Sun.

An especially striking feature of Figure 9.8 is the contrast in behavior of the kinetic temperature and the excitation temperatures.   The qualitative behavior is precisely of the form expected for a "photoelectrically controlled" line like Hα.

9.5 A General Analytical Procedure

In this section we shall attempt to present in detail a procedure for the analysis of solar multiplet lines which is more general than those described above.   We shall not suppose that the lines are so strong that continuous opacity is negligible, nor shall we suppose that the line absorption coefficients are gaussian or constant with depth; we shall, however, suppose them to have a common profile.   The theoretical foundations for the analysis have all been laid down in this and the preceding chapter.   They are few and simple consisting of the recognition, first, that, over some part of the line, at least, the line source function is independent of frequency and, second, that, because of the close coupling between the lines of a multiplet, the line source functions of both should be identical at any given location in the atmosphere except perhaps in the outermost layers.*   These two results represent a synthesis of enormous potential for the analysis of multiplet lines. The same results apply in LTE; our synthesis differs, however, in making no assumption as to the form of the line source function nor as to its relationship to the continuum source function.   It is not implied that this is the ultimate synthesis which can be made; it is, though, a first step in that direction and one which removes the degeneracy discussed in Section 9.1 without unjustifiable assumption.

Suppose that we are given limb darkening data for two (or more) lines of a multiplet at each of a number of frequencies spanning the line. Consistent with the observational limitations discussed above, we may invert the monochromatic limb darkening equation in a variety of ways; for example, we may try a three-term power series (9.27), or the quadrature procedure outlined in Section 9.2.3.

The composite quantities S_ν and τ_ν are not those which we seek, but rather are related to them through Equations (9.2) to (9.4).   To determine the spectroscopic parameters S_l, S_c, r_0, and ϕ_ν as functions of depth, and ϕ_ν as a function of frequency across the line, we make use of the basic conclusions above that S_l is frequency-independent across the line and that, at a given physical depth, S_l has the same value for each of two close-lying lines of a multiplet.   We shall further take the shape, ϕ_ν, of the absorption coefficient equal in both lines.   Our observations are then, in principle, sufficient to determine the spectroscopic parameters provided that we have observations at two frequencies, at least.

In practice we might proceed with the analysis as follows.   Consider

---

* Strictly speaking, this would apply only to lines of small wavelength separation; for widely spaced multiplet lines (like $H\alpha$ and $H\beta$) a more sophisticated treatment will be necessary.

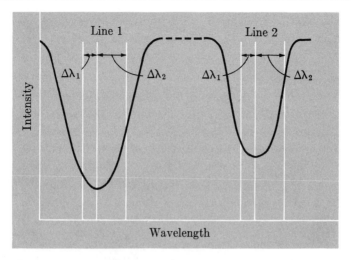

Figure 9.9. Schematic representation of the quantities $\Delta\lambda_1$ and $\Delta\lambda_2$ in the two illustrated profiles of a multiplet pair.

the values of $S_\lambda(\tau_\lambda)$ as derived from the inversion of the integral equation (9.1) at two wavelength distances $\Delta\lambda_1$ and $\Delta\lambda_2$ from the line center, in each of two lines of a multiplet (see Figure 9.9) and suppose we denote the values of each of these four quantities *at a given physical depth* by $S_{11}, S_{12}, S_{21}, S_{22}$—the first subscript indexing the particular line of the multiplet and the second the wavelength distance $\Delta\lambda$ from the relevant line center.* It is important to note that the observations themselves will not allow us directly to determine these four quantities since the composite source function S_λ is given as a function of the composite variable τ_λ whose relationship to physical depth is not known *a priori*. We may eliminate first S_l, and then S_c, from the defining equations (9.2) for the S_{ij} and we shall find, after some algebra, the following equations for r_{11} and r_{12} [cf. Jefferies (1965), Curtis and Jefferies (1965a, b)],

$$a_1 r_{11} + a_2 r_{12} = 1,$$
$$b_1/r_{11} + b_2/r_{12} = 1, \tag{9.35}$$

where

$$a_1 = (S_{11} - S_{21})/D_1, \qquad b_1 = (S_{11} - S_{21})/D_2,$$
$$a_2 = (S_{22} - S_{12})/D_1, \qquad b_2 = (S_{22} - S_{12})/D_2, \tag{9.36}\dagger$$

---

* This same notation is used to denote the other parameters of the problem, for example, r_λ and τ_λ.

† Note that this equation is incorrectly printed in Jefferies (1965).

and

$$D_1 = (S_{12} - S_{11}) + (S_{21} - S_{22})g,$$
$$D_2 = (S_{12} - S_{11}) + (S_{21} - S_{22})/g,$$

(9.37)

with $g = \kappa_2(\lambda)/\kappa_1(\lambda)$.

These equations only apply if the S_{ij} refer to the same atmospheric location; our next step, therefore, must be to determine what values of τ_λ refer to the same physical depth so that the corresponding S_{ij} can be found. This may be done iteratively by assuming initially that r_λ varies with depth in some specified manner. Suppose, for example, one takes r_λ to be independent of depth so that, from Equations (9.3) and (9.4), we find

$$\tau_{11} = t_{11}r_{11}(1 + r_{11}^{-1}),$$
$$\tau_{12} = t_{11}r_{11}(1 + r_{12}^{-1}),$$
$$\tau_{21} = t_{11}r_{11}(1 + gr_{11}^{-1}),$$
$$\tau_{22} = t_{11}r_{11}(1 + gr_{12}^{-1}),$$

(9.38)

where the line optical depth at $\Delta\lambda_1$ in the line referenced as number 1 has been chosen as the reference depth variable t_{11}. If we assumed a pair of values of r_{11} and r_{12}, then for a selected value of t_{11} we could find the values of $\tau_{11}, \tau_{12}, \tau_{21}, \tau_{22}$ corresponding to the same physical location. With these values of τ_λ we could enter the $S_\lambda(\tau_\lambda)$ equations as determined from the limb darkening data and determine the four quantities $S_{11}, S_{12}, S_{21}, S_{22}$. To the extent that the adopted r_{11} and r_{12} were correct, and that they did not vary with depth, these values of S_{ij} would refer to the same position in the atmosphere so that they are the appropriate values to be used, in Equation (9.35), to solve for r_{11} and r_{12}. These solutions are in turn to be entered in Equations (9.38) to determine a new set of τ_{ij}, hence new S_{ij}, and so a third approximation to r_{11} and r_{12}. This iterative procedure, if convergent, will yield values for r_{11} and r_{12} appropriate to the particular value of t_{11} used for the transformation (9.38).

We could next turn to another value of t_{11}, repeat the above operations, and in this way build up a set of values of r_{11} and r_{12} as a function of the reference depth t_{11}. In general these will not be independent of depth, as we have assumed, so that a necessary next step is to replace the simple linear transformations (9.38) by their corresponding integral forms, for example,

$$\tau_{11} = \int_0^{t_{11}} [1 + r_{11}(t'_{11})] \, dt'_{11}.$$

(9.39)

We may now again determine the τ_{ij} appropriate to a given value of the line optical depth t_{11} and repeat the procedure described above until we converge on a final self-consistent set of values for r_{11} and r_{12} as functions of t_{11}.

The detailed method may sound laborious, but it is conceptually simple and well adapted for high-speed computation. In practice it has the drawback that Equations (9.35) are sensitive to small changes in the quantities S_{ij}, so we have found it more convenient to proceed in a slightly different fashion, outlined in the following Section.

9.6 An Application to the Solar *D* Lines

As an illustration of the above general method we shall, with Curtis and Jefferies (1965a, b), consider the solar *D* lines, using Waddell's (1962a) corrected photoelectric observations of the intensities at various distances from the corresponding line centers and at various positions across the disk from $\mu = 1.0$ to $\mu = 0.3$. His published results are based on an average of at least four tracings at each position on the disk; the tracings were made along an east–west axis and active regions were avoided. These averaged profiles still suffer from telluric absorption, and in an attempt to eliminate this trouble the averaged profiles were reflected about the line center and the smooth curve obtained in this way was tabulated. It is on these values that our analysis rests.

The representation of $S_\lambda(\tau_\lambda)$ may be chosen in any convenient form adequate to fit the data. At the same time, if we have an *a priori* reason for believing one form to be superior to others, we should use that. The theoretical developments of the preceding chapters indicate that a source-function variation is smoother when plotted on a logarithmic than on a linear scale, and we have accordingly adopted the form

$$S_\lambda(\tau_\lambda) = a_\lambda + b_\lambda \log \tau_\lambda + c_\lambda (\log \tau_\lambda)^2 \qquad (9.40)$$

using common logarithms. The divergence of the form (9.40) as τ_λ tends to zero is really of no concern here since we only seek $S_\lambda(\tau_\lambda)$ over the range, at most, of 0.2 to 2 in τ_λ (corresponding to the limited range for μ). The values of a_λ, b_λ, and c_λ for each wavelength in each line are, therefore, to represent the source function over a very limited depth range. We are not, in other words, trying to represent the variation of S_λ over all depths and at all frequencies by a *single* relationship of the form (9.40).

If we adopt the expansion (9.40), the limb darkening law for the emergent intensity must be represented by the equation

$$I_\lambda(0, \mu) = A_\lambda + B_\lambda \log \mu + C_\lambda(\log \mu)^2 \qquad (9.41)$$

where

$$
\begin{aligned}
A_\lambda &= a_\lambda - b_\lambda k\gamma + c_\lambda k^2 F, \\
B_\lambda &= b_\lambda - 2c_\lambda k\gamma, \\
C_\lambda &= c_\lambda,
\end{aligned}
\qquad (9.42)
$$

with $k = \log e \simeq 0.4343$; $\gamma \simeq 0.57722$ is Euler's constant and $F = \pi^2/6 + \gamma^2 \simeq 1.9781$ [cf. Busbridge as quoted by Kourganoff (1952), p. 258].

A representative fit for D_1 at $\Delta\lambda = 0.025$ Å is shown in Table 9.3;

TABLE 9.3. Representative least-square fit to limb darkening. D_1 at $\Delta\lambda = 0.025$ Å, $A_\lambda = 0.0572$, $B_\lambda = 0.0337$, $C_\lambda = 0.0138$

μ	I_{observed}	I_{fit}
1.0	0.0572	0.0572
0.8	0.0548	0.0541
0.6	0.0496	0.0504
0.5	0.0480	0.0483
0.4	0.0470	0.0460
0.3	0.0430	0.0434

here, as elsewhere, the units for S_λ have been chosen as those of the center disk continuum at 5900 Å, that is, 3.6×10^{14} erg-cm^{-2}-sec^{-1}-sterad^{-1} in $\Delta\lambda = 1$ cm. The first column shows the value of μ, the second gives the observed intensity, and the third column shows the corresponding intensity as calculated from the fit by Equation (9.41). The appropriate values of A_λ, B_λ, C_λ are shown above the table. The variation of S_λ with τ_λ for this case is reproduced in Figure 9.10 together with the corresponding results for $\Delta\lambda = 0.05$ Å. The sets of numbers A_λ, B_λ, C_λ—or rather their counterparts a_λ, b_λ, c_λ as derived from Equations (9.42)—form the basic data for the analysis. However, uncertainties in S_{ij} prohibit a direct solution of the equations (9.35),

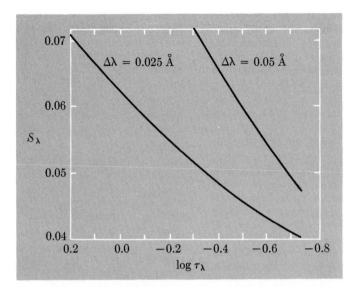

Figure 9.10. Variation of the composite (line and continuum) source function S_λ with composite optical depth for the solar D_1 line at $\Delta\lambda = 0.025, 0.050$ Å.

and we have adopted the following least-square procedure for their solution.

Let us write the equations for S_{ij} in the form

$$S_l + r_{ij}S_c = (1 + r_{ij})S_{ij}. \qquad (9.43)$$

There will be four such relations. Now for a particular value of t_{11} (or τ_{11}) we choose an r_{11} and r_{12}, and determine, via Equations (9.38), the appropriate τ_{ij}. From the empirical relations $S_\lambda(\tau_\lambda)$, we next determine the corresponding S_{ij}, and finally we solve the four equations (9.43) as a least-squares system for S_l and S_c. We may then judge how well the set S_l, S_c, r_{11}, r_{12} satisfies these equations by computing, for example, the sum D of the absolute values of the relative residuals, that is,

$$D = \sum \left| 1 - \frac{(S_l + r_{ij}S_c)}{(1 + r_{ij})S_{ij}} \right|. \qquad (9.44)$$

By varying r_{11} and r_{12} we may select the "best" solution as that which minimizes D. Again, this may not be the optimum method for solution on a desk calculator, but it is easily adapted for machine computation.

In practice, we find the expected result that we can infer little on the r_{ij} when they are either very large (i.e., line opacity is small) or very small (continuous opacity small). We can also expect to determine only S_c when r is large and only S_l in the opposite case. Accordingly, we have found it convenient to introduce the following two forms of Equation (9.43) called the "core formulation" (CF) and the "wing formulation" (WF)

$$S_l + r_{ij}S_c = (1 + r_{ij})S_{ij} \qquad \text{(CF)},$$

$$\frac{1}{r_{ij}} S_l + S_c = \left(\frac{1}{r_{ij}} + 1\right)S_{ij} \qquad \text{(WF)}. \tag{9.45}$$

While, of course, identical in principle the formulations sometimes yield different results in practice because of the statistical nature of the method of solution. Even now, however, we cannot expect to solve these equations over the whole range of $\Delta\lambda$. As we shall see, it is necessary to consider simpler formulations for the limiting cases of the extreme core and the extreme wings and to reserve the full treatment based on Equations (9.35) to the intermediate wavelengths.

9.6.1 The Extreme Cores ($\Delta\lambda \lesssim 0.1$ Å)

For very small r, the analysis is simplified since the basic inversion of the limb darkening equation essentially yields S_l as a function of $t_l(\lambda)$ for each wavelength in the line. The basic requirement that S_l be independent of wavelength then allows us to map $t_l(\lambda)$ as a function of $t_l(\lambda')$ by determining the optical depths $t(\lambda)$, $t(\lambda')$ at which S and S' are equal.* As an example, let us consider the results shown in Figure 9.10 for $\Delta\lambda = 0.025$ Å, 0.050 Å. From a point-by-point match of the quantities S_λ we find the relationship between $t(0.050$ Å$)$ and $t(0.025$ Å$)$ illustrated in Figure 9.11. The slope of this curve gives the absorption coefficient ratio (RA) according to the relationships

$$t(\lambda') = \int_0^{t(\lambda)} \frac{\kappa(\Delta\lambda')}{\kappa(\Delta\lambda)} \, dt(\lambda), \tag{9.46}$$

$$\text{RA} \equiv \frac{\kappa(\Delta\lambda')}{\kappa(\Delta\lambda)}. \tag{9.47}$$

We shall adopt the convention that $\Delta\lambda' > \Delta\lambda$. The wavelength variables in $t(\lambda)$, $t(\lambda')$ are abbreviated notations for $\Delta\lambda$, $\Delta\lambda'$.

---

* Throughout the remainder of this subsection we generally shall omit the subscript l; the quantities refer to the *line* parameters only.

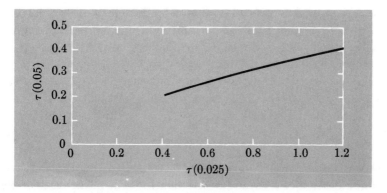

Figure 9.11. Optical depth in D_1 at $\Delta\lambda = 0.050$ Å as a function of that at $\Delta\lambda = 0.025$ Å.

Within the accuracy of the inversion, RA is constant with depth, i.e., the curve in Figure 9.11 is a straight line. Corresponding reductions for other wavelengths in both D_1 and D_2 are found to yield essentially linear curves of $t(\lambda)$ against $t(\lambda')$. As will be seen later in the analysis, it is consistent to interpret RA as a ratio of two Doppler profiles, so that we may write

$$\mathrm{RA}(\lambda, \lambda') = \exp\left[\frac{(\Delta\lambda)^2 - (\Delta\lambda')^2}{(\Delta\lambda_\mathrm{D})^2}\right]; \qquad (9.48)$$

Doppler widths inferred from this equation are shown in Table 9.4.

TABLE 9.4. Inferred values for $\Delta\lambda_\mathrm{D}$ from various wavelength pairs in D_1 and D_2

$\Delta\lambda, \Delta\lambda'$	$\Delta\lambda_\mathrm{D}$ (in Å)	
	D_1	D_2
0 to 0.025	0.034	0.041
0.0125 to 0.025	0.031	0.031
0.025 to 0.050	0.037	0.037
0.050 to 0.075	0.038	

Unfortunately, it is not possible to extend the table to larger $\Delta\lambda$, since the overlap of the $S_\lambda(t)$ curves between $\Delta\lambda = 0.075$ Å and 0.100 Å occurs only for monochromatic optical depths $t(\lambda') < 0.3$ or $t(\lambda) > 1.0$ where the inversion of the limb darkening equation does not yield

reliable data on the source function.   In this region of the line profile
the intensity is changing rapidly and data are needed for one intermediate wavelength (at least) before the method can be applied.   The
same remark holds for the range 0.050 to 0.075 Å where, for D_2, the
same value for the source function is obtained for $t(0.050) = 1.0$ and
$t(0.075) = 0.30$—so that the graph $t(0.050)$ vs. $t(0.075)$ for D_2 has only
one point in the range well defined by the observations.   This accounts
for the absence of an entry for the corresponding Doppler width in the
table.

The values shown in Table 9.4 are reasonably consistent and give no
strong indication of a variation with depth.   The mean value of about
0.036 Å is to be contrasted with the value in excess of 0.05 Å obtained
by Waddell in his application of Goldberg's method to the same data
(see Figure 9.5).   The origin of the significant difference between these
results can be seen if we refer to Figure 9.11—which is a typical plot of
$t(\lambda)$ vs. $t(\lambda')$.   The fact that the line in this plot does not pass through
the origin when extrapolated backward can only be interpreted to mean
that $\Delta\lambda_D$ is, in fact, not constant with depth, so that Goldberg's procedure is, strictly, inapplicable.   The Doppler width seems to be
essentially constant over the range 0.2 to 1.0 in the line center optical
depth t_0, since the $t_\lambda(t_0)$ relations are found to be linear.   It must
therefore be depth-dependent in the extreme outer layers.

This suggestion can be strengthened as follows: *If we assumed* $\Delta\lambda_D$
to be depth independent, Equation (9.46) would lead to

$$\text{RA} = \frac{t(\lambda')}{t(\lambda)} = \exp\left[\frac{(\Delta\lambda)^2 - (\Delta\lambda')^2}{(\Delta\lambda_D)^2}\right].\qquad(9.49)$$

Values of $\Delta\lambda_D$ obtained from this equation are shown in Table 9.5 for

TABLE 9.5. Doppler widths
inferred   using   Equation
(9.49) for the 0.025, 0.05 Å
pair of D_1

$\tau(0.025)$	$\Delta\lambda_D(\text{Å})$
0.41	0.051
0.60	0.047
0.85	0.044
1.20	0.041

the 0.025 Å, 0.05 Å wavelength pair of the D_1 line. These are typical results; they are depth-dependent (in contrast to the assumption on which Equation 9.49 was based) and are substantially higher than the estimates of Table 9.4. They agree well both in magnitude and depth-dependence with Waddell's results. Nevertheless, to the extent that they disagree with the values in Table 9.4, they cannot be acceptable. Thus, Goldberg's procedure must be used with appropriate care; in the present instance it leads to errors of as much as 50% for the Doppler width since it is applied to situations for which its basic assumptions are not valid.

The Doppler width for $t_0 < 0.3$ in either D_1 or D_2 cannot be estimated with any certainty since the observations give little reliable information on these layers. From the 0, 0.025 Å pair in D_1 and D_2 Curtis and Jefferies (1965a) obtained a rough estimate of 0.055 Å for the mean Doppler width in the region $t_0(D_2) < 0.3$. Hence, to the accuracy permitted by the data, we can infer the approximate $t_\lambda(t_0)$ transformation for both D_1 and D_2 from the relationship

$$t_\lambda(t_0) = \int_0^{t_0} \left(\frac{\kappa_\lambda}{\kappa_0}\right) dt_0.$$

In this way we find

$$t_\lambda(t_0) = \begin{cases} 0.3 \exp\left[-\left(\frac{\Delta\lambda}{\Delta_1}\right)^2\right] + (t_0 - 0.3)\exp\left[-\left(\frac{\Delta\lambda}{\Delta_2}\right)^2\right], & t_0 > 0.3 \\ t_0 \exp\left[-\left(\frac{\Delta\lambda}{\Delta_1}\right)^2\right], & t_0 < 0.3 \end{cases}$$

$$(9.50)$$

with $\Delta_1 = 0.055$ Å; $\Delta_2 = 0.036$ Å. In addition, of course, $t_\lambda(D_2) = 2t_\lambda(D_1)$.

Using this equation and the individual $S_\lambda(t_\lambda)$ curves obtained from the limb darkening inversion for the extreme core wavelengths ($\Delta\lambda \leq 0.05$ Å) we obtain the composite $S_l(t_0)$ variation shown in Figure 9.12. An interesting aspect of this figure is that the D_1 and D_2 line source functions are in fact found to be equal at a given depth. This conclusion was, of course, already reached by Waddell in his original study of the data but was in no way assumed in any steps leading to this result. The D_1 and D_2 data have here been analyzed separately.

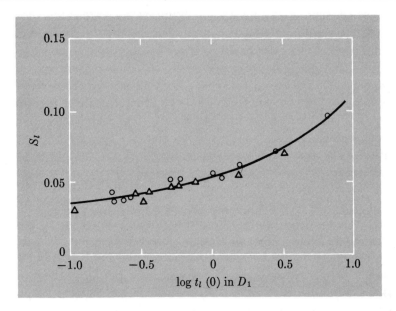

Figure 9.12. Variation of the line source functions with optical depth in the center of D_1. Data for D_1 are indicated by circles, those for D_2 by triangles.

9.6.2 The Extreme Wings ($\Delta\lambda \gtrsim 0.7$ Å)

To interpret the $S_\lambda(\tau_\lambda)$ curves for the extreme wings, we suppose that r_λ is large so that $S_\lambda \simeq S_c$. In fact, we might expect that $S_l \simeq S_c$ at depths where the wings are formed and in that case $S_\lambda \simeq S_c$ independently of the value of r_λ. The fact that r_λ *is* large in this case only makes this a better approximation.

To determine the wavelength variation of r_λ we make use of the requirement that S_c is independent of wavelength within a line. If the graph $S_{\lambda'}(\log \tau_{\lambda'})$ must be moved a distance Δ along the abscissa to place it into coincidence with the $S_\lambda(\log \tau_\lambda)$ curve, then, to the extent that r_λ may be assumed independent of depth, it follows from Equation (9.38) that

$$\Delta = \log\left(1 + \frac{1}{r_{\lambda'}}\right) - \log\left(1 + \frac{1}{r_\lambda}\right) \tag{9.51}$$

or, since r_λ is large in this case,

$$\Delta \simeq 0.434\left[\frac{1}{r_{\lambda'}} - \frac{1}{r_\lambda}\right]. \tag{9.52}$$

By a process of superimposition of the graphs of $S_\lambda(\log t_\lambda)$ on $S_{\lambda'}(\log t_{\lambda'})$

for both D_1 and D_2 we may obtain values of the corresponding abscissa shifts Δ. Table 9.6 contains values of Δ (estimated to ± 0.005) obtained

TABLE 9.6. Variation of Δ with $\Delta\lambda'$

$\Delta\lambda(\text{Å})$	D_2		D_1	
	Δ_1	Δ_2	Δ_1	Δ_2
1.3	0	$+0.010$	0	-0.005
1.1	$+0.025$	-0.020	-0.020	-0.020
1.0	0	-0.035	-0.025	-0.020
0.9	-0.025	-0.055	-0.040	-0.030
0.8	-0.055	-0.075	-0.055	-0.040
0.7	-0.115	-0.100	-0.070	-0.055
0.6	-0.160	-0.145	-0.100	-0.080

in this way from the $S_\lambda(\log \tau_\lambda)$ curves; in each case $\Delta\lambda' = 1.5$ Å and the entries headed Δ_1 and Δ_2 refer respectively to the two abscissa shifts measured at $\log \tau(\Delta\lambda')$ of -0.5 and 0.0. This procedure is represented schematically in Figure 9.13. To test the anticipated variation $r_\lambda \propto \Delta\lambda^2$, we show in Figure 9.14 graphs of $-\Delta_2$ vs. $\Delta\lambda_A^{-2}$ for both D_1 and D_2; the relationship is linear for both spectral lines, while the slopes

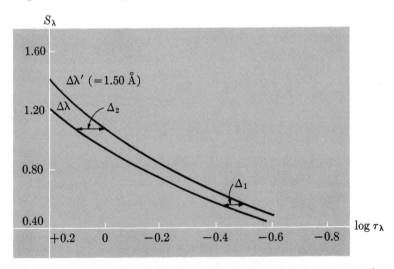

Figure 9.13. Illustration of the procedure involved in measuring the quantities Δ_1 and Δ_2 ; see text. The figure is schematic only.

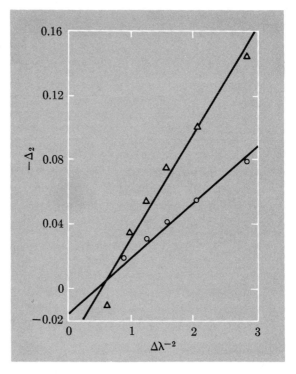

Figure 9.14. Wavelength variation of the quantity $-\Delta_2$; see text : D_1 data are indicated by circles, D_2 by triangles.

and the intercepts for each line lead respectively to the following results:

$$\left. \begin{array}{l} r_\lambda \simeq 7\Delta\lambda_{\rm A}^2 \\ r_{1.5\,{\rm A}} \simeq 13 \end{array} \right\} \text{ for } D_2,$$

$$\left. \begin{array}{l} r_\lambda \simeq 13\Delta\lambda_{\rm A}^2 \\ r_{1.5\,{\rm A}} \simeq 29 \end{array} \right\} \text{ for } D_1, \qquad (9.53)$$

where $\Delta\lambda_{\rm A}$ indicates that the quantity is measured in angstroms. Within the uncertainties of the data, these numbers are internally consistent and yield the theoretical ratio $r_\lambda(D_2)/r_\lambda(D_1) = 0.5$.

One might reasonably ask whether the depth variation of r_λ which is suggested from the difference between Δ_1 and Δ_2 in Table 9.6 might not invalidate these results, just as in the preceding section an assumed depth independence of $\Delta\lambda_{\rm D}$ led to an incorrect value. To investigate this question we have mapped $\tau(\lambda)$ onto $\tau(\lambda')$ using the requirement

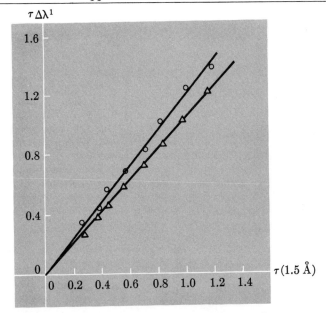

Figure 9.15. Variation of $\tau(\Delta\lambda)$ with $\tau(1.5$ Å$)$ for $\Delta\lambda = 0.6$ Å (circles) and 1.0 Å (triangles) for the sodium D_1 line.

that, at a common depth, $S_\lambda = S_{\lambda'} (= S_c)$ in the extreme wings. In keeping with the defining equation (see Equation 9.46),

$$\tau(\lambda') = \int_0^{\tau(\lambda)} \frac{\kappa(\lambda') + \kappa_c}{\kappa(\lambda) + \kappa_c} \, dt(\lambda) \,,$$

the slope of the $\tau(\lambda')$ vs. $\tau(\lambda)$ curve is, for large r_λ, simply equal to

$$\frac{d\tau(\lambda')}{d\tau(\lambda)} = 1 + \frac{1}{r_{\lambda'}} - \frac{1}{r_\lambda}. \tag{9.54}$$

Curves of $\tau(\lambda')$ vs. $\tau(\lambda)$ are shown in Figure 9.15 for the D_1 wings and for $\Delta\lambda_A = 0.6$ and 1.0 with $\Delta\lambda'_A = 1.5$. The relationships are essentially linear and pass through the origin; from this and the corresponding curves for D_2 we find

$$\begin{aligned} r_\lambda &\simeq 7\Delta\lambda_A^2 &&\text{for } D_2, \\ r_\lambda &\simeq 12\Delta\lambda_A^2 &&\text{for } D_1, \end{aligned} \tag{9.55}$$

which are essentially the same as those found above.

The depth variation of S_c with τ_c is essentially equivalent to the $S_\lambda(\tau_\lambda)$ curve for D_1 at $\Delta\lambda_A = 1.5$; it is reproduced in Figure 9.16.

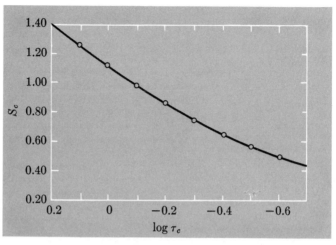

Figure 9.16. Variation of the continuum source function with continuum optical depth at 5900 Å.

9.6.3 The Intermediate Wavelengths (0.1 Å $\leq \Delta\lambda \leq$ 0.7 Å)

In that region of the line where we cannot suppose r_λ to be either very small or very large, a full solution of Equations (9.35) is necessary. It will be recalled that to formulate these equations, values referring to a single geometrical depth are needed of S_λ at two wavelength separations $(\Delta\lambda, \Delta\lambda')$ from the centers of each of the two lines D_1, D_2—these values were denoted S_{11}, S_{12}, S_{21}, S_{22}. In principle one may choose any pair of values $(\Delta\lambda', \Delta\lambda)$, but in practice it is necessary that the corresponding total optical depths $\tau(\lambda)$, $\tau(\lambda')$ should turn out to be in the "physically accessible zone" $0.3 \lesssim \tau(\lambda) \lesssim 1$. Normally this allows sufficient latitude that one may choose a fixed $\Delta\lambda$ and run through a set of $\Delta\lambda'$. We may distinguish, in this way, a number of "series" within each of which the value of $\Delta\lambda$ is fixed while $\Delta\lambda'$ varies. Thus the "0.2 series" represents the solution of the basic set (9.35) for the cases $\Delta\lambda = 0.200$ Å; $\Delta\lambda' = 0.250, 0.300, 0.400, 0.450, 0.500$ Å. For each case the equations were solved in the "core" and in the "wing" formulations; the best fit was chosen as that which minimized the quantity D of Equation (9.44).

Having chosen a $\Delta\lambda$, $\Delta\lambda'$ pair, we select a set of four values for the total (line plus continuum) D_1 optical depth $\tau_\lambda(D_1)$ and a solution of the basic system may then be sought for each of these depths. Rather than work in terms of the parameters r_λ, $r_{\lambda'}$ it is found convenient instead to use r_λ, and the ratio $\mathrm{RA} = r_\lambda/r_{\lambda'}$. Then for a specific choice of r_λ and RA the transformation from $\tau_\lambda(D_1)$ to $\tau_\lambda(D_2)$, $\tau_{\lambda'}(D_1)$, $\tau_{\lambda'}(D_2)$ is effected through the equations (see Equation 9.38)

$$\tau_{\lambda'}(D_1) = \frac{(r_\lambda + \mathrm{RA})}{1 + r_\lambda} \tau_\lambda(D_1),$$

$$\tau_\lambda(D_2) = \frac{2 + r_\lambda}{1 + r_\lambda} \tau_\lambda(D_1), \qquad\qquad (9.56)$$

$$\tau_{\lambda'}(D_2) = \frac{2\mathrm{RA} + r_\lambda}{1 + r_\lambda} \tau_\lambda(D_1).$$

We may note again that

$$r_\lambda = \frac{\kappa_c}{\kappa_\lambda(D_1)}$$

$$\mathrm{RA} = \frac{\kappa_{\lambda'}(D_1)}{\kappa_\lambda(D_1)} = \frac{\kappa_{\lambda'}(D_2)}{\kappa_\lambda(D_2)}.$$

Using the expansion coefficients a_λ, b_λ, c_λ of Equations (9.40) we may now compute values of $S_\lambda(D_1)$, $S_{\lambda'}(D_1)$, $S_\lambda(D_2)$, $S_{\lambda'}(D_2)$ which would correspond to the same physical depth—defined by the chosen value of $\tau_\lambda(D_1)$—if the assumed values for r_λ and RA were correct. The best fit for each form of Equations (9.45) was found by Curtis and Jefferies by varying r_λ and RA independently. For a given value of RA this basic set of equations was solved with different assumed values for r_λ; the best (for the assumed RA) was chosen as that with the smallest value of the dispersion parameter D—defined in Equation (9.44). This procedure was repeated for each of a number of values of RA, and

TABLE 9.7. Variation of D and r with RA in the core and wing formulations

RA	CF		WF	
	r	D	r	D
0.45	0.54 to 1.33	$0.13.10^{-1}$	0.54 to 1.17	$0.13.10^{-1}$
0.50	0.35 to 1.50	$0.89.10^{-2}$	0.35 to 1.50	$0.89.10^{-2}$
0.55	0.16 to 1.65	$0.46.10^{-2}$	0.16 to 1.65	$0.46.10^{-2}$
0.60	1.80	$0.46.10^{-3}$	1.80	$0.44.10^{-3}$
0.65	2.60	$0.59.10^{-2}$	1.82	$0.58.10^{-2}$
0.70	Indefinite	$0.18.10^{-1}$	>1.26	$0.12.10^{-1}$

the minimum of the set of D values thus generated was chosen as giving the best estimate jointly of r and RA consistent both with the observed limb darkening *and* with the two physical requirements of (1) frequency independence of the line (and continuum) source functions and (2) equality of the D_1 and D_2 line (and continuum) source functions at a given physical depth. Results for a typical case (the 0.200, 0.250 Å pair) are shown in Table 9.7.

The sharp minimum in D (near RA $= 0.6$, $r_\lambda = 1.8$) makes it easy to select the best fit and once the optimum values for r_λ and RA have been found, the corresponding values of S_l and S_c follow immediately from the definitions

$$S_\lambda = \frac{S_l + r_\lambda S_c}{1 + r_\lambda}, \tag{9.57a}$$

$$S_{\lambda'} = \frac{S_l + (r_\lambda/\text{RA})S_c}{1 + (r_\lambda/\text{RA})}. \tag{9.57b}$$

As Curtis and Jefferies emphasize, the results of the calculations must be interpreted with intelligent care. First, it is clear that if the values of $\Delta\lambda$, $\Delta\lambda'$ are too close together, the corresponding intensities will not differ significantly, the basic equations will become ill-conditioned, and the results will be unreliable. On the other hand, if the pair $\Delta\lambda$, $\Delta\lambda'$ are too far separated, it will prove impossible to determine an optical depth pair τ_λ, $\tau_{\lambda'}$ which refers to the same physical depth and which are yet each within the "physically accessible zones" within which the data on S_λ are reliably given by the limb darkening. Thus, for a given value of $\Delta\lambda$ we should not be surprised to find inconsistent solutions for the parameters r_λ, RA, S_c, and S_l when $\Delta\lambda'$ is either too close to $\Delta\lambda$, or too distant from $\Delta\lambda$. To illustrate this point, Table 9.8 shows values

TABLE 9.8. Radiation parameters inferred from the 0.300 series at $\log t_\lambda(D_1) = -0.4$

$\Delta\lambda'(A)$	RA	r	S_l	S_c
0.350	0.76	0.6 to 4.0	0.28 to 0.56	0.50 to 0.27
0.400	0.61	0.8 to 1.6	0.51	0.40
0.450	0.51	0.8 to 1.6	0.51	0.39
0.500	0.46	1.0	0.51	0.39
0.550	0.41	0.90	0.50	0.40
0.600	0.41	0.7	0.52	0.37

inferred for these parameters for the 0.300 series (that is, $\Delta\lambda = 0.3$ Å); the values refer to the depth at which $\log \tau_\lambda(D_1) = -0.4$. In this case we would have good reason to reject the results for $\Delta\lambda' = 0.350$ Å, which are less well determined, and are inconsistent with those for the other values of $\Delta\lambda'$, and to question those for $\Delta\lambda' = 0.600$ Å.

THE WAVELENGTH VARIATION OF RA

For the specific case of the D lines, an estimate of RA for each selected optical depth $\tau_\lambda(D_1)$ and for each wavelength pair was obtained by Curtis and Jefferies and, since depth variations of the ratio RA were quite small and not systematic, a mean of RA over depth was used throughout. Making use of the identity

$$\text{RA} \equiv \frac{\kappa(\lambda')}{\kappa(\lambda)} \equiv \frac{\kappa(\lambda')}{\kappa(\lambda'')} \frac{\kappa(\lambda'')}{\kappa(\lambda)}, \tag{9.58}$$

estimates of the depth-averaged RA were obtained for all available λ''. The values were expressed in terms of the ratio $\kappa(\lambda')/\kappa(0.100$ Å$)$ and are illustrated in Table 9.9; the last two values ($\Delta\lambda' = 0.25, 0.30$ Å) were

TABLE 9.9. Depth-averaged
ratios $\kappa(\Delta\lambda')/\kappa(0.100)$

$\Delta\lambda'$ (Å)	Ratio
0.125	0.35
0.150	0.18
0.175	0.12
0.200	0.073
0.250	0.046
0.300	0.032

obtained from the averages $\kappa(\Delta\lambda')/\kappa(0.2)$ multiplied by the ratio $\kappa(0.2)/\kappa(0.1)$.

In a parallel analysis, a test of the anticipated inverse-square-law variation of $\kappa(\Delta\lambda)$ was made by finding, for each $\Delta\lambda$ series, the value $\text{RA}(\Delta\lambda'/\Delta\lambda)^2$; to the extent that this is close to unity the law is valid. The results are shown in Table 9.10 and illustrate clearly that, at least for $\Delta\lambda \gtrsim 0.20$, the absorption coefficient does in fact vary closely as $(\Delta\lambda)^{-2}$. Rather coarse steps in RA were used in the basic computer

TABLE 9.10. Test of inverse-
square-law variation of $\kappa(\Delta\lambda)$

Series	$RA(\Delta\lambda'/\Delta\lambda)^2$
0.125	0.52
0.15	0.62
0.20	1.03
0.30	1.03
0.40	1.05
0.50	1.08
0.60	0.95
0.70	0.93

program and the corresponding estimates in Table 9.10 could perhaps
be improved. To a good approximation these results may be summarized in the statement that for $\Delta\lambda_A \gtrsim 0.2$,

$$\kappa(\Delta\lambda) = \frac{2.9 \times 10^{-3}}{\Delta\lambda_A^2} \kappa(0.100). \tag{9.59}$$

THE DEPTH AND WAVELENGTH VARIATIONS OF r_λ

The best estimate of the asymptotic form for the depth averaged
value of r_λ is obtained from the solutions of the basic equations (9.35) as

$$r_\lambda(D_1) \simeq 14\Delta\lambda_A^2,$$

and therefore,

$$r_\lambda(D_2) \simeq 7\Delta\lambda_A^2.$$

This is in good agreement with the results obtained from the line wings
(see Equation 9.53) but these values are not reliable to much better
than about 50%.

9.6.4 Discussion of the Results

THE DOPPLER WIDTH

The mean Doppler width in Table 9.4 is about 0.036 Å, which corresponds to a random velocity of 1.8 km/sec, i.e., to a kinetic tempera-

ture of the sodium atoms of about 4600 °K. We may accordingly conclude that only thermal motion is important in broadening the D line cores; the derived kinetic temperature compares very well with the solar boundary temperature given by all recent workers (see, e.g., Heintze, Hubenet, and de Jager, 1964) and—as we shall see—it is also consistent with the temperature structure derived in this analysis.

THE VALUES OF RA AND A DETERMINATION OF THE DAMPING CONSTANT

The inverse square dependence of RA on $\Delta\lambda$ derived in this analysis indicates that the line absorption coefficient has the standard form of the Voigt function $H(a, v)$. If the values of RA in Table 9.10 corresponded to a single depth we could presumably try a best fit of the ratios in Table 9.9 to $H(a, v)$ to determine the damping constant a. The values refer, however, to a variety of depths and this should, if possible, be allowed for; Curtis and Jefferies therefore proceeded as follows. It seems reasonable to require that the Doppler width in the line-forming region lies between the values 0.036 and 0.0425 Å—corresponding to the temperatures 4650 °K ($\tau_c = 0$) and 6500 °K ($\tau_c \sim 1$) derived from our analysis (see below). For a series of values of a, Hummer's (1965) tables of $U(a, v) \equiv H(a, v)/\sqrt{\pi}$ were used to evaluate $\kappa(\Delta\lambda')/\kappa(0.100 \text{ Å})$ for a series of values of $\Delta\lambda_D$ lying within the above

TABLE 9.11. Theoretical absorption coefficient ratios for various values of the Doppler widths

	$\Delta\lambda_D$	$\dfrac{\kappa(0.125)}{\kappa(0.100)}$	$\dfrac{\kappa(0.150)}{\kappa(0.100)}$	$\dfrac{\kappa(0.175)}{\kappa(0.100)}$	$\dfrac{\kappa(0.200)}{\kappa(0.100)}$
$a = 0.005$	0.0360	0.30	0.19	0.14	0.10
	0.0391	0.18	0.11	0.07	0.06
	0.0425	0.13	0.06	0.04	0.03
$a = 0.01$	0.0360	0.39	0.25	0.18	0.14
	0.0391	0.26	0.16	0.12	0.09
	0.0425	0.18	0.10	0.07	0.05
$a = 0.02$	0.0360	0.46	0.30	0.22	0.16
	0.0391	0.35	0.22	0.16	0.12
	0.0425	0.26	0.15	0.11	0.08

range. Some critical cases are shown in Table 9.11; these are to be compared with the values of Table 9.9 inferred from the analysis.

For $a = 0.005$ reasonable agreement can only be found for $\Delta\lambda_D = 0.0360$; the values in Table 9.9, however, refer to depths ($\tau_c \sim 0.1$ to 0.3) where the Doppler width is significantly larger than this. The computed ratios $\kappa(\Delta\lambda')/\kappa(0.100\ \text{Å})$ for $a = 0.005$ are rather too small, therefore, for agreement with Table 9.9. Similarly the values for $a = 0.02$ are rather too large. The value $a = 0.01$ is as good as we can infer in this manner; this refers to a region about $\log_{10} \tau_c \simeq -0.7$.

THE QUANTITY $r_\lambda(D_1)$ AND THE ABUNDANCE OF SODIUM

The ratio r_λ was taken to be constant through the atmosphere largely for convenience and as the first step in an iterative process. However, the values determined from the far wings and those from the line core are in such good agreement as to suggest that in fact this ratio *is* essentially constant in the solar atmosphere. The general internal consistency found throughout the analysis adds weight to this conclusion. Curtis and Jefferies were able to show, as follows, that this is entirely reasonable due to a pure coincidence.

The ratio r_λ is defined as

$$r_\lambda(D_1) = \kappa_c/\kappa_1(\Delta\lambda),$$

where κ_c is the continuous absorption coefficient at 5900 Å and $\kappa_1(\Delta\lambda)$ the D_1 line absorption coefficient. In the line wings we may write the absorption coefficient per atom for Lorentzian broadening (see Equation 4.95),

$$\alpha(\Delta\lambda) = \frac{e^2 f}{mc^3} \frac{\lambda^4 \delta}{(\Delta\lambda)^2} = \frac{3.8 \times 10^{-25}\delta}{\Delta\lambda_A^2}, \qquad (9.60)$$

where $\delta = \gamma/4\pi$, γ is the damping constant, and $f(D_1) = 0.32$. In addition, we have the relation (4.98),

$$\delta = \frac{ac\Delta\lambda_D}{\lambda^2}, \qquad (9.61)$$

so that (at $\tau_c \sim 0.2$) $\delta \simeq 3.4 \times 10^7 \text{ sec}^{-1}$ and $\gamma = 4.3 \times 10^8 \text{ sec}^{-1}$. The *radiation* damping constant for the D lines ($6.2 \times 10^7 \text{ sec}^{-1}$) is a factor of 10 lower than this, so that the damping must be due to collisional effects. In the solar photosphere the mechanism responsible for the broadening of the D lines is probably the van der Waals interaction (by H atoms). We therefore write,

$$\delta_H = K_H n_H \tag{9.62}$$

where K_H is taken to be independent of temperature and density. The appropriate concentration (at $\tau_c = 0.2$) is given in the Utrecht average model as $n_H = 1.2 \times 10^{17}$ (cm^{-3}) so that, with $\delta = 3.4 \times 10^7$ sec^{-1} we find $K_H = 2.8 \times 10^{-10}$ in cgs units.

In the line wings ($\Delta\lambda \gtrsim 0.2$ Å) this analysis gave the result

$$r_\lambda(D_1) = \frac{\alpha(H^-)n_{H^-}}{\alpha_\lambda(Na\ I)n_{Na\ I}} \simeq 14(\Delta\lambda_A)^2 \tag{9.63}$$

if—as is reasonable—we attribute all the continuous opacity to H^-. According to Geltman (1963), $\alpha(H^-) \simeq 3.3 \times 10^{-17}$ cm^2 at 6000 Å, so that

$$\frac{n_{H^-}}{n_{Na\ I}} = 1.6 \times 10^{-7}\delta, \tag{9.64}$$

while the modified Saha relation (see Equation 6.3) for the situation when the neutral sodium atoms are nearly all in the ground state gives

$$\frac{n_{H^-}}{n_{Na\ I}} \simeq \frac{1}{6b_1} \frac{n_H}{n_{Na\ II}} 10^{-2.21 \times 10^4/T}, \tag{9.65}$$

with b_1 the usual nonequilibrium parameter, while the partition function for Na I is taken as 3. Finally, from these two equations we obtain

$$b_1 \frac{n_{Na\ II}}{n_H} \simeq \frac{10^{(6 - 2.21 \times 10^4/T)}}{\delta}. \tag{9.66}$$

Since, in the photosphere, the sodium will be essentially all singly ionized while the hydrogen will be neutral, the left-hand side of this equation represents the sodium abundance A_{Na}, relative to hydrogen, multiplied by the factor b_1. The quantity on the right-hand side of Equation (9.66) was determined as a function of the 5000 Å continuum optical depth (τ_5) using the Utrecht average model of the photosphere; results are shown in Table 9.12. To the extent that these values are constant with depth, so we see from Equations (9.63) to (9.66) that the ratio r_λ is also constant. The relative constancy of r_λ over the lower layers of the atmosphere is due simply to a coincidental partial cancellation of the changes in the "Saha" term $10^{2.21 \times 10^4/T}$ with changes in the H atom concentration. Curtis and Jefferies concluded that, to a factor of order 2, the product $b_1 A_{Na}$ was 4×10^{-6} or, in a scale in which $n_H = 10^{12}$, $\log (b_1 A_{Na}) = 6.6$, and this value is within a factor 2 of that obtained by the standard LTE analysis. One may tentatively

TABLE 9.12. Values of the product $b_1 A_{Na}$ for broadening by neutral hydrogen atoms

τ_0	$b_1 A_{Na}$
0.10	1.8×10^{-6}
0.20	2.8×10^{-6}
0.45	4.8×10^{-6}
0.70	7.0×10^{-6}
1.00	10.0×10^{-6}

conclude that, for the formation of those parts of the D lines lying beyond $\Delta\lambda \simeq 0.15$ Å from the line center, LTE is a valid hypothesis. The same conclusion was reached in an entirely different manner by Johnson (1962, 1965).

THE DEPTH VARIATIONS OF THE LINE AND CONTINUUM SOURCE FUNCTIONS

The values of S_l and S_c yielded by this analysis may be referred to a single depth scale if we make use of the results of the preceding sections. The optical depth in the line is given as a function of that in the continuum by the relationship

$$\tau_l(\lambda) = \int_0^{\tau_5} \frac{\kappa_l(\lambda)}{\kappa_5} d\tau_5 \qquad (9.67)$$

with Equation (4.97),

$$\kappa_l(\lambda) = \frac{\pi e^2 f}{mc} \frac{1}{\sqrt{\pi} \Delta\nu_D} H(a, v) n_{Na\,I}, \qquad (9.68)$$

and $\kappa_5 = n_{H^-} \alpha_{H^-}$ (5000 Å) and τ_5 the continuum optical depth at 5000 Å. At 5000 Å, Geltman (1963) gives $\alpha_{H^-} = 2.8 \times 10^{-17}$ cm^2. To evaluate the integral (9.67), using the expression (9.68), Curtis and

Jefferies supposed that the Doppler width was purely thermal, that the ionization of Na I (and of H^-) followed LTE, that the sodium abundance was 2×10^{-6} (the LTE value) and that the opacity was entirely due to H^-. To relate n_H and T_e to τ_5 they used the Utrecht Reference Photosphere (1964). Their resulting depth variations for S_l and S_c are shown plotted as a function of τ_5 in Figure 9.17.

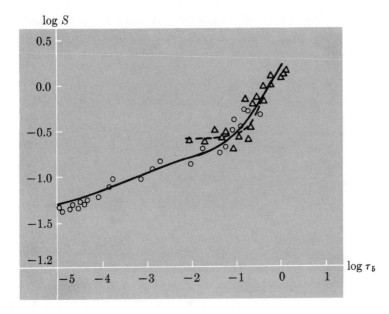

Figure 9.17. Variation with λ5000 continuum optical depth of the line (complete curve) and continuum (broken curve) source functions. The recovered values of S_l are shown by circles, those for S_c by triangles.

The relative values of S_l and S_c indicate that these two quantities are not significantly different over the range $\log \tau_5 > -2$. Very marginal evidence—based on two points of the $\Delta\lambda = 0.100$ Å series—suggests that the two source functions begin to separate at about $\tau_5 = 10^{-2}$. Thus we can conclude that the analysis of the D lines beyond $\Delta\lambda = 0.100$ Å from the line center can be carried out as in LTE. Since the D lines are the strongest lines of Na I, we can probably be confident that other lines of Na which will be formed deeper in the photosphere will be in LTE also. We may therefore anticipate that the standard LTE abundance analyses for Na I (based on curves of growth) should give reliable results.

THE TEMPERATURE STRUCTURE

If we suppose that S_c is Planckian, the depth variation of T_e follows at once. The temperature model given by the Utrecht workers and that given by Pierce and Waddell (1961) are compared with Curtis and Jefferies' results in Figure 9.18. The D line analysis yields a substantially more rapid temperature gradient than do the analyses of the continuum. The origin of this difference *may* lie in the different expansion forms for S_c adopted for the solution of the limb darkening equation, but the continuum analyses are not very trustworthy for

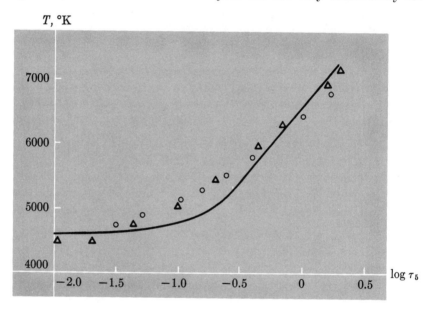

Figure 9.18. Photospheric temperature distributions. The full line shows the results obtained in this analysis of the *D*-line wings. Pierce-Waddell (1961) model is shown by circles; Utrecht 1964 model by triangles. The abscissa is continuum optical depth at 5000 Å.

$\tau_5 \lesssim 0.2$ since reliable data at such small depths must rely on observations out to $\mu \lesssim 0.2$. The influence of "seeing" on these observations is, of course, to yield a smoother temperature gradient than that which actually exists. The analysis reviewed above, while allowing an inference of T_e out to smaller optical depths, suffers from uncertainties associated with the transformation from the composite variable τ_λ to the continuum optical depth τ_5.

The boundary temperature $T \simeq 4600\ °K$ of Figure 9.18 is in agreement with the best recent estimates as summarized in the Utrecht model; it also agrees remarkably well with the value inferred from the mean Doppler width which was, of course, obtained by an entirely independent procedure. It is to be noted, however, that this latter value applies to the region ($\tau_5 \sim 10^{-4}$) where the *cores* of the D lines are formed (see Figure 9.17). We infer, therefore, that the temperature at $\tau_5 \sim 10^{-4}$ is still close to 4600 °K. There is a suggestion that the layers farther out than this have higher kinetic temperatures (a conclusion indicated in Section 9.6.1), but the analysis gives no support to the idea that a chromospheric temperature minimum is located near $\tau_5 \simeq 10^{-2}$—where it is sometimes placed.

THE LINE SOURCE FUNCTION

Values of S_l are obtained from the core and intermediate wavelength analyses discussed in Sections 9.6.1 and 9.6.3. To represent these on a common depth scale, say that at the line center, requires knowledge of the transformation $t_\lambda(t_0)$. This can be readily accomplished using the data obtained above for the line and continuum absorption coefficients. The variation of S_l thus obtained is shown as a function of $t_l(0)$ in D_1 in Figure 9.19. We lack the apparatus for a full analysis of

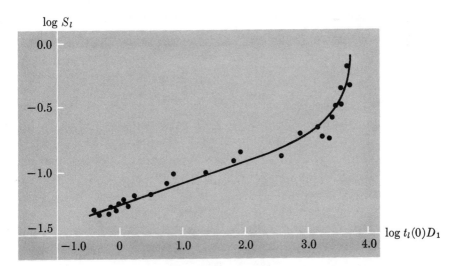

Figure 9.19. The inferred depth variation of the Na D-line source function as a function of depth in the center of D_1.

this curve in terms of the atmospheric structure and shall have to limit the discussion to some semi-quantitative remarks. First, the sudden increase in S_l near $t_l(0) \sim 3 \times 10^3$ is simply a result of the increasing degree of ionization of Na I at these depths which results in a nonlinear transformation between $t_l(0)$ and τ_5. Of more interest is the scale of variation, and the surface value, of S_l. According to the theory developed in Chapter 7, the D line source function should be inter-pretable in terms of the relation (Equation 7.33),

$$S_l \simeq \frac{\int J_\nu \phi_\nu \, d\nu + \varepsilon B + \eta B^*}{1 + \varepsilon + \eta}. \qquad (9.69)$$

In our discussion (see Section 7.1.5) of the excitation mechanisms for neutral and singly ionized atoms in the sun's atmosphere, we drew attention to an important dichotomy according to whether lines were "collisionally" controlled or "photoelectrically" controlled. Essen-tially the former case corresponds to that in which $\varepsilon B > \eta B^*$, $\varepsilon > \eta$, while for the latter $\varepsilon B < \eta B^*$, $\varepsilon < \eta$. As a general rule, resonance lines of neutral atoms like Na I belong to the second category while those of ionized metals have source terms controlled by collisions. In fact, as shown by Johnson (1965), this conclusion turns out to be incorrect for Na D mainly because the photoionization cross section from the ground ($3\,^2S$) state is very small. Rough estimates of the transition rates are shown in Table 9.13 and from those we find at once

TABLE 9.13. Na I transition rates (cgs units)

Photoelectric transitions

Transition	Rate
$3S \to \kappa$	4×10^1
$3P \to \kappa$	9×10^3
$\kappa \to 3S$	$10^{-16} n_e$
$\kappa \to 3P$	$10^{-15} n_e$

Collision Transitions

Transition	$T_e = 4.7 \times 10^3$	$T_e = 10^4$
$3S \to 3P$	$10^{-9} n_e$	$3 \times 10^{-8} n_e$
$3P \to 3S$	$8 \times 10^{-8} n_e$	$1 \times 10^{-7} n_e$

that $\varepsilon \simeq 10^{-15} n_e$ while $\eta \simeq 10^{-5}$ and that $\eta B^*/\varepsilon B \simeq 3 \times 10^{10}/n_e$. Since $n_e > 10^{10}$ cm^{-3} in any region of interest to us, the Na D source functions will be controlled by the ε, εB terms rather than by the photoelectric η, ηB^* terms. This conclusion is somewhat tentative, however, because of the extremely oversimplified atomic model used for the derivation of Equation (9.69).

Solutions of the transfer equation have mainly concentrated on the isothermal uniform density case for which

$$S_l(0) = \sqrt{(\varepsilon/1 + \varepsilon)}B. \tag{9.70}$$

The solar photosphere is not isothermal but to sufficient accuracy for discussion of our results we may suppose that Equation (9.70) applies with ε constant and with B referring to some mean atmospheric temperature between 4650 °K ($\tau_c = 0$) and 6500 °K ($\tau_c = 1$). From Figure 9.19 we have

$$S_l(0) \simeq 5 \times 10^{-2} B', \tag{9.71}$$

where B' is the Planck function at 5900 Å for the effective temperature of the emergent continuum radiation, from the center of the sun's disk. In other words, B' is equal to the emergent continuum intensity at $\mu = 1$ at 5900 Å. Since B' refers to depths at $\tau_c \simeq 1$, it cannot be less than the B entering Equation (9.70). We therefore must have, as a mean value,

$$\varepsilon \gtrsim 2 \times 10^{-3}, \tag{9.72}$$

that is,

$$n_e \gtrsim 2 \times 10^{12} \text{ cm}^{-3}. \tag{9.73}$$

This is not unreasonable; in the Utrecht model such electron densities occur at $\tau_5 \gtrsim 0.03$. These results are not inconsistent with the crude theory; however, a much more detailed study is necessary before we could interpret Figure 9.19 with any confidence.

The theoretical scale length, $1/\varepsilon$, for variation of S_l is also reasonably consistent with that shown in Figure 9.19.

9.6.5 Conclusions

In this concluding section we shall try to place the method in a broader perspective than has been possible in the detailed study above.

In the first place, it is necessary to re-emphasize the logical development and, to avoid any misunderstandings, to contrast the procedure with the standard LTE analyses. Curtis and Jefferies' general method rests on the facts, *established outside the analysis*, that the line source function is independent of frequency, and that two lines in a multiplet share a common value for S_l at a given physical depth. These conclusions also hold for the special case of LTE but are far more general in their application and are derived, of course, without recourse to that assumption. The procedure, therefore, neither asserts nor denies *a priori* the existence of LTE; it seeks instead to determine separately the depth variations of S_l and S_c and of the parameters r_λ and RA.

For the special case of the D lines (and only for this case) they found the result that $S_l \simeq S_c$ for depths $\tau_5 \gtrsim 10^{-2}$. Thus, within its limitations, the procedure *proves* that LTE validly describes the excitation of Na I (at least insofar as S_c is given by the Planck function) over a substantial part of the photosphere. It proves nothing more; it does not establish that LTE is valid for the excitation of any other element nor does it disprove it. It does, however, give a procedure for *testing* the assumption in any particular case.

We should not presume that the fact that LTE has been established for the D lines is a *post hoc* justification for the arguments adduced in its support as a general principle. Sodium is (next to H^-) the most easily ionized element in the sun's atmosphere. It can be ionized by radiation of 2000 Å, a spectral region where the continuum is still very significant. As pointed out by Johnson (whose conclusions are similar to ours) this fact will be important in determining the Na excitation.

9.7 The Empirical Determination of Doppler Widths from Profiles of Multiplet Lines

It was shown by Goldberg* (1958) that under certain assumptions the Doppler width for multiplet lines may be inferred directly from the observed line profiles. A method somewhat more general than Goldberg's may be derived as follows. In the core of a strong line (i.e., when r_λ is negligible) the emergent intensity is given by the familiar expression

$$I(\Delta\lambda, \mu) = \int_0^\infty S_l(z) \exp\left[-\int_0^z \kappa(\Delta\lambda)\frac{dx}{\mu}\right]\kappa(\Delta\lambda)\frac{dz}{\mu}, \qquad (9.74)$$

---

* Goldberg's method is similar to one introduced earlier by de Jager (1952) and used by Athay and Thomas (1958) to study the profiles of the solar Balmer lines.

where z is a depth variable. Suppose we take $S_l(z)$ to be independent of frequency across a line, and agree that two close-lying lines of the same multiplet will share a common value of the line source function at each location z. It then follows at once that, if the two lines have equal intensities for a given value of μ at distances $\Delta\lambda_1$ and $\Delta\lambda_2$, respectively, from their line centers,

$$\int_0^\infty S_l(z)\left\{\kappa_1(\Delta\lambda_1)\exp\left[-\int_0^z \kappa_1(\Delta\lambda_1)\frac{dx}{\mu}\right]\right.$$
$$\left.-\kappa_2(\Delta\lambda_2)\exp\left[-\int_0^z \kappa_2(\Delta\lambda_2)\frac{dx}{\mu}\right]\right\}\frac{dz}{\mu} = 0. \quad (9.75)$$

Equation (9.75) can be satisfied for arbitrary pairs $\Delta\lambda_1$, $\Delta\lambda_2$ only if the expression in braces vanishes. If the absorption coefficient is independent of depth, this in turn requires that

$$\kappa_1(\Delta\lambda_1) = \kappa_2(\Delta\lambda_2). \quad (9.76)$$

If the lines originate from lower levels differing in statistical weight, though of essentially the same energy, so that the Boltzmann factor can be neglected, the condition (9.76) may be written (see Equation 4.97),

$$\frac{\phi(\Delta\lambda_1)}{\phi(\Delta\lambda_2)} = \frac{(gf)_2}{(gf)_1}, \quad (9.77)$$

where the $\phi(\Delta\lambda)$ are the usual normalized absorption coefficient profile functions. In particular, in the line core where ϕ may be taken as gaussian, the Doppler width is found from the relation

$$\Delta\lambda_D = \frac{\lambda\overline{V}}{c}, \quad (9.78)$$

with the Doppler velocity $\overline{V}$ given by the formula

$$\frac{\overline{V}^2}{c^2} = \frac{(\Delta\lambda_2/\lambda_2)^2 - (\Delta\lambda_1/\lambda_1)^2}{\ln k}, \quad (9.79)$$

where

$$k = \frac{(gf\lambda)_2}{(gf\lambda)_1}. \quad (9.80)$$

The method formulated by Goldberg has been applied extensively by Unno (1959) and, as mentioned above, it was used by Waddell in inferring the Doppler widths of the solar D lines. The method is limited, however, by the restriction that $\Delta\lambda_D$ be depth-independent; when this is not so, serious errors can be made, as we have seen in

Section 9.6.   An even more extreme case of failure of the procedure was illustrated by Pecker and Roddier (1965), who constructed artificial profiles using a Doppler width which decreased with depth, and who found that an analysis of these profiles using Goldberg's procedure yielded, in fact, a Doppler width which *increased* with depth and generally bore little relation to that assumed in computing the line profiles. It is, however, a little difficult to see how such an extreme effect can be obtained, and the conclusion needs checking.

REFERENCES

ATHAY, R. G., and R. N. THOMAS, 1958, "On the Use of the Early Balmer Lines to Extend the Photospheric Model," *Astrophys. J. 137*, 96.

BÖHM, K. H., 1961, "A Basic Limit of the Information Contained in Center-To-Limb Observations," *Astrophys. J. 134*, 264.

BRILLOUIN, L., 1956, *Science and Information Theory*.   New York: Academic Press.

CURTIS, G. W., and J. T. JEFFERIES, 1965, "Inference of the Line Source Function for the Sodium D Lines," *Proceedings, Second Harvard–Smithsonian Conference on Stellar Atmospheres*, p. 297.

CURTIS, G. W., and J. T. JEFFERIES, 1965, "The Analysis of Spectral Line Profiles," *Final Report; AFSWC Contract No. AF 29(601)-6013*, Ch. III.

DAVID, H., 1961, "Die Mitte-Rand-Variation der Balmerlinien Hα-Hδ auf der Sonnenscheibe," *Z. Astrophys. 53*, 37.

DE JAGER, C., 1952, "The Hydrogen Spectrum of the Sun," *Rech. Astr. Obs. Utrecht 13*, 50.

FINN, G. D., and D. MUGGLESTONE, 1967, "The Sodium D Line Profiles in Pure Absorption," *Mon. Not. R. Astron. Soc.* (in press).

GELTMAN, S., 1963, "The Bound-Free Absorption Coefficient of the Hydrogen Negative Ion," *Astrophys. J. 136*, 935.

GOLDBERG, L., 1958, "On the Empirical Determination of Line-Absorption Coefficients," *Astrophys. J. 127*, 308.

HEINTZE, J. R. W., H. HUBENET, and C. DE JAGER, 1964, "A Reference Model of the Solar Photosphere and Low Chromosphere," *Bull. Astron. Inst. Netherlands 17*, 442.

HUMMER, D. G., 1965, "The Voigt Function, An Eight-Significant-Figure Table and Generating Procedure," *R. Astron. Soc. Memoirs 70*, 1.

HUMMER, D. G., and J. T. JEFFERIES, 1965, "Derivation of the Source Function from the Inversion of the Limb Darkening and Emergent Flux Equations," *Final Report; AFSWC Contract No. AF 29(601)-6013*, Ch. IV.

JEFFERIES, J. T., 1965, "The Theory of the Chromospheric Spectrum," Symposium: *The Solar Spectrum*.   Dordrecht-Holland: D. Reidel.

JEFFERIES, J. T., and F. Q. ORRALL, 1960, "The Numerical Solution of Fredholm Integral Equations of the First Kind," *Geophys. Res. Directorate Notes 48*, 1960.

JOHNSON, H. R., 1962, "The Equilibrium of Na I in the Solar Photosphere," *Ann. d'Astrophys. 25,* 35.

JOHNSON, H. R., 1965, "Sodium Equilibrium and the Na I D Lines," *Proceedings, Second Harvard–Smithsonian Conference on Stellar Atmospheres,* p. 333.

KING, J. I. F., 1964, "Inversion by Slabs of Varying Thickness," *J. Atmos. Sci. 21,* 324.

KING, J. I. F., 1965, "Reply" (to comments by S. Twomey), *J. Atmos. Sci. 22,* 96.

KOURGANOFF, V., 1952, "Basic Methods in Transfer Problems," Oxford: Clarendon Press.

PECKER, J. C., 1965, "Model Atmospheres," *Ann. Rev. Astron. and Astrophys. 3,* 135.

PECKER, J. C., and F. RODDIER, 1965, "Micromotions, Macromotions, and Non-LTE Effects," *Proceedings, Second Harvard–Smithsonian Conference on Stellar Atmospheres,* p. 437.

PIERCE, A. K., and J. H. WADDELL, 1961, "Analysis of Limb Darkening Observations," *Mem. Roy. Astr. Soc. 58,* 89.

PIERCE, A. K., and J. H. WADDELL, 1964, "Excitation-Temperature Equality in the Balmer Lines," *Astrophys. J. 140,* 1160.

SUEMOTO, Z., 1957, "Interferometric Study of Profiles of Faint Fraunhofer Lines," *Mon. Not. R. Astron. Soc. 117,* 2.

SYKES, J. B., 1953, "The Integral Equation of Limb-Darkening," *Mon. Not. R. Astron. Soc. 113,* 198.

TWOMEY, S., 1965, "Comments on the 'Inversion by Slabs of Varying Thickness'," *J. Atmos. Sci. 22,* 95.

UNNO, W., 1959, "Turbulent Motion in the Solar Atmosphere; I, Doppler Widths of Photospheric Lines," *Astrophys. J. 129,* 375.

WADDELL, J. H., 1958, "Study of Solar Turbulence Based on Profiles of Weak Fraunhofer Lines," *Astrophys. J. 127,* 284.

WADDELL, J. H., 1962a, "Center-to-Limb Observations of the Sodium D Lines," *Astrophys. J. 136,* 223.

WADDELL, J. H., 1962b, "Analysis of the Center to Limb Observations of the Sodium D Lines," *Astrophys. J. 136,* 231.

WADDELL, J. H., 1963, "The Source Functions of the Magnesium b Lines," *Astrophys. J. 137,* 1210.

WHITE, O. R., 1962, "Limb-Darkening Observations of Hα, Hβ, and Hγ," *Astrophys. J. Suppl. No. 70,* p. 333.

WHITE, O. R., 1963, "Analysis of Center-to-Limb Variations in Hα, Hβ, and Hγ," *Astrophys. J. 137,* 1217.

WHITE, O. R., 1964, "On the Empirical Temperature Structure of the Solar Chromosphere," *Astrophys. J. 140,* 1164.

WHITE, O. R., 1965, "An Analysis of Solar Balmer Line Profiles," *Proceedings, Second Harvard–Smithsonian Conference on Stellar Atmospheres,* p. 355.

WHITE, O. R., 1967, "Inversion of the Limb Darkening Equation Using the Prony Algorithm," *Astrophys. J.* (submitted for publication).

WHITTAKER, E. T., and G. ROBINSON, 1932, "The Calculus of Observations," London: Blackie and Son, p. 368.

10

The Analysis of Spectral Line Profiles: II. The Validity of LTE for Photospheric Analyses

It has been recognized for a long time that difficulties exist in explaining, in terms of LTE, the core intensities of certain strong solar lines, such as those of the Mg b group and the D lines, since their low central intensities would require that the atmospheric temperature drop to values far below those which we can reasonably associate with the level of formation of the line cores. For example, the central intensity of the solar D_2 line is observed to be about 4% of that of the neighboring continuum. If this were interpreted on an LTE model it would require the temperature near unit optical depth in the center of D_2 to be about 3500 °K, a value much too small to be consistent with that derived from many other lines of evidence, e.g., the analyses of the photospheric and chromospheric continua. Various attempts have been made to account for such low central intensities in the framework of LTE by appealing to the mechanism of "line blanketing" which, by increasing the opacity in the extreme outer layers of a star, reduces the temperature in the region of formation of the line below that corresponding to the radiative equilibrium model for the observed total continuum flux. For the sun, at least, such attempts have failed quantitatively to give sufficient temperature reductions, and it would now generally be conceded that the cores of the strong solar lines

256

cannot be explained on the LTE assumption. Their analysis must, therefore, proceed from a more general basis such as that given in the preceding chapter.

On the other hand, the excitation of atoms having complicated energy-level structures (e.g., neutral Ti, Fe, Cr) has almost always been described in terms of LTE distributions. It is not an easy matter to establish theoretically whether this is a valid approach, and the case for its acceptance has usually been argued on the basis of consistency of the derived results, e.g., that Fe I and Fe II analyses give the same abundance—Aller, O'Mara, and Little (1964)—or that the derived solar abundances are independent of the excitation of the lines used, or of the angle ($\cos^{-1} \mu$) at which the observations are made; cf. Müller and Mutschlecner (1964). Such arguments are strong and may indeed ultimately be decisive. In contrast to these stand the equally straightforward analyses by Pecker and his colleagues which lead to the conclusion that the assumption of LTE is not a consistent one.

The tremendous simplification in spectral-line analysis made possible by the LTE assumption lies in the fact that it immediately provides one implicit relationship between the intensities of each line of a given element which is emitted by the gas. While there is still a long way to go, even when granted the LTE assumption, to complete a quantitative analysis of a given spectrum, the procedure is then nevertheless relatively simple in principle. Because of this, and of the fact that a tremendous volume of work is based on LTE, it is important to establish whether the assumption is, or is not, likely to be valid for a stellar atmosphere.

In this chapter we shall discuss some aspects of the question without, however, considering the detailed techniques of the LTE analysis which are described fully, for example, by Aller (1960). In Section 10.1 a summary is given of some theoretical arguments for and against the assumption and, since it seems impossible at this time to reach a conclusion on those grounds, we turn in Sections 10.3 and 10.4 to a discussion of the evidence available on empirical grounds both for and against the hypothesis.

10.1 Theoretical Arguments

Complete local thermodynamic equilibrium is a state in which the population distribution among *all* the bound and free states of a gas may be described to first order by the corresponding thermodynamic equilibrium distributions associated with the local kinetic temperature. Less restrictively, we can consider a state of LTE between a pair of levels as applying when their relative populations are described by the Boltzmann formula at the local temperature.   In such a case the source function for the line formed between these levels is just equal to the Planck function $B_\nu(T)$ for the same temperature.   For example, since we feel justified in supposing the free (kinetic) energy modes as being distributed relative to one another as in LTE, the source function for *free–free* radiation is Planckian. The ultimate reason for this, of course, lies in the dominance of collision processes among the free levels.

One way to establish that LTE applies between the continuum and a particular bound level is to prove that it is populated primarily by collisions. If we wish, in these terms, to justify the LTE assumption for a specific line transition, we must establish that the upper *and* the lower states are populated predominantly by collisions. In other words, we must show that the energy of each photon arises directly from the thermal energy of the gas through a collision, and that it goes back into thermal energy on absorption as a result of a de-exciting collision. Unless this is so, the photon cannot reflect the *local* kinetic temperature in a unique way. Under stellar atmospheric conditions it is very difficult to show that the states of an atom will be so populated simply because the collision transition rates are too small—as shown in Section 6.3.1, we generally require electron densities in excess of 10^{15} cm^{-3} before collisional processes compete with their radiative counterparts in permitted lines.

If radiative transitions predominate, however, we can still establish LTE in a given line provided the radiation intensity is equal to the Planck function at the local temperature—this is the situation in a blackbody, or deep enough in a stellar atmosphere where the absorption and emission transitions in the line balance in detail.*

Various theoretical attempts have been made to prove the validity or consistency of LTE in a stellar atmosphere, but none carries conviction. Unsöld's arguments and those of Böhm, are discussed earlier (see Section 3.4) and need not be repeated here; as we pointed out there, they are essentially circular. There seems to be a general feeling,

---

* Strictly, S_ν tends to $B_\nu(T_e)$ at large depths only for a restricted class of temperature variations.   It will not hold, for example, across a region where the electron temperature changes discontinuously. (Cf. Kourganoff (1952), p. 50 *et seq.* for further details.)

however, that in an atom with a complex structure the multiplicity of energy levels will lead to an LTE distribution simply because there are so many levels which can interact.   However, the lower levels are found to be grouped in narrow energy regions ($\Delta E \sim 0.1$ ev) between each of which exists a substantial energy separation ($\Delta E \sim 1$ ev).   The mere existence, within an individual group, of a large number of closely spaced levels between which collisional transitions are highly probable may establish the populations in proportion to their statistical weights *within the group* but will do nothing to establish the *relative* group populations in LTE.   In the limit, a narrow band of many levels is the equivalent of a single level as broadened by collisional damping, and there is certainly no case to be made for the adoption of LTE simply because a line is pressure-broadened.

There is the important point here, however, that the existence of strong collisions among the close-lying energy levels will cause the corresponding spectral lines arising from transitions between two such groups to be closely coupled, and so to reflect a common depth variation in their source functions—equivalently they will possess a common run of excitation temperature (T_{ex}) with depth.   The same is true in LTE —when $T_{ex} = T_e$—and this fact may lead to difficulties in empirical attempts to establish LTE as a valid description of the excitation state.

Theoretical attempts to establish whether or not LTE is valid in a stellar atmosphere have been essentially qualitative and along the lines given above.   It is hard to see why LTE *should* be a good description, bearing in mind the generally low electron densities in the line-forming regions of stars, but it may be that some influences are being over-looked in the qualitative physical arguments—perhaps the background continuum plays a more significant role than is obvious and perhaps the general density increase with depth, with the consequent reduction in the photon diffusion lengths, is more critical than we have envisaged. An answer can only come from a detailed solution to the transfer and statistical equilibrium equations, and with the rapid progress of the past years this should be clarified soon.

In summary, the situation is unclear; on theoretical grounds there are no obvious reasons to justify the assumption of LTE for the analysis of photospheric lines; in fact, there seem good reasons to believe that it is not a correct description.   As a matter of practical importance, however, we have no way yet to estimate the influence of any de-partures from LTE on the derived properties of the gas.

10.2 Empirical Arguments against LTE

It is true that the LTE assumption permits a tremendous simplification in the analysis of a spectrum; it is equally true that in principle it carries ample opportunity for testing its self-consistency from empirical studies of observed spectral line profiles because of the great range and variety of these. A large part of the task of testing this self-consistency has been undertaken by Pecker and his colleagues and students in Paris; in the first part of this section we discuss their work in detail before turning to the equally significant discussion of Müller and Mutschlecner (1964).

10.2.1 Pecker's Analysis of the Solar Ti I Lines

In the first of a series of papers "Ecarts à l'équilibre et abondances dans les photosphères solaire et stellaires," Pecker (1959) attempted an analysis of the solar spectrum of neutral titanium with the specific aim of determining whether LTE provided a self-consistent assumption for the analysis simultaneously of the whole profiles of these lines, and of the continuum intensities. His procedure, which is reviewed below, centered on testing the agreement between the observed central intensities and those which would be predicted from the LTE theory.

The emergent intensity in the direction μ is given by the usual relation

$$I_\nu(0, \mu) = \int_0^\infty S(\tau)e^{-\tau/\mu} \frac{d\tau}{\mu}, \qquad (10.1)$$

where frequency subscripts on S and τ have been suppressed for convenience and where S is the composite source function of Equation (9.2) while τ is the total (line plus continuum) optical depth. For a monotonic source function we can always determine an "effective" depth of formation τ^* such that

$$I_\nu(0, \mu) = S(\tau^*); \qquad (10.2)$$

for example, if S is linear in τ, the Eddington-Barbier relation gives

$$\tau^* = \mu. \qquad (10.3)$$

More complicated dependencies of S on τ have been discussed by Dumont and Pecker (1958); however, as a first approximation we shall adopt, with Pecker, the result (10.3) with the understanding that we may always return to modify it if the subsequent analysis allows a determination of $S(t)$.

At the center of a strong line, where the absorption coefficient in the line is much greater than that in the continuum, the value of S is essentially that of the *line* source function—if LTE is valid this point is trivial since both S_l and S_c are identical at a given depth and frequency. Taking S_l to be independent of frequency over the core of the line, we may rewrite Equation (10.2) for the line center ν_0 in the form,

$$I_{\nu_0}(0, \mu) = B_\nu[T^{\ell a}_{\text{ex}}(\tau^*_0)], \tag{10.4}$$

where τ^*_0 refers to the line center, and the excitation temperature $T^{\ell a}_{\text{ex}}$ between the lower (ℓ) and upper (a) levels of the line is defined, in our usual notation, by the equation

$$\frac{n_a}{n_\ell} \equiv \frac{g_a}{g_\ell} \exp\left(-\frac{\chi_{a\ell}}{kT^{\ell a}_{\text{ex}}}\right) \equiv \frac{b_a}{b_\ell} \frac{g_a}{g_\ell} \exp\left(-\frac{\chi_{a\ell}}{kT_e}\right). \tag{10.5}$$

For a specific line a value of the excitation temperature in Equation (10.4) follows at once from the measured central intensity. For a meaningful comparison with other lines and with the continuum model, we must transform τ^*_0 onto some standard scale of optical depth —say that of the continuum at 5000 Å, which we shall denote by τ_c. The required transformation is then

$$\tau_0 = \tau_c + \int_0^{\tau_c} \frac{\kappa_l(0)}{\kappa_c} \, d\tau_c, \tag{10.6}$$

where $\kappa_l(0)$ and κ_c denote the absorption coefficients at the line center and in the 5000 Å continuum respectively. Following Claas (1951), the ratio κ_l/κ_c for the line center is expressible in the form (see Equation 4.97)

$$\frac{\kappa_l(0)}{\kappa_c} = Agf \frac{n_\ell}{g_\ell n_T} \left[1 - \frac{n_a}{n_\ell} \frac{g_\ell}{g_a}\right] \frac{\lambda_0 \sqrt{\pi}}{mc\overline{V}} \frac{e^2}{} \frac{H(a, 0)}{\overline{k}_c} \tag{10.7}$$

with n_T the total concentration of atoms of the element of interest, $\overline{V}$ the mean velocity appearing in the Doppler width, $\overline{k}_c$ the continuous absorption coefficient, at 5000 Å, per atom of the total hydrogen content (i.e., H atoms plus protons) and A is the abundance ratio (by number of atoms) of the element to the total hydrogen concentration.

A test as to whether LTE is a self-consistent assumption for the analysis of spectral lines and of the continuum is now straightforward, provided that we have an adequate model of the temperature, gas pressure, electron pressure, and the "microturbulence" parameter entering $\bar{V}$, as functions of depth. The first three are given by an LTE analysis of the continuum observations, together with the usual assumption of hydrostatic equilibrium. The depth variation of the microturbulence is obtained from studies of line profiles, and is often the most uncertain of all the parameters. On the basis of such a model and the assumption of LTE, the abundance A of an element may be deduced from measured equivalent widths and known values of the line strengths gf in the usual manner described, for example, in the comprehensive treatment by Goldberg *et al.* (1960).

In order to compute the absorption coefficient ratio (10.7) required for the optical depth transformation (10.6), Pecker adopted the LTE abundance A and the Saha and Boltzmann relations for the ratio n_ℓ/n_T. He investigated a number of lines of neutral titanium, grouping them into multiplets when the excitation potentials of the lower levels of the lines fell within rather narrow energy ranges. The multiplet assignments are shown in Figure 10.1. To compute the corresponding

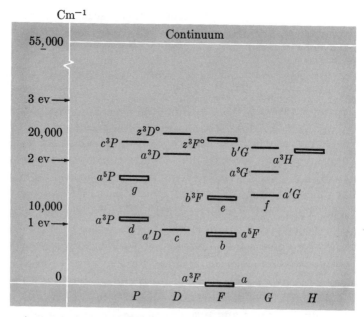

Figure 10.1. Partial energy level diagram for neutral titanium showing the assignment of "multiplets" adopted by Pecker.

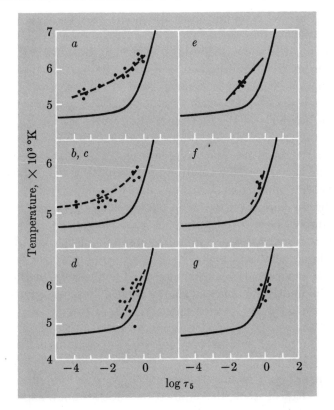

Figure 10.2. Excitation temperatures for Ti I lines deduced by Pecker for lines of the different multiplets shown in Figure 10.1. The full lines illustrate the assumed photospheric temperature distribution. The values for multiplets *f* and *g* are incorrect; see text. (After Pecker, 1959, Figure 3.)

excitation temperatures from Equation (10.4), Pecker used corrected central intensities from the Utrecht Atlas; these refer to the center of the solar disk. The derived excitation temperatures were then plotted at the appropriate value of $\tau_c(\tau_0^* = 1)$ and an immediate comparison made between T_{ex} and the corresponding value of T_e given by the model. Pecker's results are reproduced in Figure 10.2, the plotted points indicating values of T_{ex} and the full line representing the photospheric temperature model, derived from the empirical analysis of the continuous spectrum, which was used in making the transformation (10.6). A reanalysis by Jefferies and Pecker (1963, unpublished) shows that the results for the *f* and *g* multiplets in Figure 10.2 are in fact incorrectly plotted; the points should be moved to the left by about

1.0 in log τ_c. The difference between the T_{ex} and T_e curves gives striking evidence that the assumption of LTE does not, in fact, provide a consistent basis simultaneously for the analysis of the *central intensities* of the solar Ti lines, of the *equivalent widths* of the Ti lines (from which the abundance A is derived), and of the *solar continuum*. To carry the analysis further, it would be necessary to determine the departure coefficients b_n which enter the transformation $\tau_c(\tau_0^*)$ and to determine a new abundance taking into account the first approximation $S_l(\tau_c)$ derived from the central intensities. Pecker indicated the outline of the corresponding iterative procedure; this was carried out by Kandel (1960) in a paper discussed later in this chapter.

We digress here from the main stream of Pecker's analysis to consider a further aspect of Figure 10.2, namely that the excitation temperature for lines arising from a common lower level, i.e., the lines in one of the lettered multiplets, seem to trace out a single curve which one might associate with a common run of line source function for each line of the multiplet. One might not immediately have expected this result if the lines are not formed in LTE. If we accepted LTE, the fact that the solar temperature decreases toward the top of the photosphere would lead us also to accept the suggestion that the central depth of a line is a measure of its "strength"—$Agfn_\ell$—that is, roughly of the distance out in the atmosphere where it is formed. We would then also expect that the equivalent width would depend almost uniquely on this strength, i.e., we would expect that a "curve of growth" could be drawn for the lines of a multiplet.

If, however, we are forced to abandon the concept of LTE, we must be prepared to accept the possibility that lines of different multiplets—or even lines of the same multiplet—may have *independent* source functions which reflect the local electron temperature distribution either not at all or in different ways. The concept of a curve of growth in such a case loses its intuitive quality altogether for lines showing some saturation.

The fact that it *is* nevertheless possible, even without LTE, to obtain a curve of growth for a single multiplet is not difficult to account for. Weak lines on the linear part of the curve act essentially as optically thin absorbers of the continuous radiation; the amount absorbed being proportional (for a given lower excitation potential) to the gf value for the transition. For stronger lines, however, the details of the depth distribution of the line source function will start to influence the dependence of equivalent width on the *gf* value.   Only if all lines of a multiplet share a common distribution of T_{ex} over most of the atmosphere can we meaningfully speak of "*a*" curve of growth* (we neglect those effects associated with differences in the damping parameter *a*).

Various suggestions have been made to account for the results in Figure 10.2 within the framework of LTE.   In particular, criticism has been made of Pecker's model, his observational data, and of the *gf* values used.   The latter can be disposed of readily; Pecker used the relative *gf* values of King and King (1938); these are in excellent general agreement with the recent measures of Corliss and Bozman (1962) and it therefore seems unlikely that this can be regarded as a serious source of error.   The Utrecht Atlas is not sufficiently accurate for determination of central intensities, especially for strong lines; however, the differences between T_{ex} and T_e are too large to be accounted for in this way, and in any case Kandel's repetition of the analysis using data obtained by Miss Müller at the McMath-Hulbert Observatory resulted in essentially the same conclusion.

A more important criticism is that directed against the adopted photospheric model.   The curves shown in Figure 10.2 are rather misleading; limb darkening gives little information on the photosphere model for $\tau_c < 10^{-1}$, and eclipse measurements are by no means entirely satisfactory in extending the model into the low chromosphere. We cannot, therefore, place much emphasis on the temperature discrepancy in regions where $\tau_c \lesssim 10^{-1}$, even accepting the results of the Na *D* analysis in Chapter 9.   Still, it remains to account for the differences at $\tau_c > 10^{-1}$.   The distribution of the velocity $\bar{V}$ is poorly known and can influence the derived excitation temperature markedly. It is not clear, however, that the discrepancy in Figure 10.2 can be accounted for by reasonable variations in $\bar{V}$—though indeed it is hard to say what is reasonable.   The *D* line analysis discussed in the preceding chapter indicates a very low value in the region where the *D* line cores are formed, but Roddier (1965) has reached an entirely different conclusion from observations of the Sr I resonance line λ4607. The question needs a closer analysis.   More important are the suggestions (a) that inhomogeneities could produce effects which could be wrongly interpreted as departures from LTE, and (b) that Pecker's

---

* This fact was clearly recognized by Pecker, who insisted, correspondingly, that the matching of curves of growth must be based on matching the 45-deg sections (weak lines), and not, as is usually done, by forcing a best fit for all lines of such multiplets.

results are, in fact, largely due to the judicious choice of a model. That these seem also unable to account for the effect is shown in the study by Pecker and Vogel (1960) of the relative behavior of solar lines of Ti I and Cr I.

10.2.2 Comparative Analyses of Ti I and Cr I

In an effort to determine the reality of Pecker's conclusion that the central intensities of the solar Ti I lines were not consistent with LTE, Pecker and Vogel (1960) undertook a similar analysis of the solar Cr I spectrum.   Since the ionization potentials of neutral Ti and Cr are equal (at 6.8 ev) then, if the atoms are excited in accordance with LTE, a line of Ti I and one of Cr I which have equal central intensities must have suffered the same influences in their formation no matter what the structure of the atmosphere—homogeneous or inhomogeneous.   If, therefore, the lines were in fact formed in LTE and it were simply some

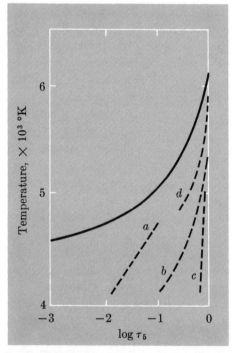

Figure 10.3. Excitation temperatures for some multiplets of the neutral chromium spectrum.   (After Pecker and Vogel, 1960, Figure 5.) The full line illustrates the assumed photospheric temperature distribution.

characteristic of the atmosphere that was introducing the appearance of departures from LTE shown in Figure 10.2, the run of $T_{ex}(\tau_c)$ for Ti I lines should be the same as that for Cr I.

If, on the other hand, the $T_{ex}(\tau_c)$ curves for the two elements were different, we should have to conclude that departures from LTE are significant in the relative populations of the levels of at least one of these atoms. Pecker and Vogel's results are illustrated in Figure 10.3; a comparison with Figure 10.2 clearly shows the marked difference in behavior between Ti and Cr; the former having $T_{ex} > T_e$, the latter $T_{ex} < T_e$.

Another observational corroboration of the opposite behavior of lines of these two elements is to be found in Unno's (1959a) study of the depth dependence of the Doppler velocity $\bar{V}$ which he obtained using Goldberg's (1958) procedure (see Section 9.7) for the determination of the Doppler width of multiplet lines, and the relationship

$$\Delta\lambda_D = \frac{\lambda}{c}\,\bar{V}. \tag{10.8}$$

Unno determined the depth variation of $\bar{V}$ in essentially the same way as Pecker later chose to find $T_{ex}(\tau_c)$, namely through the Eddington-Barbier relation and the transformation (10.6) between τ_0^* and τ_c. If Unno's results produce different curves $\bar{V}(\tau_c)$ for lines of different elements, therefore, we must question the self-consistency of the assumption of LTE applied simultaneously to the analysis of the continuum and to the excitation of the energy levels of these elements. The pertinent results from Unno's tabulation have been extracted by Pecker and Vogel and are reproduced in Figure 10.4. The difference in behavior is marked; we may produce the common $\bar{V}(\tau_c)$ curve in which any meaningful analysis must result by decreasing the opacity in the Ti I lines or increasing that in Cr I.

That Unno's results are in agreement with those of Pecker and Vogel is seen from the following simple argument. Unno determined the depth of formation of the Cr I lines from their measured central intensities which he translated into an equivalent temperature via the LTE result

$$I_\nu(0,\,1) \simeq B_\nu(T_e^*), \tag{10.9}$$

where T_e^* is the temperature at the "effective depth of formation." This depth was determined as that at which the empirical solar model had the temperature T_e^*. Now, if a line is too strong for consistency

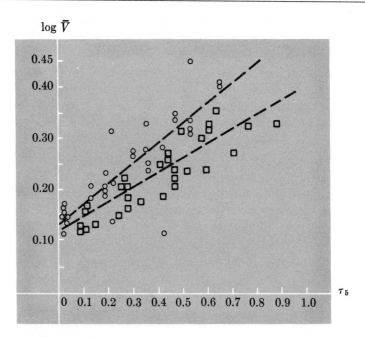

Figure 10.4. The variation of turbulent velocity $\bar{V}$ with the 5000 Å continuum optical depth; as deduced by Unno (1959 *a*). The plotted values are taken from Unno's Table 2. The open squares refer to lines of Ti I, the open circles to Cr I. The broken lines are least-square fits to the two sets of data.

with LTE (as are the Cr I lines), then its effective depth of formation will be underestimated; correspondingly, if the line is weaker than in LTE (as for Ti), the depth will be overestimated. Unno recognized quite well that his result implied an inconsistency in the application of LTE, and in an attempt at interpretation (Unno 1959*b*) he suggested that noncoherent scattering by the chromosphere could preferentially deepen the Cr I lines over those of Ti I. His detailed treatment is inadequate—since he regards the chromosphere as a purely scattering medium—nevertheless, his suggestion is important as pointing the way to an explanation of his anomalous results in terms of departures from LTE.

10.2.3 Lefèvre and Pecker's Analysis of the Center-Limb Variation of the Central Intensities of Solar Ti I Lines

If we have available data on the center-to-limb variation of the central intensity of a line, we can use the Eddington-Barbier relation, in an obvious extension of Pecker's (1959) analysis, to map out the depth variation of the line source function for a single line. If we have such center-limb data for many lines of a multiplet, we may perform this analysis for each one of them and determine, for example, whether the excitation temperatures are indeed the same for each line of a multiplet, as has been suggested above. Such an analysis was carried out by Lefèvre and Pecker (1961) for lines of Ti I observed with the large spectrograph at the Pic du Midi Observatory.

Their study proceeds in the usual way via the pair of equations

$$I_{v_0}(0, \mu) \simeq B[T_{ex}(\tau_0^*)] \qquad (10.10)$$

and

$$\tau_0^* = \tau_c + \tau_l(0) = \mu. \qquad (10.11)$$

For the transformation (10.11) they adopted Kandel's abundance (see Section 10.2.4) and used a model atmosphere which included the Athay, Menzel, Pecker, and Thomas (1954) representation of the chromosphere. We have reproduced their results for some lines of multiplet a in Figure 10.5—the other multiplets behave similarly but the behavior is more clearly seen when they are omitted. In the figure the full lines represent the variation $T_{ex}(\tau_c)$ derived from Equations (10.10) and (10.11); the broken line represents that deduced by Pecker (1959) from the central intensities observed only at the center of the disk.

It is clear from the figure that the curves of $T_{ex}(\tau_c)$ for the different lines of the multiplet do not in fact coincide but are systematically displaced in a way which gives the diagram the appearance of half a herringbone, and the authors have accordingly named this the "fishbone effect" ("effet 'arête de poisson' "). The tendency for the effect to become less pronounced in the outer layers is claimed by Lefèvre and Pecker to be real, though the evidence does not seem strong.

It should be clear from our remarks in Chapter 8 that there is nothing necessarily unexpected about the "fishbone effect." The analysis of Lefèvre and Pecker was made for the line centers, i.e., as far out in the atmosphere as possible for each line, and it is just there that one might expect to observe departures from source function equality as the lines become uncoupled. These authors, however, have rejected this possibility on the rather slight basis of an analogy with some strong lines of Fe and, after rejecting several other possible sources of error (Eddington-Barbier relation, anisotropy of turbulence) as insignificant,

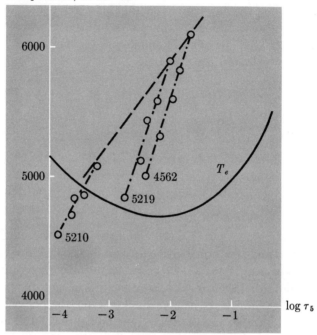

Figure 10.5. The "fishbone" effect. The depth variation of the excitation temperature of three lines of Ti I of Pecker's multiplet *a*. The individual points for each line are deduced from observations of the central intensities at $\mu = 1$, 0.6, 0.45, 0.30, and 0.15. The broken line represents the curve $T_{ex}(\tau_5)$ deduced from observations at $\mu = 1$ only, as in Figure 10.2. (After Lefèvre and Pecker, 1961, Figure 1.)

have concluded that the explanation is to be sought in the influence of small-scale inhomogeneities in the solar photosphere.

Lefèvre and Pecker attempted to answer two questions on the influence of inhomogeneities; first, whether these were the source of the failure of the LTE hypothesis in Pecker's analysis of the central intensities, and second, whether the "fishbone effect" arose because the photosphere is, in fact, not homogeneous. Their analysis was a first approximation which attempted to derive the consequences of the supposition that the photosphere, instead of being homogeneous, consisted of three columns; one hot, one cold, and one of intermediate temperature; the physical properties of the columns were based on Böhm's (1954) "three stream" model. In each of these columns the center of a specific line has effective "continuum depths of formation" τ_{c1}^*, τ_{c2}^*, τ_{c3}^* and at these depths the temperatures are denoted T_1, T_2, and T_3. Then, denoting by a_1, a_2, a_3 the corresponding relative cross-sectional areas of the three columns, Lefèvre and Pecker defined an effective temperature $\overline{T}_\mu$ for this inhomogeneous atmosphere through the equation

$$B(\overline{T}_\mu) = \sum_{i=1}^{3} a_i B(T_i),\qquad (10.12)$$

and then associated the effective depth of formation of the line with the continuous optical depth (τ_{ci}^*) at which the *intermediate* temperature column had the temperature $\overline{T}_\mu$. When the same line was analyzed assuming a homogeneous atmosphere, of structure identical with the intermediate column, the mean depth of formation τ_{ch}^* was found to be rather smaller than τ_{ci}^*. This result is shown in Figure 10.6, which illustrates the temperature distribution in the three "streams" along with the excitation temperature distributions E_h (inferred on the basis of a homogeneous model) and E_i (inferred on the basis of an inhomogeneous model) for observations, at five values of μ, of the central intensities in the lines $\lambda 5219$ and $\lambda 4562$ of Ti I. The error in neglecting inhomogeneities is given by the translation parallel to the optical depth axis between the curves E_i and the corresponding E_h curves. As it

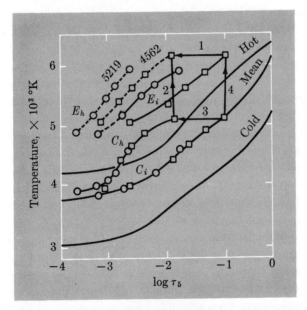

Figure 10.6. Pecker and Lefèvre's analysis of the influence of inhomogeneities on the derived depth variation of excitation temperature ; see text for details.

stands, however, interpretation of this figure is a little obscure, and for clarification one should isolate the effect due solely to the inhomogeneities from that of possible departures from LTE. To do this, Lefèvre and Pecker considered an artificial case in which the two lines were supposed formed in LTE in an inhomogeneous atmosphere of the given structure, and *analyzed* the computed emergent radiation, first on the assumption of a homogeneous atmosphere, and second by using the inhomogeneous model. The optical depths of formation of the two lines in the various columns are the same as before—since in this first approximation LTE is used to determine the transformation $\tau^*(\tau_c)$. If we adopted the inhomogeneous model we would again obtain values of τ_{c1}^*, τ_{c2}^*, τ_{c3}^* for the effective depths of formation $\tau^* = \mu$ and correspondingly, via Equation (10.12), we would find a $\overline{T}_\mu$ and a mean depth of formation τ_{ci}^* to which this temperature corresponds in the mean model. If $\lambda4562$ were in fact formed in LTE, if the photosphere were in fact described by the three-stream model adopted by Lefèvre and Pecker, and if the Eddington-Barbier relation were exact, the emergent central intensity would be given by

$$I(0, \mu) = B(\overline{T}_\mu), \tag{10.13}$$

and the analysis of the spectral line would then yield points lying along the $T(\tau_c)$ curve of the mean temperature model, i.e., it would give points like those shown on the curve labeled C_i in Figure 10.6.

If, on the other hand, the line were still formed in LTE and in an inhomogeneous model, but we chose to analyze the intensities as if the atmosphere were *homogeneous* and of structure identical with the mean column of the three-stream model, we would derive the different value τ_{ch}^* for the effective depth of formation. In fact, the analysis of the line central intensity would then result in a $T(\tau_c)$ distribution of the type shown as curve C_h in Figure 10.6. If the analysis of the observed solar Ti I lines had resulted in a curve like that labeled C_h, we could have said that the apparent inconsistency of LTE was due only to the assumption of a homogeneous model for the analysis of lines formed in LTE in an inhomogeneous atmosphere, and that had we taken instead a proper inhomogeneous model we would have found consistency. The influence of inhomogeneities *alone* is represented by the arrows 1 and 3 in Figure 10.6, while the influence of departures from LTE, once inhomogeneities have been accounted for, is represented by the arrows 2 and 4; these, clearly, remain very large. We can conclude then, with

Lefèvre and Pecker, that the apparent departures from LTE do *not* arise from inhomogeneities in the solar photosphere—this is in agreement with Pecker and Vogel's conclusions based on the different behavior of the lines of Ti I and Cr I.

The fact that both lines $\lambda5219$ and $\lambda4562$ overlap in the curve C_h, when we assume LTE to be valid, implies that the "fishbone effect" does not have its origin in the assumption of a homogeneous model to analyze lines formed in an inhomogeneous atmosphere. This, however, turns out to be due to the fact that we are implicitly supposing in Equation (10.12) that the horizontal scale size of the inhomogeneities is very much greater than the vertical height down to the effective depth of formation of the line. As Lefèvre and Pecker point out, the depth at which $\tau^* = \mu$ is not the same in each column; in fact, for the Ti I lines discussed here the opacity increases as the temperature decreases, so that the effective depth of formation of the cold column lies highest. As one observes toward the limb, therefore, the emission from the hot and the mean columns will be absorbed preferentially over that in the cold column, and for a line formed in LTE one will therefore observe a greater limb darkening than would be found in a homogeneous atmosphere of the same mean structure. The amount of such shadowing of the hotter columns by the cold one depends on the differences between the depths of formation of the line in the three columns, and on the scale size of the structure. Lefèvre and Pecker concluded that structures of about 300 to 500 km were necessary to produce enough shadowing to give rise to an observable "fishbone effect" in the observable range of μ. Structures smaller than this would give rise to the effect also, but the variation of central intensity with μ near the disk center would then be extreme. Larger structures, of course, would only show the effect far out in the atmosphere corresponding to a differential limb darkening at very small values of μ.

Thus, with a judiciously chosen size for the elements, one may reproduce the fishbone effect for lines formed in LTE. There is, however, a difficulty in this picture; if inhomogeneities manifest themselves in the analysis in this way, how are we to account for Waddell's demonstration that at a given depth the line source functions for D_1 and D_2 are equal? Here the assumption of a homogeneous atmosphere has resulted in no "fishbone effect" in the analysis, since otherwise it would have been impossible to superimpose the cores of the observed profiles $I_{D_2}(\mu)$ and $I_{D_1}(\mu/2)$. It may be that the inhomogeneities are too large, where the cores of the D lines are formed, to show a "fishbone effect"; however, Waddell's profiles match out to a wavelength where their intensity is about 40% of the continuum, and the depth of formation of this radiation is surely below that of the core of $\lambda4562$. There is good reason, therefore, to question the conclusion that the fishbone effect arises in the analytical method as a result of a false assumption of a homogeneous photosphere. On the other hand, as we have seen above, there is no occasion for surprise at the existence of this effect— it is, indeed, to be expected under certain circumstances.

A critical test between the two suggestions for the origin of the effect can readily be devised. If it arises from the presence of inhomogeneities, the "fishbone effect" should be observed in the limb darkening at all points on the profile—indeed, it should increase away from the core, if, as Lefèvre and Pecker assert, the effect increases with depth. If, on the other hand, the effect is a natural one arising from the decoupling of the lines in the outer layers, we should expect to see the opposite behavior, namely that the fishbone effect decreases toward the line wings.

10.2.4 Kandel's Self-Consistent Analysis of the Ti I Lines of Pecker's Multiplet *a*

The principal aim of the investigations described so far in this chapter was to determine whether LTE was a self-consistent assumption for the analysis of the neutral titanium spectrum of the Sun. On the basis of a procedure outlined by Pecker (1959), Kandel attempted to extend the earlier studies to determine a self-consistent solution for the line source function, and the abundance, for lines of Pecker's multiplet a, using data obtained by E. A. Müller on the McMath-Hulbert high-resolution spectrograph, and equivalent widths measured by Claas from the Utrecht Atlas. Kandel's computations were based on Minnaert's (1953) model atmosphere with a modification to include a chromospheric temperature rise. Because the "turbulence" is rather uncertain, Kandel discussed two extreme possibilities, one (his model S) with no turbulence, the other (model T) based on van Regemorter's (1959) tabulation.

The first step in Kandel's iterative procedure, as in Pecker's original analysis, lay in the determination of the distribution of the excitation temperature $T_{ex}(\tau_c)$ for the various lines of Ti I. From a first approxi-

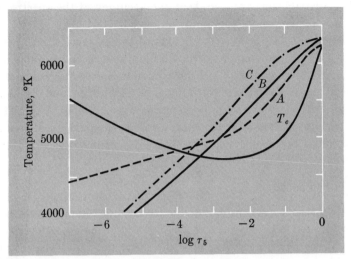

Figure 10.7. Depth variation of the excitation temperatures deduced by Pecker in a first approximation (curve *A*), and by Kandel in his models neglecting "turbulence" (*C*) and including "turbulence" (*B*).

mation to $S_l(\tau_c)$ for each line, Kandel first computed the equivalent widths W, and so the curve of growth, by a standard method. From the observed equivalent widths he was then able to determine a new abundance which allowed a new transformation $\tau^*(\tau_c)$ and so, as the start of a new iteration cycle, a new distribution $T_{ex}(\tau_c)$. This iterative scheme was found to converge rather slowly, and Kandel used an interpolation procedure to accelerate convergence once the general character of the $T_{ex}(\tau_c)$ curves had been established. His final results are illustrated in Figure 10.7; abundances for the two turbulence models T and S are a factor 4 to 7 larger than those found by Claas on the basis of LTE. This result has such significant implications that it should be confirmed.

10.3 Empirical Arguments Favoring LTE

The evidence presented above gives a clear-cut case against the adoption of LTE for the analysis of the cores of the photospheric metal lines. Nevertheless, there are unsatisfactory aspects, perhaps mainly associated with the facts (a) that a fully satisfying iterative treatment has never been applied, (b) that the influence of the model on the results is indefinite and incompletely studied—especially for the "microturbulent velocity" distribution—and (c) that the accuracy of the spectroscopic data is too low to permit a definite conclusion.

In any case, it has been strongly argued that, even if the line center intensities do show departures from LTE, these have no influence on abundance determinations.*   Major contributions to this point of view have been made by Müller and Mutschlecner (1964), and by Warner (1964a, b)—cf. also in this connection the discussion by Pagel (1965). Before considering these arguments, we must first briefly review their formulation of the problem of abundance determination.

10.3.1 Formulation

The determination of abundances from photospheric spectra normally proceeds via a discussion of the curve of growth which relates the equivalent width of a spectral line to atomic and atmospheric parameters.   The definition (2.58) of the equivalent width W may be restated in the form, appropriate for solar analyses, for which limb darkening data are available,

$$W(\lambda, \mu)I_c(\lambda, \mu) = \int_0^\infty [I_c(\lambda, \mu) - I_l(\lambda, \mu)]\, d\lambda.\dagger \qquad (10.14)$$

Hence, for radiation emerging in the direction μ, $W(\lambda, \mu)$ is that wavelength interval in the neighboring continuous spectrum which contains the same amount of energy as is extracted from the continuum by the line.   As may be seen from its definition, W is positive or negative respectively for an absorption or an emission line.

A considerable algebra has grown up around the theoretical description of the equivalent width.   We shall not give a full discussion of the various formulations here; we shall merely derive some of the more significant results.

For a semi-infinite, plane parallel, layer the emergent intensity in a spectral line is given by Equation (2.57).   With some trivial algebraic and notational changes, this result may be written

$$I_l(\lambda, \mu) = \int_0^\infty [S_l\eta_\lambda + S_c] \exp\left[-\int_0^{t_c} (1 + \eta_\lambda)\frac{\kappa_c^\lambda}{\kappa_c}\frac{dt_c}{\mu}\right]\left(\frac{\kappa_c^\lambda}{\kappa_c}\right)\frac{dt_c}{\mu}, \qquad (10.15)$$

---

* By implication, therefore, these arguments deny the validity of Kandel's results.

† Note that in contrast to $I_c(\lambda, \mu)$, $I_l(\lambda, \mu)$ varies substantially over a given spectral line.   The integration element $d\lambda$ is essentially a wavelength interval in the neighborhood of the line.

in which t_c is the continuum optical depth at some reference wavelength, say 5000 Å. The continuum absorption coefficients κ_c^λ and κ_c are defined analogously and η_λ is the ratio $\kappa_l^\lambda/\kappa_c^\lambda$.

The emergent continuum intensity $I_c(\lambda, \mu)$ is simply obtained from Equation (10.15) by setting η_λ to zero. A formal expression for the depression of the line below the continuum may then be written

$$I_c(\lambda, \mu) - I_l(\lambda, \mu) = \int_0^\infty \left[S_c \exp\left(\frac{-t_c^\lambda}{\mu}\right)\left\{ 1 - \exp\left(-\int_0^{t_c} \eta_\lambda \frac{\kappa_c^\lambda}{\kappa_c} \frac{dt_c}{\mu}\right)\right\} \right.$$
$$\left. - \eta_\lambda S_l \exp\left\{\frac{-t_c^\lambda}{\mu} - \int_0^{t_c} \eta_\lambda \frac{\kappa_c^\lambda}{\kappa_c} \frac{dt_c}{\mu}\right\}\right] \frac{\kappa_c^\lambda}{\kappa_c} \frac{dt_c}{\mu}, \quad (10.16)$$

in which t_c^λ is the continuum optical depth at wavelength λ.

For computational purposes it is convenient to simplify this expression by making a partial integration of the first term on the right-hand side, which we can readily do after expressing it in the form;

$$\int_0^\infty \left[-\frac{d}{dt_c} \int_{t_c}^\infty S_c \exp\left\{\frac{-t_c^\lambda}{\mu}\right\} \frac{\kappa_c^\lambda}{\kappa_c} dt_c \right] \times \left[1 - \exp\left\{-\int_0^{t_c} \eta_\lambda \frac{\kappa_c^\lambda}{\kappa_c} \frac{dt_c}{\mu}\right\}\right] \frac{dt_c}{\mu}.$$
$$(10.17)$$

In this way we find, after a little algebra, that

$$r(\lambda, \mu) \equiv \frac{I_c(\lambda, \mu) - I_l(\lambda, \mu)}{I_c(\lambda, \mu)}$$
$$= \int_0^\infty \eta_\lambda \frac{\kappa_c^\lambda}{\kappa_c} \exp\left\{ -\int_0^{t_c} \eta_\lambda \frac{\kappa_c^\lambda}{\kappa_c} \frac{dt_c}{\mu}\right\} G_\lambda(t_c, \mu) \frac{dt_c}{\mu}, \quad (10.18)$$

in which the "weighting function" G_λ is defined as

$$G_\lambda(t_c, \mu) = \frac{\displaystyle\int_{t_c}^\infty S_c \exp\left(\frac{-t_c^\lambda}{\mu}\right) \frac{\kappa_c^\lambda}{\kappa_c} \frac{dt_c}{\mu} - S_l e^{-t_c^\lambda/\mu}}{\displaystyle\int_0^\infty S_c \exp\left(\frac{-t_c^\lambda}{\mu}\right) \frac{\kappa_c^\lambda}{\kappa_c} \frac{dt_c}{\mu}}. \quad (10.19)$$

Note that $G_\lambda(t_c, \mu)$ varies negligibly across a spectral line provided that S_l behaves similarly.

Now, in view of Equation (4.97) the ratio η_λ can be written

$$\eta_\lambda = \frac{\pi e^2 f \lambda^2}{mc^2} \frac{H(a, v)}{\sqrt{\pi} \, \Delta\lambda_D} n_l \left[1 - \frac{n_u}{n_l} \frac{g_l}{g_u}\right] \frac{1}{\kappa_c^\lambda}, \quad (10.20)$$

in which the dimensionless parameter v is defined as $\Delta\lambda/\Delta\lambda_D$; it is to be noted that in general $\Delta\lambda_D$ and a are functions of depth.

It is convenient to measure Doppler widths in terms of some representative value $\Delta\lambda_D^*$ (for example, $\Delta\lambda_D^*$ may be taken as the Doppler width at $t_c = 1$) and to define correspondingly a quantity p such that

$$p \equiv \frac{\Delta\lambda_D^*}{\Delta\lambda_D}. \tag{10.21}$$

In general, of course, p will be a function of depth. If then we define a wavelength parameter v^* such that

$$v^* = \frac{\Delta\lambda}{\Delta\lambda_D^*} = \frac{v}{p}, \tag{10.22}$$

it is readily seen, from Equations (10.18) through (10.22), that the equivalent width can be obtained, by integrating $r(\lambda, \mu)$ over the line, in the form

$$W(\lambda, \mu) = 2\Delta\lambda_D^* \int_0^\infty G_\lambda(t_c, \mu)\left[\int_0^\infty y_\lambda(t_c, v^*)\right.$$
$$\left. \times \exp\left\{-\int_0^{t_c} y_\lambda(t_c, v^*)\frac{dt_c}{\mu}\right\} dv^*\right]\frac{dt_c}{\mu}, \tag{10.23}$$

where it is assumed that S_l varies negligibly with λ and where

$$y_\lambda(t_c, v^*) = \eta_\lambda \frac{\kappa_c^\lambda}{\kappa_c} = \frac{\pi e^2 f \lambda^2}{mc^2} n_\ell\left(1 - \frac{n_u}{n_\ell}\frac{g_\ell}{g_u}\right)\frac{pH(a, pv^*)}{\sqrt{\pi}\,\Delta\lambda_D^*}\frac{1}{\kappa_c}. \tag{10.24}$$

In many problems it is permissible to neglect the depth dependence of the quantity $H(a, pv^*)$ in the integral in the exponent in Equation (10.23). In that case, an expression for the equivalent width follows as

$$W(\lambda, \mu) = \frac{\pi e^2 f \lambda^2}{mc^2} \int_0^\infty G_\lambda(t_c, \mu)\phi_\lambda[x(t_c), a]n_\ell\left(1 - \frac{n_u}{n_\ell}\frac{g_\ell}{g_u}\right)\frac{dt_c}{\kappa_c\mu}, \tag{10.25}$$

in which the "saturation function" ϕ_λ is defined as

$$\phi_\lambda[x(t_c), a] = \frac{2}{\sqrt{\pi}}\int_0^\infty pH(a, pv^*)\exp\left[-x(t_c)H(a, pv^*)\right]dv^*, \tag{10.26}$$

with

$$x(t_c) = \frac{\sqrt{\pi}\,e^2 f \lambda^2}{mc^2}\int_0^{t_c} \frac{n_\ell\left(1 - \dfrac{n_u}{n_\ell}\dfrac{g_\ell}{g_u}\right)}{\Delta\lambda_D}\frac{dt_c}{\kappa_c\mu}. \tag{10.27}$$

It follows immediately that $\mu x(t_c)$ is approximately equal to the line center optical depth at the level t_c.

The abundance of the particular atom enters the expression for W through the ratio of the line and continuum absorption coefficients. In Equation (10.25), for example, this is reflected in the ratio n_ℓ/κ_c.

The expression (10.25) may be written in a variety of equivalent ways; one, which is often convenient, is

$$\frac{W(\lambda, \mu)}{\lambda} = \frac{\pi e^2}{mc^2} \frac{gf\lambda A}{\mu} \int_0^\infty G_\lambda(t_c, \mu)\phi_\lambda[x(t_c), a] \frac{n_\ell}{g_\ell n_T} \left(1 - \frac{n_a}{n_\ell} \frac{g_\ell}{g_a}\right) \frac{dt_c}{\bar{k}_c},$$
(10.28)

in which n_T is the total number density (atoms and ions) of the particular atomic species, and $\bar{k}_c$ is the continuous absorption coefficient (at 5000 Å) per atom of the total hydrogen content (neutral H and protons) so that A is the abundance of the element relative to hydrogen.

Equation (10.28) may be applied to a particular spectral line whose gf value and energy levels are known. *If we can evaluate the integral,* therefore, a simple measure of the equivalent width of the line in the radiation emerging in the direction μ should suffice to determine the abundance A of the atomic species in the atmosphere. In practice, we are rarely, if ever, sufficiently sure either of the quality of our observational data W or of the experimental or theoretical data on gf values to place much reliance on the abundance determined from the equivalent width of a single line. Instead, we try to combine information on a number of lines of the same element with the hope of reducing the error of determination of A.

In order to evaluate the integral in Equation (10.28) we need to know, as functions of t_c, the source functions entering the quantity $G(t_c, \mu)$, the population ratios n_ℓ/n_T and n_a/n_ℓ, and the quantity $x(t_c)$. The simplest course, and that most widely used, is to assume LTE so that the source functions are Planckian and the population ratios are given by the Saha and Boltzmann relations. In that case it can readily be seen from Equations (10.19), and (10.26) to (10.28) that $W(\lambda, \mu)$ can be computed as a function of $gf\lambda A$, and of λ, μ, a, and the excitation potential χ_ℓ of the lower state, once we specify the atmospheric structure. The abundance could then be obtained by comparing the computed and observed equivalent widths for each line of a given atom.

To study this question further it is convenient to write Equation

(10.28) in the form adopted by Müller and Mutschlecner—cf. Aller (1960)—

$$\frac{W(\lambda, \mu)}{\lambda} = \frac{M}{\mu} \mathscr{L}_\lambda^\mu,$$

(10.29)

in which

$$M \equiv \frac{\pi e^2 g f \lambda A \, 10^{\theta_0 \Delta x}}{mc^2 m_\mathrm{H} \mu_0 \log_{10} e},$$

(10.30)

where m_H is the mass of the hydrogen atom, and μ_0 is the mean molecular weight of the solar material with respect to hydrogen. The final factor in the numerator is introduced for convenience in computing $\mathscr{L}_\lambda^\mu$; the quantity θ_0 ($\equiv 5040/T_0$) is chosen to refer to some characteristic temperature in the sun and, for neutral atoms, $\Delta\chi$ is defined to be the energy difference between the ionization potential and the lower level of the line.

A simple comparison with Equation (10.28) shows that the remaining factor in Equation (10.29) may be written

$$\mathscr{L}_\lambda^\mu = \int_0^\infty G_\lambda(t_c, \mu)\phi_\lambda[x(t_c), a]\left(1 - \frac{n_u}{n_\ell}\frac{g_\ell}{g_u}\right)10^{-\theta_0\Delta x}10^{-\theta_\mathrm{ex}\chi_\ell}\frac{t_c \, d(\log_{10} t_c)}{k_c u_r(n_T/n_r)},$$

(10.31)

where k_c is the mass absorption coefficient in the continuum at the standard wavelength, n_r and u_r are respectively the population and the partition function in the ionization stage with which the line is associated, and θ_ex is defined by

$$\frac{n_\ell}{n_r} = \frac{g_\ell}{u_r} 10^{-\theta_\mathrm{ex}\chi_\ell}.$$

(10.32)

For weak lines, for which the saturation function ϕ_λ is essentially unity, Müller and Mutschlecner write the expression (10.29) as

$$\frac{W(\lambda, \mu)}{\lambda}\bigg]_{\mathrm{weak\ line}} \simeq \frac{M}{\mu} L_\lambda^\mu \equiv C_\lambda^\mu A,$$

(10.33)

in which (see Equation 10.30),

$$C_\lambda^\mu = K g f \lambda L_\lambda^\mu 10^{\theta_0 \Delta x}/\mu,$$

(10.34)

where K is a constant and L_λ^μ is the unsaturated form of Equation (10.31).

A *theoretical* curve of growth for a given atmosphere and spectrum is basically a plot of the *computed* value of $\log\left[W(\lambda,\mu)/\lambda\right]$ as ordinate, against $\log\left(gf\lambda A\right)$ as abscissa, obtained for specified values of a, λ, χ_ℓ, and μ. It is convenient sometimes to use as abscissa the related quantity $\log\left(C_\lambda^\mu A\right)$, in which case the theoretical curve of growth is found to have the form shown schematically in Figure 10.8 for the three

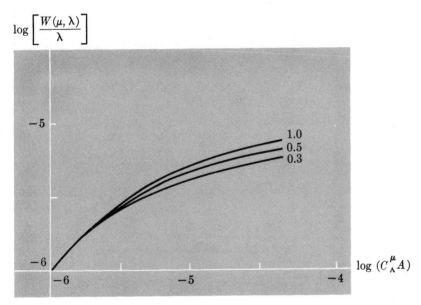

Figure 10.8. Theoretical curves of growth for the three values of μ shown against the curves. The figure is patterned after Figure 10 of Müller and Mutschlecner.

values of μ shown. Variations in a, χ_ℓ, and λ introduce similar small influences in the saturated region. Obviously, a theoretical curve of growth can only be drawn if we know the excitation state of the atom; in other words, the curve depends on the theory.

An *empirical* curve of growth for lines of a given atomic spectrum emitted in a direction μ, is constructed for lines of similar a, χ_ℓ, and λ values by computing first the relevant values of L_λ^μ and then plotting *observed* values of $\log\left[W(\lambda,\mu)/\lambda\right]$ vs. $\log C_\lambda^\mu$. Figure 10.9 shows a schematic illustration of an empirical curve of growth. The plotted points are obtained from observation, while the full curve is a fit to a theoretical curve of growth such as Figure 10.8. Now from Equation (10.33), the abundance is numerically equal to the weak line value of

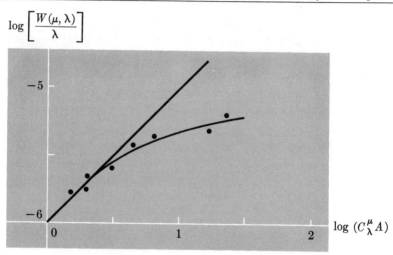

$$\log \left[\frac{W(\mu, \lambda)}{\lambda} \right]$$

Figure 10.9. A schematic representation of an empirical curve of growth obtained by fitting the theoretical curve to the data points represented by dots.

$W(\lambda, \mu)/\lambda$ for C_λ^μ unity. Hence, A may be found by fitting the theoretical to the empirical curve of growth and noting the intercept of the straight-line section of the theoretical curve on the ordinate drawn through $\log C_\lambda^\mu = 0$. Thus in Figure 10.9, we would find $\log A = -6.0$.

10.3.2 Müller and Mutschlecner's Analysis

Müller and Mutschlecner (1964) considered the lines of each of the elements Ca, Ti, V, Cr, Mn, Fe, and Co as observed at three locations on the solar disk: $\mu = 1.0, 0.5, 0.3$. For each element they grouped the lines according to wavelength and χ_ℓ, the value of a was taken as 10^{-2} throughout since variations in this parameter do not significantly alter the results. In the manner indicated in the preceding paragraph they obtained LTE abundances for each grouping—a typical example of their results is given in Table 10.1. In each case they found that, to within the accuracy of the data, the derived abundances were independent of μ or χ_ℓ. They concluded, therefore, that deviations from the LTE hypothesis were unimportant in the determination of solar abundances by the curve of growth method.

This is, however, not necessarily a correct conclusion to draw from the results. To see this, let us consider the analysis of solar equivalent widths from a viewpoint more general than LTE. The relevant theoretical relationships are contained in Equations (10.29) to (10.32);

TABLE 10.1. Iron abundances derived from different multiplets at three positions on the solar disk. [From Müller and Mutschlecner *loc. cit.*, Table 20]

$\Delta\chi$	$\log[N(\mathrm{Fe})/N(\mathrm{H})] + 12.00$		
(*in ev*)	$\mu = 1.0$	0.5	0.3
7.7 to 7.9	6.77	6.78	6.75
6.2 to 7.0	6.67	6.67	6.66
5.4 to 5.7	6.72	6.73	6.73
5.0 to 5.3	6.65	6.65	6.71
4.2 to 4.9	6.73	6.73	6.72
3.4 to 4.0	6.85	6.83	6.83

however, to compute the quantities entering these equations for a given line, we need to know the source function for that line, the population ratios n_r/n_T, n_u/n_ℓ, and the excitation temperature $T_{\mathrm{ex}} = 5040/\theta_{\mathrm{ex}}$.

In a simple extension of the theoretical and observational results found for the Na D and Mg b lines, we may assume that the line source functions for all lines of a given element in a particular (χ_ℓ, λ) grouping will share a common depth variation. Hence, the integral L_λ^μ will have essentially the same value for each line in the group. In other words, we would expect to find a unique curve of growth relationship covering all the lines in a given grouping—at least in the 45-deg slope region. Now, from Equations (10.29) to (10.34) it follows that the equation to this linear section of the theoretical curve of growth can be written in the approximate form,

$$\log \frac{W(\lambda, \mu)}{\lambda} = \log Q_\lambda^\mu + \log\left(\frac{gf\lambda A}{\mu}\right) + \bar{\theta}_{\mathrm{ion}}\chi_{\mathrm{ion}} - \bar{\theta}_{\mathrm{ex}}\chi_\ell, \qquad (10.35)$$

where

$$Q_\lambda^\mu \propto \int_0^\infty G_\lambda(t_c, \mu)\, dt_c \qquad (10.36)$$

is independent of the particular line in a (χ_ℓ, λ) group, while $\bar{\theta}_{\mathrm{ion}}$ is a mean of the ionization temperature parameter entering the population ratio, n_T/n_r, of the ionized to the neutral state* and $\bar{\theta}_{\mathrm{ex}}$ is a similar mean

---

* Strictly, n_T is the total population of the atom in all stages of ionization. However, under solar atmospheric conditions n_T is essentially equal to the population of the singly ionized state for the atoms of interest to us here.

(see Equation 10.32). Equation (10.35) exhibits the dependence of the equivalent width on atomic and atmospheric parameters in a more explicit fashion than Equation (10.31), and so is useful for expository purposes.

Now, let us consider the curves of growth corresponding to two line groupings in which $\chi_\ell = \chi_1$ and χ_2 and for which the line wavelengths are approximately equal. Viewed in terms of the approximation (10.35), Müller and Mutschlecner's contribution lay in showing that the separation of the linear sections of the empirical curves of growth was, in fact, equal to $\bar{\theta}_e(\chi_2 - \chi_1)$, where $\bar{\theta}_e$ is the quantity $\bar{\theta}_{ex}$ evaluated for LTE. In the general case the separation of the empirical curves of growth would be $\bar{\theta}_{ex}(\chi_2 - \chi_1)$. The difference in separation in the two cases is therefore just

$$(\bar{\theta}_{ex} - \bar{\theta}_e)(\chi_2 - \chi_1), \qquad (10.37)$$

and this difference must be distinguishable in the empirical curves if we are to decide whether or not LTE is valid. In point of fact, Müller and Mutschlecner's results indicate that a difference of at least 0.1 in $|\bar{\theta}_{ex} - \bar{\theta}_e|$ would not be detectable from the data, and only to this extent could one claim that the relative populations of the relevant levels are given by the Boltzmann formula. The corresponding abundance uncertainty is, of course, just that found by Müller and Mutschlecner—one may attribute it to errors in the data or to errors in the theory.

However, the derived abundance depends not only on the excitation term but also on the ionization term $\bar{\theta}_{ion}\chi_{ion}$ in Equation (10.35), and Müller and Mutschlecner's procedure allows no test of the validity of evaluating *this* term as in LTE. Still, if it could be shown that the LTE abundance invariance held for χ_ℓ ranging up to one or two electron volts below the continuum, then we could claim that LTE was a valid description of the excitation since, on very general grounds, we can be sure that levels lying close to the continuum are populated as in LTE with respect to each other and the continuum. In other words, if $\bar{\theta}_{ex}$ has its LTE value for χ_ℓ ranging up close to χ_{ion}, then $\bar{\theta}_{ion}$ and $\bar{\theta}_{ex}$ must be equal, i.e., the ionization is also in LTE.

On the other hand, if significant departures from LTE exist, then an LTE analysis will yield abundances which depend systematically on χ_ℓ but only provided one spans a range in χ_ℓ through which the excitation temperature varies significantly. It can well be argued that the analyses of Müller and Mutschlecner did not span a sufficient range due to limitations forced by the lack of data on equivalent widths, or *gf* values, for transitions lying higher in the energy-level diagram.   Some evidence for this point of view is found in two publications by Warner, which we now discuss.

10.3.3 The Solar Iron Abundance

An inconsistency is found between abundance analyses of the coronal spectrum and the usual LTE analyses of the photospheric spectrum.   Thus, using data on both the forbidden and the permitted spectrum of iron, Pottasch (1963*a*, *b*) has shown that the solar coronal iron abundance greatly exceeds that derived from the LTE photospheric analyses.   In a later study—Pottasch (1964)—he concluded that the same kind of discrepancy exists for other elements of the iron group, specifically for Ni, Cr, Co, and Mn.   His results are compared with those of Müller and Mutschlecner in Table 10.2.   It has been suggested

TABLE 10.2. Comparison of solar coronal and photospheric abundances of the iron-group elements

Element	LOG *A*	
	Corona[1]	*Photosphere*[2]
Hydrogen	12.0	12.0
Chromium	6.0	5.1
Manganese	5.7	4.8
Iron	7.9	6.7
Cobalt	5.6	4.4
Nickel	6.7	5.5 to 6.2[3]

[1] Pottasch (1964); [2] Muller and Mutschlecner (1964); [3] Goldberg, Muller, and Aller (1960).

that Pottasch's results depend critically on the assumed coronal model —especially on the electron density distribution—and on the collisional excitation cross sections used to compute the emissivity of coronal material.   However, from an analysis of the spectrum of a bright coronal condensation, Jefferies and Orrall (1966) have been able to set a firm lower limit to the iron and the calcium abundances in the corona—independent of the model or of the collisional rates—and have shown that in each case the coronal abundance must be at least a factor of 3 to 4 greater than the LTE photospheric value, while the true iron abundance must almost certainly be still higher. There can be little doubt remaining that a real discrepancy exists.

Warner (1964b) attempted to test the applicability of LTE for the analysis of the photospheric spectra of neutral atoms of the iron group elements. Since the ionization potentials of these atoms are much the same, one would expect their excitation temperatures and curves of growth to be similar. On the other hand, Pecker's results for Ti, V, and Cr would imply significant differences in the excitation temperatures and curves of growth for these elements. To the extent that differences are found which cannot be interpreted on an LTE basis, they would constitute a case against that assumption. As did Müller and Mutschlecner, Warner arranged the lines of each element into groups according to their χ_ℓ values—in general he used 0.5 ev groupings, though this energy width was reduced for the lower energies. Within each grouping he then subdivided the lines into the wavelength ranges 4000 to 4500 Å and 4500 to 6500 Å. For each such group of each element he then formed empirical curves of growth—log W/λ vs. log $(gf\lambda)$—using equivalent widths W from the Utrecht Atlas and values of gf from the tables of Corliss and Bozman (1962) and, for Fe I, of Corliss and Warner (1964). From the curves of growth he determined for each element the horizontal shifts needed to superpose the weak line (45-deg) segments of the curves for χ_ℓ onto that for $\chi_\ell = 0$. His plots of these horizontal shifts—which he designated $\Delta \log \eta'$—vs. χ_ℓ are shown, for the grouping 4000 to 4500 Å, in Figure 10.10; the results for different elements were adjusted along the ordinate to obtain the best fit for all elements.

Two features are significant in Figure 10.10; first, the consistency among the different elements, and second, the curvature, which sets in at about $\chi_\ell = 3.0$ ev. Since the ionization potentials of these neutral atoms are essentially equal, one would expect that the individual curves shown in Figure 10.10 would overlap if LTE were a valid hypothesis; the fact that they do has been interpreted by Warner as observational evidence for LTE in the solar photosphere. He finds additional support for this view in the fact that the lines in the range 4500 to 6500 Å also exhibit a common behavior—for these the curvature sets in at about 3.7 ev and is less marked.

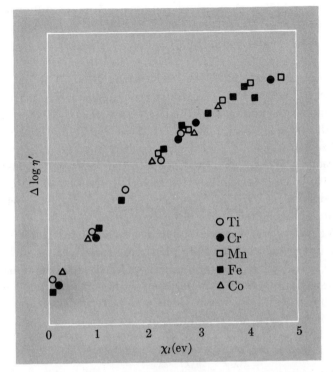

Figure 10.10. Variation of $\Delta \log \eta'$ with χ_ℓ for the iron-group elements in the Sun. (From Warner, 1964 *b*.)

Now, from Equation (10.35) we may write, assuming Q_μ^λ constant,

$$\Delta \log \eta' = \chi \bar{\theta}_{ex}(0, \chi), \qquad (10.38)$$

where $\bar{\theta}_{ex}(0, \chi)$ refers to the population ratio between states at χ and the ground state (see Equation 10.32). The slope of the curve in Figure 10.10, i.e., the derivative with respect to χ of $\Delta \log \eta'$, defines another excitation temperature $\bar{\theta}_{ex}(\chi)$. It is readily shown that the populations of any two levels at χ and χ' are then related by the equation

$$\frac{n(\chi')}{g(\chi')} = \frac{n(\chi)}{g(\chi)} \, \text{dex} \left[-\int_\chi^{\chi'} \bar{\theta}_{ex}(\chi) \, d\chi \right], \qquad (10.39)$$

where dex is the decimal exponentiation operator.

For $\chi_\ell \lesssim 3$ ev it is clear, from Figure 10.10, that $\bar{\theta}_{ex}(\chi)$ is constant and close to unity, a value which is consistent with LTE. However, for $\chi_\ell > 3$ ev, the excitation temperatures rise to values exceeding 10^4 °K, and under no circumstances can these be understood in the framework of LTE. Certainly $\overline{T}_{ex}$ corresponds to no real atmospheric temperature even in LTE, but it is a form of average and with a realistic solar model could never achieve values in excess of about 6000 °K.

Two separate explanations have been advanced to account for the curvature in Figure 10.10. First, it was pointed out by Warner (1964a), in his study of the photospheric Fe I spectrum, that the original f-values obtained by Corliss and Bozman for these high lying lines had been normalized by them to agree with an f-sum rule and with theoretical calculations. If these unnormalized data had been used in constructing Figure 10.10, the curvature would have been greatly reduced—at the cost, however, of accepting f-values of 10 to 20 for lines originating between highly excited states of Fe I.

On the other hand, Jefferies (1966) has suggested that the curvature may be interpreted in terms of a departure from LTE in such a sense that the lower lying states are underpopulated while the upper states are approaching their LTE populations with respect to the continuum $(Fe^+ + e)$ state.

If we write Equation (10.39) in the form

$$\frac{n(\chi')}{g(\chi')} = \frac{n(\chi)}{g(\chi)} \frac{b(\chi')}{b(\chi)} 10^{-\overline{\theta}_e(\chi'-\chi)}, \tag{10.40}$$

in which $\overline{\theta}_e$ is the mean electron temperature through the atmospheric region contributing to the equivalent width, and if we adopt a reasonable value for $\overline{\theta}_e$, Warner's measures of $\Delta \log \eta'$ allow us to infer average values of the ratio $b(\chi')/b(\chi)$ of the coefficients measuring the departures from LTE. Results of this procedure—applied to Warner's (1964a) Fe I analysis of the group 4000 to 4500 Å—are shown in Table

TABLE 10.3. Empirical values of $\log [b(4.25 \text{ ev})/b(\chi)]$ for Fe I

$\chi(\text{ev})$	$\int_{\chi}^{4.25} \overline{\theta}_{ex}(\chi)\, d\chi$	$\log [b(4.25 \text{ ev})/b(\chi)]$	$b(\chi)_{\max}$
3.25	−0.3	0.70	0.20
2.75	−0.5	1.00	0.10
2.25	−0.9	1.10	0.08
1.50	−1.8	0.95	0.11
1.00	−2.5	0.75	0.18
0.00	−3.6	0.65	0.22

10.3 for $\bar{\theta}_e = 1.0$, $\chi' = 4.25$ ev and various values of χ.   Since $b(\chi)$ must approach unity as χ approaches the ionization potential and since the convergence is surely monotonic, Table 10.3 shows that $b(4.25 \text{ ev}) \leq 1$. *Upper* limits on $b(\chi)$ are given by setting $b(4.25 \text{ ev}) = 1$, and these are given in the fourth column of the table.

From Table 10.3 we can see that the variation in $b(\chi)$ is such that fairly consistent abundances would be found were these lines to be analyzed in LTE.   Since, however, $b(\chi) \leq 1/5$ to $1/10$, the LTE abundance would be low by a factor exceeding 5 to 10.

Certainly the curvature in Figure 10.10 shows that an LTE curve of growth analysis of these high-lying lines cannot yield an abundance equal to that obtained from the lower-lying lines.   In other words, if the f-values are correct the LTE abundance must depend on the value of χ_ℓ.   This, of course, is in clear contrast to Müller and Mutschlecner's conclusion.   Their analysis, however, could not show this effect since they were unable to include these high-lying Fe I lines as no suitable f-value data were available to them.

Aller, O'Mara, and Little (1964) determined the solar iron abundance for both Fe I and Fe II lines and obtained the same value, $\log A = 6.59$, from each analysis.   Again, this is consistent with LTE but does not constitute a definite case.

Two criticisms of Jefferies' interpretation have been given by Warner (1966) on the counts (a) that the highly excited states do not converge to LTE populations, as shown by the excitation temperatures of 10,000 to 15,000 °K derived for these states, and (b) that the same curvature is found for all iron group atoms, so that departures from LTE would have to affect all these elements identically.   Neither of these objections is tenable, however.   First, it is a physical requirement that the high states approach LTE populations with respect to the continuum levels because of the increasingly close coupling between the high lying states and the continuum.   If the populations of the lower states with respect to the continuum state are less than their LTE values, then small values of $\bar{\theta}_{ex}(\chi)$ will apply to excitation potentials which lie in the region where the excitation is changing from non-LTE to LTE.   Correspondingly, if the lower states are overpopulated large values of $\bar{\theta}_{ex}(\chi)$ will be found.   It should, perhaps, be pointed out that this interpretation of Figure 10.10 envisages that we would find the slope of the curve increasing to about unity again if we could obtain data on lines with $\chi_\ell > 4.25$ ev.   Second, the equivalent behavior of all iron-group elements, illustrated in Figure 10.10, is not surprising; the atoms are excited and ionized by common processes in a single atmosphere, and one would expect departures from LTE to exhibit themselves at about the same place in the energy level diagram.

At present the situation is far from clear; until we have *f*-values of assured accuracy, we do not know whether the curvature in Figure 10.10 is real or not. If it turns out to be real, the photospheric and coronal abundance determinations may perhaps be rationalized, at the cost of abandoning the LTE analyses. If, on the other hand, new *f*-values show that the curvature is spurious then, and only then, may we have some faith that the LTE analyses are valid. For this, however, we shall have to establish that the *f*-sum rules can be violated by factors of 10 to 20, and to accept an iron-group abundance a factor of 10 to 20 greater in the solar corona than in the photosphere.

One could hardly ask for a more clear-cut issue. Since the validity of almost all solar and stellar abundance estimates hangs on the resolution of this simple question, reliable *f*-values for these high-lying lines of neutral iron are anxiously awaited.

REFERENCES

ALLER, L. H., 1960, "Stellar Atmospheres," edited by J. L. Greenstein. Chicago: Chicago University Press, Chap. 4.

ALLER, L. H., B. J. O'MARA, and S. LITTLE, 1964, "The Abundances of Iron and Silicon in the Sun," *Proc. Nat. Acad. Sci. 51*, 1238.

ATHAY, R. G., D. H. MENZEL, J. C. PECKER, and R. N. THOMAS, 1954, "The Thermodynamic State of the Outer Solar Atmosphere; V, A Model of the Chromosphere from the Continuum Emission," *Astrophys. J. Suppl. 1*, 505.

BÖHM, K.-H., 1954, "Die Temperaturschichtung der Sonnenatmosphäre im nichtgrauen Strahlungsgleichgewicht," *Z. Astrophys. 34*, 182.

CLAAS, W. J., 1951, "The Composition of the Solar Atmosphere," *Rech. Astr. Obs. Utrecht 12*, 1.

CORLISS, C. H., and W. R. BOZMAN, 1962, "Experimental Transition Probabilities for Spectral Lines of Seventy Elements," *Nat. Bur. Stand., Monog. 53*.

CORLISS, C. H., and B. WARNER, 1964, "Absolute Oscillator Strength for Fe I," *Astrophys. J. Suppl. 8*, No. 83.

DUMONT, S., and J.-C. PECKER, 1958, "La géneralisation des relations d'Eddington-Barbier et ses applications," *C.R. Acad. Sc. 247*, 425.

GOLDBERG, L., E. A. MÜLLER, and L. H. ALLER, 1960, "The Abundances of the Elements in the Solar Atmosphere," *Astrophys. J. Suppl. 5*, No. 45.

JEFFERIES, J. T., 1966, "The Solar Abundance of Iron," *I.A.U. Symposium 26*, p. 207.

JEFFERIES, J. T., and F. Q. ORRALL, 1966, "Loop Prominences and Coronal

Condensations; III, The Abundances of Iron and Calcium," *Astrophys. J. 145*, 231.

KANDEL, R., 1960, "Écarts a l'équilibre et abondances dans les photosphères solaire et stellaires V. L'abondance du titane," *Ann. d'astrophys. 23*, 995.

KING, R. B., and A. S. KING, 1938, "Relative *f*-Values for Lines of Fe I and Ti I," *Astrophys. J. 87*, 24.

KOURGANOFF, V., 1952, "Basic Methods in Transfer Problems," Oxford: Clarendon Press.

LEFEVRE, J., and J.-C. PECKER, 1961, "Écarts a l'équilibre et abondances dans les photosphères solaire et stellaires VI. La variation des intensités centrales des raies métalliques entre le centre et le bord du Soleil," *Ann. d'astrophys. 24*, 238.

MINNAERT, M. G., 1953, *The Sun*, edited by G. P. Kuiper. Chicago: University of Chicago Press, Chap. 3.

MÜLLER, E. A., and J. P. MUTSCHLECNER, 1964, "Effects of Deviations from Local Thermodynamic Equilibrium on Solar Abundances," *Astrophys. J. Suppl. 9*, No. 85, p. 1.

PAGEL, B. J., 1965, "Deductions as to Accuracy of LTE from Excitation Temperature Measurements, and a Comment on the Abundance of 'Trace Elements'," *Proceedings, Second Harvard–Smithsonian Conference on Stellar Atmospheres*, p. 425.

PECKER, J.-C., 1959, "Écarts à l'équilibre et abondance dans les photosphères solaire et stellaires I. Le spectre du titane neutre—Ecarts à l'E.T.L.," *Ann. d'astrophys. 22*, 499.

PECKER, J.-C., and L. VOGEL, 1960, "Écarts à l'équilibre et abondance dans les photosphères solaire et stellaires II. Les cas des atomes neutres de titane, vanadium, chrome dans l'atmosphère solaire," *Ann. d'astrophys. 23*, 594.

POTTASCH, S. R., 1963a, "The Lower Solar Corona, Interpretation of the Ultraviolet Spectrum," *Astrophys. J. 137*, 945.

POTTASCH, S. R., 1963b, "The Lower Solar Corona: The Abundance of Iron," *Mon. Not. R. Astr. Soc. 125*, 543.

POTTASCH, S. R., 1964, "On the Chemical Composition of the Solar Corona," *Mon. Not. R. Astr. Soc. 128*, 73.

REGEMORTER, H. VAN, 1959, "Recherches sur les Problèmes Théorique de Classification Stellaire," *Ann. d' astrophys. 22*, 249.

RODDIER, F., 1965, "Etude à Haute Résolution de Quelques Raies de Fraunhofer par Observation de la Résonance Optique d'un Jet Atomique. II. Résultat des Observations Solaires," *Ann. d'astrophys. 28*, 478.

UNNO, W., 1959a, "Turbulent Motion in the Solar Atmosphere; I, Doppler Widths of Photospheric Lines," *Astrophys. J. 129*, 375.

UNNO, W., 1959b, "Turbulent Motion in the Solar Atmosphere; II, Turbulent Velocities in the Lower Chromosphere," *Astrophys. J. 129*, 388.

WARNER, B., 1964a, "Solar Curves of Growth for Neutral Iron," *Mon. Not. R. Astron. Soc. 127*, 413.

WARNER, B., 1964b, "On Departures from Local Thermodynamic Equilibrium in the Solar Atmosphere," *Mon. Not. R. Astron. Soc. 128*, 63.

WARNER, B., 1966, *I.A.U. Symposium 26, discussion remark*, p. 211.

Author Index

Subject Index